PRENTICE HALL

Teacher's Edition

SCIENCE EXPLORER

Sound and Light

Prentice
Hall

Needham, Massachusetts
Upper Saddle River, New Jersey
Glenview, Illinois

ISBN 0-13-054104-4
1 2 3 4 5 6 7 8 9 10   05 04 03 02 01

Chart your own course.

15 motivational hardcover books make it easy for you to create your own curriculum; meet local, state, and national guidelines; and teach your favorite topics in depth.

Prepare your students with rich, motivating content...

Science Explorer is crafted for today's middle grades student, with accessible content and in-depth coverage of all the important concepts.

...and a wide variety of inquiry activities.

Motivational student- and teacher-tested activities reinforce key concepts and allow students to explore science concepts for themselves.

Check your compass regularly.

Science Explorer gives you more ways to regularly check student performance than any other program available.

Utilize a variety of tools.

Integrated science sections in every chapter and Interdisciplinary Explorations in every book allow you to make in-depth connections to other sciences and disciplines. Plus, you will find a wealth of additional tools to set your students on a successful course.

Chart the course you want with 15 motivating books that easily match your curriculum.

Each book in the series contains:
- Integrated Science sections in every chapter
- Interdisciplinary Explorations for team teaching at the end of each book
- Comprehensive skills practice and application—assuring that you meet the National Science Education Standards and your local and state standards

EXPLORATION TOOLS: BASIC PROCESS SKILLS

Observing

Measuring

Calculating

Classifying

Predicting

Inferring

Graphing

Creating data tables

Communicating

LIFE SCIENCE TITLES

From Bacteria to Plants
1. Living Things
2. Viruses and Bacteria
3. Protists and Fungi
4. Introduction to Plants
5. Seed Plants

Animals
1. Sponges, Cnidarians, and Worms
2. Mollusks, Arthropods, and Echinoderms
3. Fishes, Amphibians, and Reptiles
4. Birds and Mammals
5. Animal Behavior

Cells and Heredity
1. Cell Structure and Function
2. Cell Processes and Energy
3. Genetics: The Science of Heredity
4. Modern Genetics
5. Changes Over Time

Human Biology and Health
1. Healthy Body Systems
2. Bones, Muscles, and Skin
3. Food and Digestion
4. Circulation
5. Respiration and Excretion
6. Fighting Disease
7. The Nervous System
8. The Endocrine System and Reproduction

Environmental Science
1. Populations and Communities
2. Ecosystems and Biomes
3. Living Resources
4. Land and Soil Resources
5. Air and Water Resources
6. Energy Resources

 Integrated Science sections in every chapter

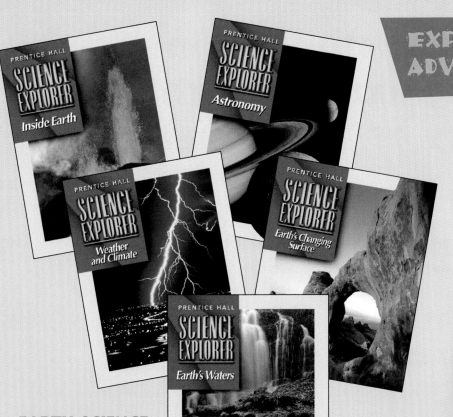

EXPLORATION TOOLS: ADVANCED PROCESS SKILLS

Posing questions

Forming operational definitions

Developing hypotheses

Controlling variables

Interpreting data

Interpreting graphs

Making models

Drawing conclusions

Designing experiments

EARTH SCIENCE TITLES 🔵

Inside Earth
1. Plate Tectonics
2. Earthquakes
3. Volcanoes
4. Minerals
5. Rocks

Earth's Changing Surface
1. Mapping Earth's Surface
2. Weathering and Soil Formation
3. Erosion and Deposition
4. A Trip Through Geologic Time

Earth's Waters
1. Earth: The Water Planet
2. Fresh Water
3. Freshwater Resources
4. Ocean Motions
5. Ocean Zones

Weather and Climate
1. The Atmosphere
2. Weather Factors
3. Weather Patterns
4. Climate and Climate Change

Astronomy
1. Earth, Moon, and Sun
2. The Solar System
3. Stars, Galaxies, and the Universe

PHYSICAL SCIENCE TITLES 🔵

Chemical Building Blocks
1. An Introduction to Matter
2. Changes in Matter
3. Elements and the Periodic Table
4. Carbon Chemistry

Chemical Interactions
1. Chemical Reactions
2. Atoms and Bonding
3. Acids, Bases, and Solutions
4. Exploring Materials

Motion, Forces, and Energy
1. Motion
2. Forces
3. Forces in Fluids
4. Work and Machines
5. Energy and Power
6. Thermal Energy and Heat

Electricity and Magnetism
1. Magnetism and Electromagnetism
2. Electric Charges and Current
3. Electricity and Magnetism at Work
4. Electronics

Sound and Light
1. Characteristics of Waves
2. Sound
3. The Electromagnetic Spectrum
4. Light

 Integrated Science sections in every chapter

Turn your students into science explorers with a variety of inquiry activities.

Motivational student- and teacher-tested activities reinforce key concepts and allow students to explore science concepts for themselves. More than 350 activities are provided for each book in the Student Edition, Teacher's Edition, Teaching Resources, Integrated Science Lab Manual, Inquiry Skills Activity Book, Interactive Student Tutorial CD-ROM, and *Science Explorer* Web Site.

STUDENT EDITION ACTIVITIES

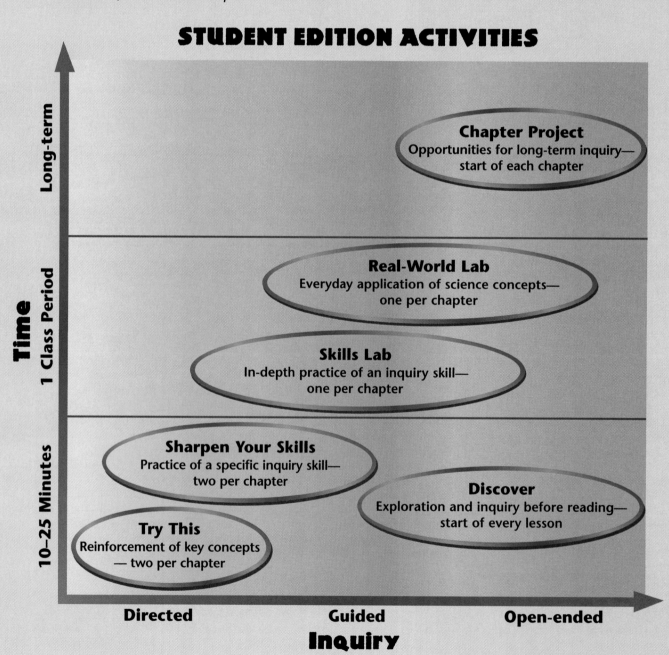

Time

Long-term

Chapter Project
Opportunities for long-term inquiry—
start of each chapter

1 Class Period

Real-World Lab
Everyday application of science concepts—
one per chapter

Skills Lab
In-depth practice of an inquiry skill—
one per chapter

10–25 Minutes

Sharpen Your Skills
Practice of a specific inquiry skill—
two per chapter

Discover
Exploration and inquiry before reading—
start of every lesson

Try This
Reinforcement of key concepts
— two per chapter

Directed   Guided   Open-ended

Inquiry

Check your compass regularly with integrated assessment tools.

Prepare for state exams with traditional and performance-based assessment.

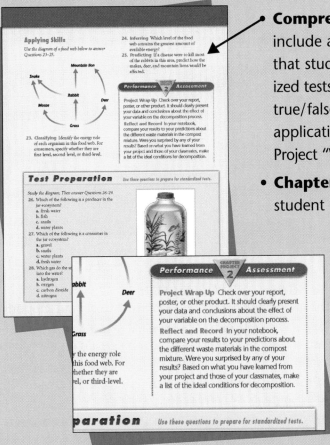

- **Comprehensive Chapter Reviews** include a wide range of question types that students will encounter on standardized tests. Types include multiple choice, enhanced true/false, concept mastery, visual thinking, skill application, and critical thinking. Also includes Chapter Project "Wrap Up."

- **Chapter Projects** contain rubrics that allow you to easily assess student progress.

- **Section Reviews** provide "Check your Progress" opportunities for the Chapter Project, as well as review questions for the section.

Additional *Science Explorer* assessment resources:

- **Computer Test Bank with CD-ROM**
- **Resource Pro® with Planning Express® CD-ROM**
- **Standardized Test Practice Book**
- **Interactive Student Tutorial CD-ROM**
- **On-line review activities** at www.phschool.com
  See pages T8 & T9 for complete product descriptions.

Self-assessment opportunities help students keep themselves on course.

- **Caption Questions** throughout the text assess critical thinking skills.

- **Checkpoint Questions** give students an immediate content check as new concepts are presented.

- **Interactive Student Tutorial CD-ROM** provides students with electronic self-tests, review activities, and Exploration activities.

- **www.phschool.com** provides additional support and on-line test prep.

Utilize a wide variety of tools.

Easy-to-manage, book-specific teaching resources

15 Teaching Resource Packages, each containing a Student Edition, Teacher's Edition, Teaching Resources with Color Transparencies, Interactive Student Tutorial CD-ROM, Guided Study Workbook, Guided Reading Audio CD, and correlation to the National Science Education Standards.

15 Teacher's Editions with a three-step lesson plan–Engage/Explore, Facilitate and Assess–that is ideal for reaching all students. Chapter planning charts make it easy to find resources, as well as to plan for block scheduling and team teaching.

15 Teaching Resource Books with Color Transparencies offer complete teacher support organized by chapter to make it easy for you to find what you need–when you need it.

15 Guided Reading Audio CD's and Audiotapes provide section summaries for students who need additional support. Available in English and Spanish.

15 Guided Study Workbooks containing blackline master worksheets for assessing, understanding, and developing study skills. Teacher's Edition available for each workbook.

Comprehensive print components

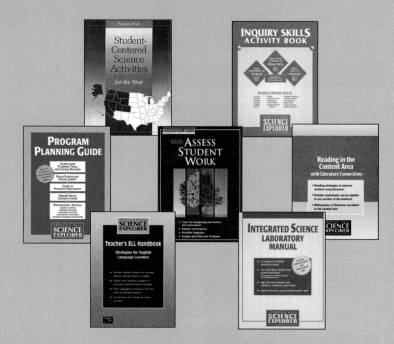

Integrated Science Lab Manual SE & TE—74 in-depth labs covering the entire curriculum, with complete teaching support.

Inquiry Skills Activity Book—additional activities that introduce basic and advanced inquiry skills and reinforce skills on an as-needed basis.

Program Planning Guide—course outlines, block scheduling pacing charts, correlations, and more.

Reading in the Content Area with Literature Connections—provides students with additional strategies for successful reading.

Standardized Test Preparation Book—provides students with hints, tips, strategies, and practice to help them prepare for state and local exams.

How to Assess Student Work—professional articles and example activities that help you design assessments, use rubrics effectively, and develop a portfolio assessment program.

Student-Centered Science Activities—five regional activity books, for the Northeast, Southeast, Midwest, Southwest, and West.

How to Manage Instruction in the Block—comprehensive collection of block scheduling resources, from managing classroom routines to checklists for monitoring and assessing small group learning.

Teacher's ELL Handbook—provides multiple strategies for reaching English language learners. Select appropriate activities to meet the needs of individual students.

Program-wide technology resources

Interactive Student Tutorial CD-ROMs—
provide students with self-tests, helpful hints, and Exploration activities. Tests are scored instantly and contain a detailed explanation of all answers.

Probeware Lab Manual—
provides detailed instructions for using probeware to perform selected labs. Blackline masters of labs are included.

Resource Pro® CD-ROM—
electronic version of the Teaching Resources for all 15 books—ideal for creating integrated science lessons. Contains Planning Express software and Computer Test Bank. Organized by chapter to save you time.

Science Explorer Web Site—
activities and teaching resources for every chapter at: www.phschool.com

Science Explorer Videotapes and Videodiscs
—explore and visualize concepts through spectacular short documentaries containing computer animations. Videotapes also available in Spanish.

Lab Activity Videotapes—
provide step-by-step instruction with students performing activities from every chapter. Promote and teach proper lab techniques, inquiry skills, and safety procedures.

iText—
An interactive text version of the Student Edition at www.phschool.com containing animations, simulations, and videos to enhance student understanding and retention of concepts.

Interactive Physics—
explore physics concepts with computer simulations that encourage what-if questions.

Computer Test Bank Book with CD-ROM—
comprehensive collection of assessment resources containing Computer Test Bank Software with Dial-A-Test; provides you with unparalleled flexibility in creating tests.

ADDITIONAL RESOURCES

Materials Kits—
Prentice Hall and Science Kit, Inc. have collaborated to develop a Consumable Kit and Nonconsumable Kit for each book. Ordering software makes it easy to customize!

Interdisciplinary Explorations—
designed to help you connect science topics to social studies, math, language arts, and students' daily lives.

Options for Pacing *Sound and Light*

The Pacing Chart below suggests one way to schedule your instructional time. The *Science Explorer* program offers many other aids to help you plan your instructional time, whether regular class periods or **block scheduling**. Refer to the Chapter Planning Guide before each chapter to view all program resources with suggested times for Student Edition activities.

Pacing Chart

	Days	Blocks		Days	Blocks
Nature of Science: Turning Down the Volume on Sonic Booms	1	$\frac{1}{2}$	**2** Waves of the Electromagnetic Spectrum	5	$2\frac{1}{2}$
Chapter 1 Characteristics of Waves			**3** Producing Visible Light	3	$1\frac{1}{2}$
Chapter 1 Project Over and Over and Over Again	Ongoing	Ongoing	**4** Integrating Technology: Wireless Communication	$5\frac{1}{2}$	2–3
1 What Are Waves?	2	1	Chapter 3 Review and Assessment	1	$\frac{1}{2}$
2 Properties of Waves	3	$1\frac{1}{2}$	**Chapter 4 Light**		
3 Interactions of Waves	4	2	Chapter 4 Project What a Sight!	Ongoing	Ongoing
4 Integrating Earth Science: Seismic Waves	$1\frac{1}{2}$	1	**1** Reflection and Mirrors	$2\frac{1}{2}$	1–2
Chapter 1 Review and Assessment	1	$\frac{1}{2}$	**2** Refraction and Lenses	3	$1\frac{1}{2}$
Chapter 2 Sound			**3** Color	3	$1\frac{1}{2}$
Chapter 2 Project Music to Your Ears	Ongoing	Ongoing	**4** Integrating Life Science: Seeing Light	2	1
1 The Nature of Sound	3	$1\frac{1}{2}$	**5** Using Light	5	$2\frac{1}{2}$
2 Properties of Sound	3	$1\frac{1}{2}$	Chapter 4 Review and Assessment	1	$\frac{1}{2}$
3 Combining Sound Waves	5	$2\frac{1}{2}$	Interdisciplinary Exploration: The Magic of the Movies		
4 Integrating Life Science: How You Hear Sound	4	2			
5 Applications of Sound	$2\frac{1}{2}$	1–2			
Chapter 2 Review and Assessment	1	$\frac{1}{2}$			
Chapter 3 The Electromagnetic Spectrum					
Chapter 3 Project You're on the Air	Ongoing	Ongoing			
1 The Nature of Electromagnetic Waves	2	1			

RESOURCE◎PRO®

The Resource Pro® CD-ROM is the ultimate scheduling and lesson planning tool. Resource Pro® allows you to preview all the resources in the *Science Explorer* program, organize your chosen materials, and print out any teaching resource. You can follow the suggested lessons or create your own, using resources from anywhere in the program.

Thematic Overview of *Sound and Light*

The chart below lists the major themes of *Sound and Light*. For each theme, the chart supplies a big idea, or concept statement, describing how a particular theme is taught in a chapter.

	Chapter 1	Chapter 2	Chapter 3	Chapter 4
Patterns of Change	Waves are periodic events that can be described by their wavelength, amplitude, frequency, and speed. Waves reflect, refract, or diffract when they reach different surfaces.	The speed of sound is determined by the properties of the medium through which it travels.		When light strikes a surface, it can be transmitted, absorbed, or reflected. If it is transmitted, the path of the light wave may be bent.
Scale and Structure	Transverse waves have crests and troughs while longitudinal waves have compressions and rarefactions. Surface waves combine the motion of these two waves. Seismic activity can generate extremely powerful transverse, longitudinal, and surface waves, such as tsunamis.	The speed that sound waves travel is determined by the elasticity, temperature, and density of the medium through which they move. Properties of sound include intensity, frequency, and timbre. The outer ear collects sound waves, the middle ear transmits the waves as vibrations, and the inner ear converts vibrations to nerve signals that travel to the brain.		Light passes through the cornea, iris, and lens, before it is focused onto the retina of the human eye. By controlling the wavelengths of light in a tube a laser beam can be produced.
Systems and Interactions	The speed of a wave depends on the properties of the medium through which the wave is traveling. Waves interact with each other and other objects by reflection, refraction, diffraction, and interference.	Musical instruments have vibrating strings or columns of air that produce sounds of a pleasing timbre. Infrasonic and ultrasonic waves can be bounced off objects and used to detect objects or communicate.	Electromagnetic waves, which include light, sometimes behave like waves and sometimes like particles. Light can be produced in many ways. A wide array of communication devices use radio waves of different frequencies. Students examine how irradiating food affects its nutritional value.	When light strikes a plane mirror, it is reflected and forms a virtual image. When it strikes a concave mirror, it can form a virtual or real image. When it changes mediums, it refracts. Convex lenses form real images. Objects appear to be the color of light they reflect. Primary colors of light combine to form white light; primary colors of pigment combine to form black. Light can be used to take photographs.
Energy	Waves are disturbances that transfer energy from one place to another. Increasing the energy in a wave affects its amplitude and frequency.	Sound is produced by vibrations that give energy to the particles of a medium. Sound is a form of energy that travels as a longitudinal wave.	Electromagnetic waves have a variety of frequencies; those with higher frequencies are more penetrating.	
Unity and Diversity				All colors of the visible spectrum are combined to form white light. Colored objects absorb some colors and reflect or transmit others. When light is transmitted the path of different colors of light is bent by different amounts, so the light is separated into its colors.

Inquiry Skills Chart

The Prentice Hall *Science Explorer* program provides comprehensive teaching, practice, and assessment of science skills, with an emphasis on the process skills necessary for inquiry. The chart lists the skills covered in the program and cites the page numbers where each skill is covered.

Basic Process SKILLS				
	Student Text: Projects and Labs	**Student Text: Activities**	**Student Text: Caption and Review Questions**	**Teacher's Edition: Extensions**
Observing	12–13, 20–21, 30–31, 60–61, 94–95, 104–106, 122, 128	14, 18, 24–25, 27, 32, 40, 46, 48, 50, 52, 54, 62–63, 66–67, 76, 78, 80, 86, 90, 92, 98, 112, 114, 117–118, 123, 125, 131, 133, 152		15–16, 19, 22, 41, 49, 51, 53, 55, 69, 77, 83, 91, 113–115, 118–120, 130–132, 135–137, 140–141
Inferring	60–61, 94–95, 128	32, 40, 52, 62–63, 66, 76, 118, 152	23, 34, 53, 59, 73, 78, 86, 90, 99, 109	15, 22, 26, 53, 79, 84, 86, 78, 99, 102, 115, 132, 137
Predicting	30–31, 60–61, 94–95, 128	18, 27, 40, 48, 125, 152	25, 29, 37, 43, 79, 103, 125	21, 26, 28, 41, 49, 67, 84, 115, 119, 126, 137
Classifying	12–13, 20–21	32, 114, 133–134, 153	37, 41, 64, 109, 145	55, 113–114, 135
Making Models	30–31	96, 153	37	26, 28, 42, 64, 68, 77, 82, 87, 99, 124
Communicating	12–13, 20–21, 38–39, 45, 74–75, 94–95, 110–111	32, 52, 55, 62, 65–66, 81, 89, 101, 126, 139, 153	36, 72, 108, 144–145	16, 19, 21, 24–26, 42, 49, 52, 68, 80, 82, 91, 96, 100, 114, 117, 123, 126, 130, 133, 137
Measuring	45, 60–61, 94–95, 104–106, 122	66, 154	19	19, 83
Calculating	45	22, 155	37, 70, 73	33, 42, 68, 81, 96
Creating Data Tables	12–13, 30–31, 60–61, 74–75, 94–95, 122	162		
Graphing	74–75	43, 162–164	73	
Advanced Process SKILLS				
Posing Questions		90, 129, 156		
Developing Hypotheses		24, 125, 156	49	125
Designing Experiments	30–31, 38–39, 45, 94–95, 104–106, 110–111, 122	67, 157		21, 25, 49, 58
Controlling Variables	30–31, 38–39, 94–95, 110–111, 122	157	73	19, 58, 91

Advanced Process SKILLS (continued)

	Student Text: Projects and Labs	Student Text: Activities	Student Text: Caption and Review Questions	Teacher's Edition: Extensions
Forming Operational Definitions		46, 80, 157		55
Interpreting Data	12–13, 60–61, 74–75	43, 157	73, 109	
Drawing Conclusions	60–61, 74–75, 94–95, 104–106	57, 78, 98, 157	109	49, 58, 83

Critical Thinking SKILLS

Comparing and Contrasting	20–21, 30–31, 60–61	14, 54, 63, 92, 96, 112, 158	16, 37, 48, 73, 79, 97, 109, 127, 132, 136, 145	16, 41–42, 53, 68, 92, 120, 130–131
Applying Concepts	30–31, 38–39, 104–106, 128	25, 134, 158	17, 33, 37, 42, 44, 47, 59, 67, 73, 82, 85, 88, 92, 98, 116, 118, 124, 145	41, 43, 56, 78, 84, 100, 114, 118, 131, 134, 136, 138
Interpreting Diagrams, Graphs Photographs, and Maps	104–106	158	15, 20, 37, 63, 81, 97, 115, 120	21, 28, 42, 56, 58, 85, 114, 141
Relating Cause and Effect		159	51, 109, 130, 145	79, 92
Making Generalizations	20–21, 60–61	76, 159	42, 54, 109, 145	98
Making Judgments		65, 89, 142, 159	93	
Problem Solving	38–39, 45, 94–95, 104–106	65, 89, 159	121, 145	114, 126

Information Organizing SKILLS

Concept Maps		160	36, 72, 108	32, 141
Compare/ Contrast Tables		160	144	90, 120
Venn Diagrams		161		
Flowcharts		161		32, 62–63, 129–130
Cycle Diagrams		161		

The *Science Explorer* program provides additional teaching, reinforcement, and assessment of skills in the Inquiry Skills Activities Book and the Integrated Science Laboratory Manual.

Throughout the *Science Explorer* program, every effort has been made to keep the materials and equipment *affordable, reusable,* and *easily accessible.*

The *Science Explorer* program offers an abundance of activity options so you can pick and choose those activities that suit your needs. To help you order supplies at the beginning of the year, the Master Materials List cross-references the materials by activity. If you prefer to create your list electronically, you can use the Materials List CD-ROM.

There are two kits available for each book of the *Science Explorer* program: a Consumable Kit and a Nonconsumable Kit. These kits are produced by **Science Kit and Boreal Laboratories,** the leader in providing science kits to schools. Prentice Hall and Science Kit collaborated throughout the development of *Science Explorer* to ensure that the equipment and supplies

in the kits precisely match the requirements of the program activities.

The kits provide an economical and convenient way to get all of the materials needed to teach each book. For each book, Science Kit also offers the opportunity to buy equipment and safety items individually. For additional information about ordering materials to accompany *Science Explorer,* please call:
1-800-848-9500
or access the *Science Explorer* Internet site at: **www.phschool.com**

Master Materials List

Consumable Materials

*	Description	Quantity per class	Textbook Section(s)	*	Description	Quantity per class	Textbook Section(s)
C	Aluminum Foil, Roll, 12" × 25'	1	3-4 (Lab)	SS	Paper, Sheet	50	3-2 (DIS) 3-3 (Lab) 4-2 (DIS) 4-2 (Lab) 4-4 (DIS)
C	Balloons, Round, 13", Pkg/10	1	3-4 (DIS)				
C	Battery, Size D	10	2-3 (DIS) 3-1 (DIS) 3-1 (TT) 4-2 (Lab) 4-3 (Lab)	SS	Paper, Tracing, Sheet	5	3-4 (DIS)
				SS	Pencil	5	1-1 (DIS) 2-3 (TT) 2-3 (Lab)
SS	Box, Cardboard	5	3-2 (DIS) 3-3 (Lab)	SS	Pencils, Colored, Pkg/12	5	3-2 (DIS) 3-3 (SYS) 4-3 (DIS) 4-3 (TT)
SS	Box, Shoe	5	4-3 (Lab)				
SS	Bulb, Fluorescent	5	3-3 (DIS) 3-3 (SYS)				
C	Bulb, Standard, 75 Watt	5	3-3 (DIS) 3-3 (SYS)	C	Pipe Cleaners, Asst Colors, 6", Pkg/110	1	4-5 (SYS)
SS	Bulbs, Incandescent, Various, Packaged	5	3-3 (Lab)	C	Pipe Cleaners, Red, 6", Pkg/100	1	4-5 (SYS)
				C	Rubber Bands, Asst. Colors & Sizes, 1-1/2 oz	1	4-5 (DIS)
SS	Cardboard	10	2-5 (SYS) 3-4 (Lab)	C	Rubber Bands, #19, 3-1/2" × 1/16" × 1/32", 1 oz	1	2-3 (TT)
SS	Cardboard Stand	5	4-2 (Lab)				
C	Cardboard, White, 5" × 5", Pkg/6	2	4-3 (DIS) 4-3 (TT)	C	Rubber Bands, #33, 3-1/2" × 1/8" × 1/32", 1 oz	1	2-3 (TT)
C	Cards, Index, Blank, 5" × 8", Pkg/30	1	3-1 (DIS)	C	Sand, Fine, 1 kg	1	1-4 (DIS)
C	Clay, Modeling (Cream), lb (water-resistant)	3	1-3 (Lab) 1-4 (DIS) 3-1 (DIS) 4-2 (Lab)	C	Straws, Plastic (Wrapped) Pkg/50	1	1-3 (SYS) 2-2 (TT)
				C	String, Cotton, 200 ft	1	2-4 (TT) 3-1 (DIS) 4-3 (DIS) 4-3 (TT)
C	Cup, Paper, 100 mL	5	4-5 (DIS)				
C	Cup, Plastic, Clear, Cocktail, 9 oz	10	3-1 (TT)	SS	Tape, Masking, 3/4" × 60 yd	2	2-3 (Lab) 2-5 (DIS) 4-1 (DIS) 4-2 (Lab) 4-3 (Lab) 4-5 (SYS)
SS	Film, UV Sensitive	1	3-2 (TT)				
SS	Gloves, Latex, Box/100	1	2-3 (DIS)				
C	Lamp, Miniature, #14 (2.47 V)	5	4-2 (Lab)				
C	Marking Pencil, Black Wax	5	2-3 (Lab)	SS	Tube, Cardboard	10	2-5 (SYS) 4-5 (SYS)
C	Oil, Vegetable, 16 oz	1	4-2 (TT)				
SS	Paper Towel Roll	1	1-3 (SYS) 1-3 (Lab)	C	Wax Paper, Roll, 75 sq ft	1	3-3 (Lab) 4-5 (DIS)

KEY: **DIS**: Discover; **SYS**: Sharpen Your Skills; **TT**: Try This; **Lab**: Lab
Quantities based on 5 lab groups per class.
* Items designated **C** are in the Consumable Kit, **NC** are in the Nonconsumable Kit, and **SS** are School Supplied.

Master Materials List

Nonconsumable Materials

*	Description	Quantity per class	Textbook Section(s)	*	Description	Quantity per class	Textbook Section(s)
NC	Alligator Clip with 3/8" Jaw	10	3-4 (Lab)	NC	Light Socket, Porcelain w/Cord	5	3-3 (SYS) 3-3 (Lab)
NC	Ball, Soft Rubber, 2-1/2" Diam	5	1-3 (DIS) 2-5 (DIS)	NC	Light Socket, Mini w/Fahn. Clips	5	4-2 (Lab)
NC	Battery Holder w/Fahnestock Clips, D-Cell	5	4-2 (Lab)	NC	Magnifying Glass, 3x, 6x	5	4-2 (DIS) 4-5 (TT)
SS	Board, Wood w/Nails	5	2-2 (DIS)	NC	Meter Stick, Half (50 cm in length)	5	1-2 (Lab) 1-3 (DIS) 2-5 (DIS) 3-3 (Lab) 4-2 (Lab)
SS	Book	5	2-5 (SYS)				
SS	Bottles, Glass	15	2-3 (Lab)				
SS	Camera	1	3-2 (TT)				
SS	Canister, Film Type w/Snap Cap	25	1-4 (DIS)	NC	Mirror, Plastic, 6" × 9", with Beveled Edges	5	1-3 (Lab)
SS	Coffee Can, Empty	5	2-1 (Lab) 2-3 (DIS)	NC	Mirror, Plastic, 1-1/2" × 1-1/2", with Beveled Edges	5	2-3 (DIS)
NC	Cork, XX, Size 7	5	1-1 (DIS) 1-3 (Lab)	NC	Mirror, Plastic 7.5 × 12.5 cm, with Beveled Edges	10	4-1 (DIS)
NC	Crystal Radio Kit (includes instructions)	5	3-4 (Lab)	SS	Mixer, Electric or Hairdryer	1	3-4 (TT)
NC	Dropper, Plastic	5	1-3 (Lab)	SS	Objects, Red, Blue, Yellow, Set	5	4-3 (Lab)
NC	Flashlight, Plastic (Size D)	5	2-3 (DIS) 3-1 (DIS) 3-1 (TT) 4-3 (Lab)	NC	Pan, Aluminum Foil, 13" × 10" × 2"	5	1-1 (DIS) 1-3 (Lab) 2-1 (DIS)
				NC	Pins, Pushpins, Plastic, Pkg/5	1	4-5 (DIS)
SS	Glass, Large	5	4-2 (TT)	NC	Plastic, 3" × 3", Pkg/18 - 3 Colors/ 6 Each (Red, Blue, Green)	2	4-3 (Lab)
SS	Glass, Small	5	4-2 (TT)				
NC	Guitar String	5	2-2 (DIS)	NC	Prism, Equilateral, Plastic, 25 mm	5	3-2 (DIS)
SS	Hole Punch	5	3-1 (DIS)	NC	Rope, Clothesline, 7/32" × 50'	1	1-2 (DIS)
SS	Hose, Vacuum Cleaner	5	2-2 (TT)	SS	Ruler, Plastic, 12"/30 cm	5	1-3 (Lab) 2-3 (TT) 3-1 (DIS) 4-3 (DIS) 4-3 (TT) 4-4 (DIS)
NC	Lens, Double Convex, 3.75 cm Dia., 15 cm Focal Length	5	4-2 (Lab) 4-5 (TT)				

KEY: **DIS**: Discover; **SYS**: Sharpen Your Skills; **TT**: Try This; **Lab**: Lab
* Items designated **C** are in the Consumable Kit, **NC** are in the Nonconsumable Kit, and **SS** are School Supplied.

Nonconsumable Materials (cont.)

*	Description	Quantity per class	Textbook Section(s)
SS	Scissors	5	2-2 (TT) 3-3 (Lab) 4-3 (DIS) 4-3 (TT) 4-3 (Lab)
SS	Sink	1	3-1 (TT)
NC	Slinky, Plastic	5	1-2 (Lab)
NC	Spectroscope	5	3-3 (SYS)
NC	Spoon, Metal, Tsp	5	2-1 (Lab) 2-3 (DIS) 2-4 (TT) 4-1 (SYS)
NC	Tape Measure, 1.5 m, Metric/English	5	2-1 (Lab)
SS	Television	1	3-4 (TT)
NC	Thermometer, −40°C to 50°C/−40°F to 120°F, Low Temp, Plastic Back	5	2-1 (Lab)
NC	Thread, Round, Elastic, 5 yd	5	1-3 (TT)

*	Description	Quantity per class	Textbook Section(s)
NC	Tuning Fork, Alloy, 256 hz, Economy, Stamped	5	2-1 (DIS)
SS	Watch, Ticking	5	2-5 (SYS)
NC	Wire, Insulated, Copper, 22 Gauge, 25 m (4 oz Spool)	1	4-2 (Lab)

Equipment

*	Description	Quantity per class	Textbook Section(s)
SS	Goggles, Chemical Splash - Class Set	1	2-2 (DIS) 2-3 (TT) 2-3 (Lab) 3-3 (DIS) 3-3 (Lab)
SS	Slide Projector	1	3-1 (TT)
SS	Stopwatch	5	2-1 (Lab) 2-5 (DIS)

KEY: **DIS**: Discover; **SYS**: Sharpen Your Skills; **TT**: Try This; **Lab**: Lab
* Items designated **C** are in the Consumable Kit, **NC** are in the Nonconsumable Kit, and **SS** are School Supplied.

Sound and Light

Book-Specific Resources

Student Edition
Annotated Teacher's Edition
Teaching Resources with Color Transparencies
Consumable and Non-Consumable Materials Kits
Guided Reading Audio CDs
Guided Reading Audiotapes
Guided Study Workbook
Guided Study Workbook, Teacher's Edition
Lab Activity Videotapes
Science Explorer Videotapes
Science Explorer Web Site at **www.phschool.com**

Program-Wide Resources

Computer Test Bank Book with CD-ROM
How to Assess Student Work
How to Manage Instruction in the Block
Inquiry Skills Activity Book
Integrated Science Laboratory Manual
Integrated Science Laboratory Manual, Teacher's Edition
Interactive Student Tutorial CD-ROM
Prentice Hall Interdisciplinary Explorations
Probeware Lab Manual
Product Testing Activities by Consumer Reports™
Program Planning Guide
Reading in the Content Area with Literature Connections
Resource Pro® CD-ROM (Teaching Resources on CD-ROM)
Science Explorer Videodiscs
Standardized Test Preparation Book
Student-Centered Science Activity Books
Teacher's ELL Handbook: Strategies for English Language Learners

Spanish Resources

Spanish Student Edition
Spanish Guided Reading Audio CDs with Section Summaries
Spanish Guided Reading Audiotapes with Section Summaries
Spanish Science Explorer Videotapes

Science Explorer Student Editions

From Bacteria to Plants

Animals

Cells and Heredity

Human Biology and Health

Environmental Science

Inside Earth

Earth's Changing Surface

Earth's Waters

Weather and Climate

Astronomy

Chemical Building Blocks

Chemical Interactions

Motion, Forces, and Energy

Electricity and Magnetism

Sound and Light

ISBN 0-13-054103-6
1 2 3 4 5 6 7 8 9 10   05 04 03 02 01

Cover: This French horn is shown
against a background of the visible
spectrum.

Teacher's Edition ISBN 0-13-054104-4

Michael J. Padilla, Ph.D.
Professor
Department of Science Education
University of Georgia
Athens, Georgia

Michael Padilla is a leader in middle school science education. He has served as an editor and elected officer for the National Science Teachers Association. He has been principal investigator of several National Science Foundation and Eisenhower grants and served as a writer of the National Science Education Standards.

As lead author of *Science Explorer,* Mike has inspired the team in developing a program that meets the needs of middle grades students, promotes science inquiry, and is aligned with the National Science Education Standards.

Ioannis Miaoulis, Ph.D.
Dean of Engineering
College of Engineering
Tufts University
Medford, Massachusetts

Martha Cyr, Ph.D.
Director, Engineering
    Educational Outreach
College of Engineering
Tufts University
Medford, Massachusetts

Science Explorer was created in collaboration with the College of Engineering at Tufts University. Tufts has an extensive engineering outreach program that uses engineering design and construction to excite and motivate students and teachers in science and technology education.

Faculty from Tufts University participated in the development of *Science Explorer* chapter projects, reviewed the student books for content accuracy, and helped coordinate field testing.

CHAPTER PROJECT

Book Author

Jay M. Pasachoff, Ph.D.
Professor of Astronomy
Williams College
Williamstown, Massachusetts

Contributing Writers

Rose-Marie Botting
Science Teacher
Broward County School District
Fort Lauderdale, Florida

John Coffey
Science/Mathematics Teacher
Venice Area Middle School
Venice, Florida

Edward Evans
Former Science Teacher
Hilton Central School
Hilton, New York

Peter Kahan
Former Science Teacher
Dwight-Englewood School
Englewood, New Jersey

Reading Consultant

Bonnie B. Armbruster, Ph.D.
Department of Curriculum
    and Instruction
University of Illinois
Champaign, Illinois

Interdisciplinary Consultant

Heidi Hayes Jacobs, Ed.D.
Teacher's College
Columbia University
New York, New York

Safety Consultants

W. H. Breazeale, Ph.D.
Department of Chemistry
College of Charleston
Charleston, South Carolina

Ruth Hathaway, Ph.D.
Hathaway Consulting
Cape Girardeau, Missouri

Tufts University Program Reviewers

Behrouz Abedian, Ph.D.
Department of Mechanical
   Engineering

Wayne Chudyk, Ph.D.
Department of Civil and
   Environmental Engineering

Eliana De Bernardez-Clark, Ph.D.
Department of Chemical Engineering

Anne Marie Desmarais, Ph.D.
Department of Civil and
   Environmental Engineering

David L. Kaplan, Ph.D.
Department of Chemical Engineering

Paul Kelley, Ph.D.
Department of Electro-Optics

George S. Mumford, Ph.D.
Professor of Astronomy, Emeritus

Jan A. Pechenik, Ph.D.
Department of Biology

Livia Racz, Ph.D.
Department of Mechanical Engineering

Robert Rifkin, M.D.
School of Medicine

Jack Ridge, Ph.D.
Department of Geology

Chris Swan, Ph.D.
Department of Civil and
   Environmental Engineering

Peter Y. Wong, Ph.D.
Department of Mechanical Engineering

Content Reviewers

Jack W. Beal, Ph.D.
Department of Physics
Fairfield University
Fairfield, Connecticut

W. Russell Blake, Ph.D.
Planetarium Director
Plymouth Community
   Intermediate School
Plymouth, Massachusetts

Howard E. Buhse, Jr., Ph.D.
Department of Biological Sciences
University of Illinois
Chicago, Illinois

Dawn Smith Burgess, Ph.D.
Department of Geophysics
Stanford University
Stanford, California

A. Malcolm Campbell, Ph.D.
Assistant Professor
Davidson College
Davidson, North Carolina

Elizabeth A. De Stasio, Ph.D.
Associate Professor of Biology
Lawrence University
Appleton, Wisconsin

John M. Fowler, Ph.D.
Former Director of Special Projects
National Science Teacher's Association
Arlington, Virginia

Jonathan Gitlin, M.D.
School of Medicine
Washington University
St. Louis, Missouri

Dawn Graff-Haight, Ph.D., CHES
Department of Health, Human
   Performance, and Athletics
Linfield College
McMinnville, Oregon

Deborah L. Gumucio, Ph.D.
Associate Professor
Department of Anatomy and Cell Biology
University of Michigan
Ann Arbor, Michigan

William S. Harwood, Ph.D.
Dean of University Division and Associate
   Professor of Education
Indiana University
Bloomington, Indiana

Cyndy Henzel, Ph.D.
Department of Geography
   and Regional Development
University of Arizona
Tucson, Arizona

Greg Hutton
Science and Health
   Curriculum Coordinator
School Board of Sarasota County
Sarasota, Florida

Susan K. Jacobson, Ph.D.
Department of Wildlife Ecology
   and Conservation
University of Florida
Gainesville, Florida

Judy Jernstedt, Ph.D.
Department of Agronomy and Range Science
University of California, Davis
Davis, California

John L. Kermond, Ph.D.
Office of Global Programs
National Oceanographic and
   Atmospheric Administration
Silver Spring, Maryland

David E. LaHart, Ph.D.
Institute of Science and Public Affairs
Florida State University
Tallahassee, Florida

Joe Leverich, Ph.D.
Department of Biology
St. Louis University
St. Louis, Missouri

Dennis K. Lieu, Ph.D.
Department of Mechanical Engineering
University of California
Berkeley, California

Cynthia J. Moore, Ph.D.
Science Outreach Coordinator
Washington University
St. Louis, Missouri

Joseph M. Moran, Ph.D.
Department of Earth Science
University of Wisconsin–Green Bay
Green Bay, Wisconsin

Joseph Stukey, Ph.D.
Department of Biology
Hope College
Holland, Michigan

Seetha Subramanian
Lexington Community College
University of Kentucky
Lexington, Kentucky

Carl L. Thurman, Ph.D.
Department of Biology
University of Northern Iowa
Cedar Falls, Iowa

Edward D. Walton, Ph.D.
Department of Chemistry
California State Polytechnic University
Pomona, California

Robert S. Young, Ph.D.
Department of Geosciences and
   Natural Resource Management
Western Carolina University
Cullowhee, North Carolina

Edward J. Zalisko, Ph.D.
Department of Biology
Blackburn College
Carlinville, Illinois

Teacher Reviewers

Stephanie Anderson
Sierra Vista Junior
    High School
Canyon Country, California

John W. Anson
Mesa Intermediate School
Palmdale, California

Pamela Arline
Lake Taylor Middle School
Norfolk, Virginia

Lynn Beason
College Station Jr. High School
College Station, Texas

Richard Bothmer
Hollis School District
Hollis, New Hampshire

Jeffrey C. Callister
Newburgh Free Academy
Newburgh, New York

Judy D'Albert
Harvard Day School
Corona Del Mar, California

Betty Scott Dean
Guilford County Schools
McLeansville, North Carolina

Sarah C. Duff
Baltimore City Public Schools
Baltimore, Maryland

Melody Law Ewey
Holmes Junior High School
Davis, California

Sherry L. Fisher
Lake Zurich Middle
    School North
Lake Zurich, Illinois

Melissa Gibbons
Fort Worth ISD
Fort Worth, Texas

Debra J. Goodding
Kraemer Middle School
Placentia, California

Jack Grande
Weber Middle School
Port Washington, New York

Steve Hills
Riverside Middle School
Grand Rapids, Michigan

Carol Ann Lionello
Kraemer Middle School
Placentia, California

Jaime A. Morales
Henry T. Gage Middle School
Huntington Park, California

Patsy Partin
Cameron Middle School
Nashville, Tennessee

Deedra H. Robinson
Newport News Public Schools
Newport News, Virginia

Bonnie Scott
Clack Middle School
Abilene, Texas

Charles M. Sears
Belzer Middle School
Indianapolis, Indiana

Barbara M. Strange
Ferndale Middle School
High Point, North Carolina

Jackie Louise Ulfig
Ford Middle School
Allen, Texas

Kathy Usina
Belzer Middle School
Indianapolis, Indiana

Heidi M. von Oetinger
L'Anse Creuse Public School
Harrison Township, Michigan

Pam Watson
Hill Country Middle School
Austin, Texas

Activity Field Testers

Nicki Bibbo
Russell Street School
Littleton, Massachusetts

Connie Boone
Fletcher Middle School
Jacksonville Beach, Florida

Rose-Marie Botting
Broward County
    School District
Fort Lauderdale, Florida

Colleen Campos
Laredo Middle School
Aurora, Colorado

Elizabeth Chait
W. L. Chenery Middle School
Belmont, Massachusetts

Holly Estes
Hale Middle School
Stow, Massachusetts

Laura Hapgood
Plymouth Community
    Intermediate School
Plymouth, Massachusetts

Sandra M. Harris
Winman Junior High School
Warwick, Rhode Island

Jason Ho
Walter Reed Middle School
Los Angeles, California

Joanne Jackson
Winman Junior High School
Warwick, Rhode Island

Mary F. Lavin
Plymouth Community
    Intermediate School
Plymouth, Massachusetts

James MacNeil, Ph.D.
Concord Public Schools
Concord, Massachusetts

Lauren Magruder
St. Michael's Country
    Day School
Newport, Rhode Island

Jeanne Maurand
Glen Urquhart School
Beverly Farms, Massachusetts

Warren Phillips
Plymouth Community
    Intermediate School
Plymouth, Massachusetts

Carol Pirtle
Hale Middle School
Stow, Massachusetts

Kathleen M. Poe
Kirby-Smith Middle School
Jacksonville, Florida

Cynthia B. Pope
Ruffner Middle School
Norfolk, Virginia

Anne Scammell
Geneva Middle School
Geneva, New York

Karen Riley Sievers
Callanan Middle School
Des Moines, Iowa

David M. Smith
Howard A. Eyer Middle School
Macungie, Pennsylvania

Derek Strohschneider
Plymouth Community
    Intermediate School
Plymouth, Massachusetts

Sallie Teames
Rosemont Middle School
Fort Worth, Texas

Gene Vitale
Parkland Middle School
McHenry, Illinois

Zenovia Young
Meyer Levin Junior
    High School (IS 285)
Brooklyn, New York

PRENTICE HALL
SCIENCE EXPLORER

Contents

Sound and Light

Prepare your students with rich, motivating content

Science Explorer is crafted for today's middle grades student, with accessible content and in-depth coverage.
Integrated Science Sections support every chapter and the **Interdisciplinary Exploration** provides an engaging final unit.

Check your compass—regularly assess student progress.

Self-assessment tools are built right into the student text and **on-going assessment** is woven throughout the Teacher's Edition. You'll find a wealth of **assessment technology** in the Resource Pro®, Interactive Student Tutorial, and Assessment Resources CD-ROMs.

Activities

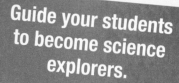

Guide your students to become science explorers.

A wide range of **student-tested** activities, **from guided to open-ended,** with options for **short-** **and long-term** inquiry.

Draw upon the world around you.

Interdisciplinary Activities connect to every discipline and give science a **meaningful, real-world context.**

Turning Down the Volume on Sonic Booms

Focus on Engineering

This four-page feature introduces the process of scientific inquiry by involving students in a high-interest, magazine-like article about a working scientist, Dr. Christine Darden. Using Dr. Darden's explorations into the causes of sonic booms, the article focuses on observing, measuring, and studying models as key elements of scientific inquiry.

Waves and the properties of sound are presented in Chapters 1 and 2 of this book. However, students need not have any previous knowledge of those chapters' content to understand and appreciate this feature.

Scientific Inquiry

◆ Before students read the feature, let them read the title, examine the pictures, and read the captions on their own. Then ask: **What questions came into your mind as you looked at these pictures?** *(Students might suggest questions such as "What is a sonic boom? What does supersonic mean? Why are they testing models if they already know what sonic booms are?")* Point out to students that just as they have questions about what they are seeing, scientists too have questions about what they observe.

◆ Ask whether any students have ever heard a sonic boom. Ask whether any students have ever heard a cannon. If any students have done so, ask them to describe what they heard.

Turning Down the Volume on SONIC BOOMS

Dr. Christine Mann Darden grew up in Monroe, North Carolina. She received her Ph.D. in Mechanical Engineering at George Washington University in Washington, D.C. A national expert on sonic booms, she now works at NASA's Langley Research Center in Hampton, Virginia. She manages a group of scientists who are developing supersonic airplanes. Dr. Darden (center) is shown here with other members of the Sonic Boom Group, Kathy Needleman (left) and Robert Mack (right).

*I*t happens every time a space shuttle returns to Earth. The spacecraft drops down from orbit and streaks toward its landing site in Florida or California. A few seconds after it passes overhead—BOOM! A window-rattling sound like a giant cannon shot is heard. Most scientists at the space center are monitoring the shuttle itself when it comes down from a mission. But Dr. Christine Darden is more interested in that big boom.

Dr. Darden is a research engineer at the National Aeronautics and Space Administration (NASA). She is in charge of the space agency's Sonic Boom Group. Her team of scientists is investigating the distinctive "sound print" made by aircraft that travel faster than the speed of sound. Dr. Darden and her co-workers are looking for ways to soften sonic booms. They hope to make supersonic travel—travel at speeds faster than the speed of sound—more common in the future.

Background

Engineering is the application of math and science knowledge to the effective use of materials and forces in nature. There are numerous branches of engineering; however, because the branches are interrelated, an engineer specializing in any field needs to have some understanding of the other fields and how they relate.

An aeronautical engineer, for example, must have some knowledge of airplane design, manufacture, and testing. The aeronautical engineer must also understand aerodynamics, structural engineering as it relates to how airplanes are built, and how jet engines work.

Aerospace engineers, who focus on craft that fly beyond Earth's atmosphere, need to know about rocket engines, satellites, astronomy, gravity and related concepts, and spacecraft design.

Talking With
Dr. Christine Darden

Breaking the Sound Barrier

The sound barrier was first broken in 1947. Since then, people have complained about sonic booms so much that the government has passed regulations. It's now against the law to fly most aircraft at supersonic speeds over the United States.

"If it is loud enough, a sonic boom can actually break windows and do damage to buildings," says Dr. Darden. "People find it very disturbing. Right now, the boom is one of the biggest obstacles to commercial supersonic air service."

Today supersonic aircraft fly mainly over the ocean. But what if scientists can find ways to lower the volume of sonic booms? Then someday supersonic commercial jets may be allowed to fly across the country.

What Is a Sonic Boom?

You have probably heard the sound that is made when an airplane breaks the sound barrier. A sonic boom sounds like a clap of thunder or a sharp explosion high in the sky. Just what are you hearing?

"A sonic boom is a compression or pressure wave," Dr. Darden

Both the SR-71 Blackbird (above) and F-16 (opposite page) are military supersonic planes.

explains. "An airplane pushes a wave of air molecules ahead of it as it travels forward, just as a ship's bow pushes out a wave as it moves through the water. Those compressions travel outward from the plane as a shock wave of high pressure. When that shock wave reaches our ears, we hear it as a boom."

"Think of blowing up a balloon," Dr. Darden says. "With the balloon inflated, the air on the inside is much more compressed than the air on the outside. When the balloon pops, the compression immediately flies outward in the form of a shock wave."

- Encourage students to tell what they already know about sonic booms or about sound waves. Stress that Dr. Darden is interested in sonic booms because she wants supersonic travel to be more common in the future.
- Encourage interested students to research how the sound barrier was first broken in 1947 by Chuck Yeager in an X-1 rocket plane. Invite them to share their findings with the class.
- Students may recall hearing reference to Mach numbers in movies. Give interested students the background information on Mach numbers on this page. Also suggest that they consult library books to learn more about supersonic flight. (See Further Reading, page 11).
- Explain that a compression wave is caused when something is compressed.
- Make sure students know which part of a ship the bow is. If possible, find a video clip of a ship moving through water, showing the waves caused by the bow. Otherwise, demonstrate the waves using a toy boat in a sink of water.

Background

The Mach number is the ratio of the speed of the airplane to the speed of sound in air. An airplane traveling at Mach 1 is traveling at the speed of sound. An airplane traveling at Mach 2 is traveling at twice the speed of sound. Above Mach 1, the plane is supersonic.

Mach numbers have no units. They are named after Ernst Mach, an Austrian physicist and philosopher. Mach numbers are used in aerodynamics and in fluid mechanics, which is the study of how fluids move.

- Ask: **Why does Dr. Darden's group study waves in water?** (*You can see waves in water. You cannot readily see waves in air.*) Ask students how many of them have informally experimented with waves in water. Ask students to share any insights they gained.

- Ask: **What was Dr. Darden's first job at NASA?** (*She was a mathematician.*) **Why did she decide to get a degree in engineering?** (*She became interested in the work of the NASA research engineers.*) **Do you think her background teaching math was useful when she studied engineering?** (*Yes, engineers often use a lot of math in solving problems and designing new technologies.*) **Why did she need to go to graduate school when she was already a mathematician?** (*She was not qualified to be an engineer and she needed to study more.*) Point out that Dr. Darden changed careers after she was already a mathematician at NASA. Lead students to understand that even after you graduate from college with a Bachelor's degree, there's no reason why you can't go back later in life and pursue a degree in something else. You are never to old to stop learning something new, and you are never too old to decide that your career is not what you wanted and to pursue something different.

- Ask: **What is hands-on work?** (*Work in which you are working with your hands to solve problems rather than just thinking about them theoretically.*)

- Ask: **Why is "fly" in quotes?** (*The model aircraft don't really fly in a wind tunnel. The air is pushed past them to simulate flying.*)

- Refer students to the photo caption on page 11. Ask: **What do you think a low-boom model is?** (*Answers may vary. Samples: a model of an aircraft that makes a quieter sonic boom than other planes; a plane that makes a sonic boom that is lower in pitch than other sonic booms*)

How Do You Research What You Can't See?

"Part of our work is coming up with new ways to observe and measure the phenomenon we're studying," says Dr. Darden. "For example, we know that all waves have similar properties. So we look at how waves behave in water to tell us something about how they behave in the air."

Choosing Engineering

Dr. Darden's study of waves in water and air is a long way from her first career as a math teacher. In the late 1960s, she was teaching in a school in Hampton, Virginia. At that time, the NASA labs nearby were working on a program to send astronauts to the moon. Dr. Darden went to work for NASA as a mathematician.

She quickly became fascinated with the work of the NASA research engineers. "They were the ones who were working with the really tough challenges of the program," she says. "They were doing the interesting, hands-on work." As a result of her experience, she decided to get a graduate degree in engineering.

How Do You Test Supersonic Aircraft?

Working hands-on is one way that Dr. Darden and her team study how airplanes create sonic booms. They

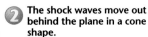

1 A sonic boom results when an airplane moves at supersonic speed. Air is compressed at the front of the plane, creating shock waves.

2 The shock waves move out behind the plane in a cone shape.

3 When the shock waves reach the ground, people hear them as a sonic boom.

Background

A wind tunnel is a device used to study how objects such as airplanes, bridges, automobiles, buildings, and spacecraft behave when moving through air. In the tunnel, the object remains fixed while air is forced through the tunnel around it. Some wind tunnels are less than a meter across while others are large enough to test a small aircraft. NASA has a wind tunnel 24 meters by 37 meters in California. The larger the wind tunnel, the more power is needed to force the air through it, so supersonic testing is usually done in small tunnels using scale models. At supersonic speeds, air friction generates heat, so wind tunnels for researching supersonic speeds include heaters to simulate this heating.

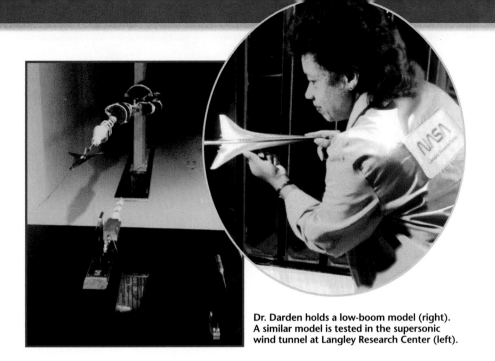

Dr. Darden holds a low-boom model (right). A similar model is tested in the supersonic wind tunnel at Langley Research Center (left).

"fly" model aircraft in a high-speed wind tunnel. The scientists place the steel models in the tunnel and watch how they behave in winds moving at up to three times the speed of sound. (The speed of sound varies with altitude and air pressure. At sea level on a 16°C day, the speed of sound is about 1,207 kilometers per hour.)

Instruments on the sides of the tunnel allow Dr. Darden to "hear" the sonic boom created by the model. By adding very fine smoke, she can even watch how the air moves over the plane. "We can actually see the shock wave," she says.

Can the Sonic Boom Effect Be Reduced?

Dr. Darden and her group at NASA have found that the shape of an aircraft determines the size of the boom it creates. They have performed tests with computer programs, on actual supersonic

jets, and in wind tunnels. Their experiments have shown that angling the wings back sharply reduces the size of the shock wave and the loudness of the sonic boom. But the same features that make planes quieter also make them harder to fly.

"You could put a needle up there supersonically and you wouldn't get a sonic boom," explains Dr. Darden. "But you wouldn't have much of an airplane, either."

In Your Journal

In her research, Dr. Darden made predictions about how the angle of an airplane wing might affect a sonic boom. Then her team set up a series of experiments to test these predictions.

Now think of different-shaped boats moving through water: a kayak, a tugboat, and a rowboat. Predict the type of wave that each boat will make. How could you use models to test your predictions?

O ◆ 11

- Challenge students to find out how the angled-back wings affects the plane's flight. Have students research how this wing design changes the way the plane takes off, lands, and maneuvers in the air.
- You may wish to have students make paper airplanes with different wing designs and compare how they fly.
- Ask: **What does Dr. Darden mean in the last paragraph?** (*A long thin airplane can fly at supersonic speeds and not make a sonic boom. But such a plane would be too thin to be practical.*)

In Your Journal If students aren't familiar with how the shapes of the hulls of the boats differ, sketch the three types of boats on the board. Students can experiment with waves by bending a piece of plastic, such as from an empty gallon milk jug, into different angles and pushing it through a sink of water.

Introducing Sound and Light

Have students look through the table of contents and the book to find the parts that relate most closely to this article. (*Chapter 1, Characteristics of Waves, particularly Section 1-2, Properties of Waves, and Chapter 2, Sound, particularly Section 2-2, The Nature of Sound.*) Ask: **Besides sound waves, what else is this book about?** (*waves, applications of sound, the electromagnetic spectrum, light*) **What kinds of things do you think you will be learning about?** (*Accept all responses without comments.*)

READING STRATEGIES

Further Reading

- Hallion, Richard P. *Supersonic Flight: Breaking the Sound Barrier and Beyond: The Story of the Bell X-1 and Douglas D-558.* Brassey's, 1997.
- Gunston, Bill. *Faster than Sound: The Story of Supersonic Flight.* Motorbooks International, 1992.
- Yeager, Chuck and James Young. *The Quest for Mach One: A First-Person Account of Breaking the Sound Barrier.* Viking Penguin, 1997.
- Owen, Kenneth. *Concorde and the Americans: International Politics of the Supersonic Transport.* Smithsonian Institution Press, 1997.
- Wolfe, Tom. *The Right Stuff.* Farrar, Straus, & Giroux, 1983.

Characteristics of Waves

Sections	Time	Student Edition Activities	Other Activities
CHAPTER PROJECT 1 **Over and Over Again** p. 013	Ongoing (2 weeks)	Check Your Progress, pp. 017, 023 Project Wrap Up, p. 037	**TE** Chapter 1 Project Notes, pp. 012–13
1 **What Are Waves?** pp. 014–17 ◆ 1.1.1 Define waves and identify what causes them. ◆ 1.1.2 Identify and compare the three main types of waves.	2 periods/ 1 block	**Discover** How Do Waves Travel?, p. 014	**TE** Demonstration, p. 015 **TE** Including All Students, p. 016 **TE** Building Inquiry Skills: Comparing and Contrasting, p. 016
2 **Properties of Waves** pp. 018–23 ◆ 1.2.1 List and describe the basic properties of waves. ◆ 1.2.2 Describe how a wave's speed is related to its wavelength and frequency and calculate a wave's speed.	3 periods/ $1\frac{1}{2}$ blocks	**Discover** How Can You Change a Wave?, p. 018 **Skills Lab: Observing** Wavy Motions, pp. 020–21	**TE** Inquiry Challenge, p. 019 **TE** Building Inquiry Skills: Controlling Variables, p. 019 **TE** Inquiry Challenge, p. 021 **TE** Demonstration, p. 022 **TE** Math Toolbox, p. 022 **TE** Building Inquiry Skills: Inferring, p. 022 **ISLM** 0-1, "Making Waves"
3 **Interactions of Waves** pp. 024–31 ◆ 1.3.1 Identify and compare reflection, refraction, and diffraction. ◆ 1.3.2 Describe the two types of interference of waves. ◆ 1.3.3 Identify and describe standing waves and resonance.	4 periods/ 2 blocks	**Discover** How Does a Ball Bounce?, p. 024 **Sharpen Your Skills** Observing, p. 025 **Try This** Standing Waves, p. 027 **Science at Home** p. 029 **Skills Lab: Making Models** Making Waves, pp. 030–31	**TE** Inquiry Challenge, p. 025 **TE** Demonstration, p. 026 **TE** Inquiry Challenge, p. 026 **TE** Demonstration, p. 028
4 *INTEGRATING EARTH SCIENCE* **Seismic Waves** pp. 032–34 ◆ 1.4.1 Describe what creates seismic waves. ◆ 1.4.2 Identify the different types of seismic waves. ◆ 1.4.3 Explain how a seismograph works.	$1\frac{1}{2}$ periods/ 1 block	**Discover** Can You Find the Sand?, p. 032 **Science at Home** p. 034	
Study Guide/Assessment pp. 035–37	1 period/ $\frac{1}{2}$ block		**ISAB** Provides teaching and review of all inquiry skills

 For Standard or Block Schedule The Resource Pro® CD-ROM gives you maximum flexibility for planning your instruction for any type of schedule. Resource Pro® contains Planning Express®, an advanced scheduling program, as well as the entire contents of the Teaching Resources and the Computer Test Bank.

Key: **SE** Student Edition
PLM Probeware Lab Manual
ISAB Inquiry Skills Activity Book

CHAPTER PLANNING GUIDE

Program Resources	Assessment Strategies	Media and Technology
TR Chapter 1 Project Teacher Notes, pp. 06–7 **TR** Chapter 1 Project Overview and Worksheets, pp. 08–11	**TE** Check Your Progress, pp. 017, 023 **TE** Performance Assessment: Chapter 1 Project Wrap Up, p. 037 **TR** Chapter 1 Project Scoring Rubric, p. 012	🌐 Science Explorer Internet Site 🎧 Audio CDs and Audiotapes, English-Spanish Section Summaries
TR 1-1 Lesson Plan, p. 013 **TR** 1-1 Section Summary, p. 014 **TR** 1-1 Review and Reinforce, p. 015 **TR** 1-1 Enrich, p. 016	**SE** Section 1 Review, p. 017 **TE** Ongoing Assessment, p. 015 **TE** Performance Assessment, p. 017	💿 Exploring Physical Science Videodisc, Unit 6 Side 2, "Waves All Around Us" 📽 Transparency 1, "Motion of Duck on a Water Wave" 📽 Transparency 2, "Transverse Wave" 📽 Transparency 3, "Longitudinal Wave"
TR 1-2 Lesson Plan, p. 017 **TR** 1-2 Section Summary, p. 018 **TR** 1-2 Review and Reinforce, p. 019 **TR** 1-2 Enrich, p. 020 **TR** Skills Lab blackline masters, pp. 029–30	**SE** Section 2 Review, p. 023 **SE** Analyze and Conclude, p. 021 **TE** Ongoing Assessment, p. 019 **TE** Performance Assessment, p. 023	📼 Lab Activity Videotape, *Sound and Light*, 1 💿 Exploring Physical Science Videodisc, Unit 6 Side 2, "A Wave Is a Wave Is a Wave" 💿 Exploring Earth Science Videodisc, Unit 2 Side 2, "The Wave"
TR 1-3 Lesson Plan, p. 021 **TR** 1-3 Section Summary, p. 022 **TR** 1-3 Review and Reinforce, p. 023 **TR** 1-3 Enrich, p. 024 **TR** Skills Lab blackline masters, pp. 031–33	**SE** Section 3 Review, p. 029 **SE** Analyze and Conclude, p. 031 **TE** Ongoing Assessment, pp. 025, 027 **TE** Performance Assessment, p. 029	📼 Lab Activity Videotape, *Sound and Light*, 2 📽 Transparency 4, "Exploring Interactions of Waves"
TR 1-4 Lesson Plan, p. 025 **TR** 1-4 Section Summary, p. 026 **TR** 1-4 Review and Reinforce, p. 027 **TR** 1-4 Enrich, p. 028 **SES** Book F, *Inside Earth,* Chapter 2	**SE** Section 4 Review, p. 034 **TE** Ongoing Assessment, p. 033 **TE** Performance Assessment, p. 034	💿 Exploring Earth Science Videodisc, Unit 2 Side 2, "Waves in the Earth" 💿 Exploring Earth Science Videodisc, Unit 3 Side 1, "Rock and Roll" 📽 Transparency 5, "Seismic Waves"
GSW Provides worksheets to promote student comprehension of content **RCA** Provides strategies to improve science reading skills **ELL** Provides multiple strategies for English language learners	**SE** Study Guide/Assessment, pp. 035–37 **TR** Performance Assessment, pp. 0138–140 **TR** Chapter 1 Test, pp. 0141–144 **CTB** *Sound and Light*, Chapter 1 Test **STP** Provides standardized test practice	💻 Computer Test Bank, *Sound and Light*, Chapter 1 Test 💻 Interactive Student Tutorial CD-ROM, 0-1

TE Teacher's Edition   **TR** Teaching Resources   **CTB** Computer Test Bank
RCA Reading in the Content Area   **ISLM** Integrated Science Laboratory Manual   **STP** Standardized Test Preparation Book
GSW Guided Study Workbook   **ELL** Teacher's ELL Handbook   **SES** Science Explorer Series Text

Meeting the National Science Education Standards and AAAS Benchmarks

National Science Education Standards	Benchmarks for Science Literacy	Unifying Themes
Science as Inquiry (Content Standard A) ◆ **Design and conduct a scientific investigation** Students make observations, control variables, and design experiments about wave behavior. *(Skills Lab, Wavy Motions; Skills Lab, Making Waves)* ◆ **Develop descriptions, explanations, predictions, and models using evidence** Students identify examples of periodic motion and collect and organize data about periodic events. *(Chapter Project)* **Physical Science** (Content Standard B) ◆ **Motions and forces** A wave can be described by its wavelength, amplitude, and frequency. When waves encounter objects, they reflect, refract, or diffract. *(Sections 2, 3)* ◆ **Transfer of energy** Waves transfer energy through a medium. *(Section 1)* **Earth and Space Science** (Content Standard D) ◆ **Structure of the earth system** The release of energy from Earth's moving plates causes seismic waves to travel through Earth's crust. *(Section 4)*	**1B Scientific Inquiry** Students control variables as they examine wave behavior. *(Skills Lab, Making Waves)* **2A Patterns and Relationships** Wavelength, amplitude, frequency, and speed can be measured. *(Section 3)* Scientists measure seismic waves to determine the epicenter of an earthquake. *(Section 4)* **4A Processes That Shape the Earth** Movement of the Earth's crustal plates releases seismic waves. *(Section 4)* **4F Motion** Waves spread outward from the source of a vibration and may change direction or speed when they encounter a different medium or barrier. *(Sections 1, 2, 3, 4; Skills Lab, Wavy Motions; Skills Lab, Making Waves)* **9B Symbolic Relationships** Wave speed is equal to wavelength multiplied by wave frequency. *(Section 2)* **11C Constancy and Change** Waves are periodic events that can be described by their wavelength, amplitude, and frequency. *(Sections 1, 2; Chapter Project; Skills Lab, Making Waves)*	◆ **Energy** Waves are disturbances that transfer energy from one place to another. Increasing the energy in a wave affects its amplitude and frequency. *(Sections 1, 2; Skills Lab, Making Waves)* ◆ **Patterns of Change** Waves are periodic events that can be described by their wavelength, amplitude, frequency, and speed. Waves may reflect, refract, or diffract when they reach different surfaces. *(Sections 1, 3, 4; Chapter Project; Skills Lab, Wavy Motions)* ◆ **Scale and Structure** Transverse waves have crests and troughs while longitudinal waves have compressions and rarefactions. Surface waves combine the motion of these two waves. *(Section 1)* Seismic activity can generate extremely powerful transverse, longitudinal, and surface waves, such as tsunamis. *(Section 4)* ◆ **Systems and Interactions** The speed of a wave depends on the properties of the medium through which the wave is traveling. Waves interact with each other and other objects by reflection, refraction, diffraction, and interference. *(Sections 1, 2, 3, 4, Skills Labs, Chapter Project)*

Take It to the Net

 Interactive text at www.phschool.com

Science Explorer comes alive with iText.

- **Complete student text** is accessible from any computer with a browser.
- **Animations, simulations, and videos** enhance student understanding and retention of concepts.
- **Self-tests and online study tools** assess student understanding.
- **Teacher management tools** help you make the most of this valuable resource.

STAY CURRENT with **SCIENCE NEWS**®

Find out the latest research and information about wave behavior at:
www.phschool.com

Go to **www.phschool.com** and click on the Science icon. Then click on Science Explorer under PH@school.

ACTIVITY	Time (minutes)	Materials Quantities for one work group	Skills
Section 1			
Discover, p. 14	10	**Consumable** water, paper towels **Nonconsumable** shallow pan at least 20 cm across, a cork	Observing
Section 2			
Discover, p. 18	10	**Nonconsumable** medium-weight rope about 3 m long	Predicting
Skills Lab, pp. 20–21	40	**Nonconsumable** spring toy, meter stick	Observing
Section 3			
Discover, p. 24	10	**Consumable** water **Nonconsumable** ball, meter stick	Developing Hypotheses
Sharpen Your Skills, p. 25	10	**Consumable** straw, paper **Nonconsumable** piece of terry cloth or towel	Observing
Try This, p. 27	10	**Nonconsumable** 3-m elastic cord; fixed, solid object, such as doorknob	Predicting
Science at Home, p. 29	home	**Consumable** water **Nonconsumable** sink, bath toy	Observing, Making Models, Communicating
Skills Lab, pp. 30–31	25	**Consumable** paper towels, water **Nonconsumable** metric ruler, modeling clay, cork or other small floating object, ripple tank (aluminum foil lasagna pan with mirror at the bottom), plastic dropper	Making Models
Section 4			
Discover, p. 32	10	**Nonconsumable** 5 empty plastic film canisters, sand, modeling clay	Inferring
Science at Home, p. 34	home	**Nonconsumable** spoon, table	Observing

A list of all materials required for the Student Edition activities can be found beginning on page T15. You can obtain information about ordering materials by calling 1-800-848-9500 or by accessing the Science Explorer Internet site at: **www.phschool.com**

Over and Over and Over Again

Students' lives are full of periodic events, such as the changing of the seasons or the progression from morning to night. This project will provide an opportunity for students to identify periodic motion and events, and to apply concepts of wave properties and interactions to describe them.

Purpose In this project, students identify examples of periodic motion or other periodic events. Then they analyze data on the frequency and duration of each periodic event, and classify each event according to concepts they learn in this chapter.

Skills Focus After completing the Chapter 1 Project, students will be able to
◆ observe and classify periodic events;
◆ interpret data about the frequency and duration of these events;
◆ communicate their results to classmates in the form of a display, poster, or demonstration.

Project Time Line This project will take approximately one week. Initially, students identify and observe periodic events, sketch or describe these events, and record data on their frequency and duration. Students should apply chapter concepts to describe chosen events. Finally, students present their observations and analyses to the class as a poster, display, or demonstration. Before beginning the project, see Chapter 1 Project Teacher Notes on pages 6–7 in Teaching Resources for more details on carrying out the project. Also, distribute to students the Chapter 1 Project Overview and Worksheets and Scoring Rubric on pages 8–12 in Teaching Resources.

Suggested Shortcuts To save time, allow students to work in small groups.

Possible Materials Students will need graph paper to sketch their observations. They may also require clocks or stopwatches to measure the duration of the periodic events and rulers for making other measurements. Pictures from magazines and newspapers may be helpful to illustrate events that show rhythmic patterns. Provide poster board,

CHAPTER 1 Characteristics of Waves

WEB ACTIVITY www.phschool.com

SECTION **1** What Are Waves?
Discover **How Do Waves Travel?**

SECTION **2** Properties of Waves
Discover **How Can You Change a Wave?**
Skills Lab **Wavy Motions**

SECTION **3** Interactions of Waves
Discover **How Does a Ball Bounce?**
Sharpen Your Skills **Observing**
Try This **Standing Waves**
Skills Lab **Making Waves**

markers, scissors, and tape for students to use in preparing their presentations.

Launching the Project To introduce the project, have the class join hands in a circle. Ask them to use their arms to make repeating patterns that go back and forth and up and down. Then have them experiment, making waves of different speeds, frequencies, and amplitudes. Students should observe how long it takes for them to repeat their movement.

Allow time for students to read the description of the project in their text and the Chapter 1 Project Overview and Worksheets on pages 8–11 in Teaching Resources. Encourage discussions on periodic events. Ask students: **What events can you think of that show a regular, repeated pattern?** (Samples: ocean tides, playground swings, hands on a clock) Have students brainstorm a list of events they could include in this project.

Over and Over and Over Again

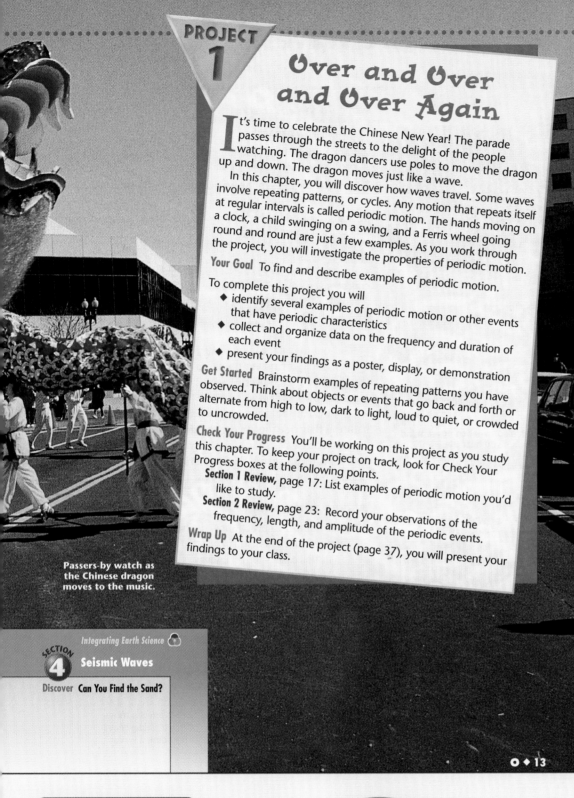

It's time to celebrate the Chinese New Year! The parade passes through the streets to the delight of the people watching. The dragon dancers use poles to move the dragon up and down. The dragon moves just like a wave.

In this chapter, you will discover how waves travel. Some waves involve repeating patterns, or cycles. Any motion that repeats itself at regular intervals is called periodic motion. The hands moving on a clock, a child swinging on a swing, and a Ferris wheel going round and round are just a few examples. As you work through the project, you will investigate the properties of periodic motion.

Your Goal To find and describe examples of periodic motion.

To complete this project you will
◆ identify several examples of periodic motion or other events that have periodic characteristics
◆ collect and organize data on the frequency and duration of each event
◆ present your findings as a poster, display, or demonstration

Get Started Brainstorm examples of repeating patterns you have observed. Think about objects or events that go back and forth or alternate from high to low, dark to light, loud to quiet, or crowded to uncrowded.

Check Your Progress You'll be working on this project as you study this chapter. To keep your project on track, look for Check Your Progress boxes at the following points.
Section 1 Review, page 17: List examples of periodic motion you'd like to study.
Section 2 Review, page 23: Record your observations of the frequency, length, and amplitude of the periodic events.

Wrap Up At the end of the project (page 37), you will present your findings to your class.

Passers-by watch as the Chinese dragon moves to the music.

Integrating Earth Science

SECTION
4
Seismic Waves

Discover **Can You Find the Sand?**

O ◆ 13

Program Resources

◆ **Teaching Resources** Chapter 1 Project Teacher Notes, pp. 6–7; Chapter 1 Project Overview and Worksheets, pp. 8–11; Chapter 1 Project Scoring Rubric, p. 12

Media and Technology

 Audio CDs and **Audiotapes**
English-Spanish Section Summaries

WEB ACTIVITY www.phschool.com

You will find an Internet activity, chapter self-tests for students, and links to other chapter topics at this site.

Performance Assessment

The Chapter 1 Project Scoring Rubric on page 12 of Teaching Resources will help you evaluate how well students complete the Chapter 1 Project. Students will be assessed on
◆ the thoroughness of their lists of periodic events;
◆ their observations and the thoroughness and organization of their data analyses;
◆ how well they are able to apply concepts of wave motion such as amplitude, speed, and frequency to their periodic events;
◆ the clarity and completeness of their presentation and written analysis.
By sharing the Chapter 1 Scoring Rubric with students at the beginning of the project, you will make it clear to them what they are expected to do.

Objectives

After completing the lesson, students will be able to
- ◆ define waves and identify what causes them;
- ◆ identify and compare the three main types of waves.

Key Terms wave, energy, medium, mechanical wave, vibration, transverse wave, crest, trough, longitudinal wave, compression, rarefaction, surface wave

1 Engage/Explore

Activating Prior Knowledge

Show a video recording of a periodic event, such as waves breaking on a beach or a Ferris wheel in motion. Ask students to look for patterns in the motion. Students should conclude that some motions have a repeating rhythm.

········ DISCOVER ·········

Skills Focus observing
Materials *shallow pan at least 20 cm across; water; a cork; paper towels*
Time 10 minutes
Tips As an alternative, place a clear pan on an overhead projector. Then carry out the activity as a teacher demonstration. The patterns of the waves will be projected onto the overhead projector screen.
Expected Outcome Patterns of waves will be seen spreading across the surface of the water. The cork will bob up and down.
Think It Over The cork bobbed up and down as the ripple went by in Step 4. The wave moves horizontally, and the cork moves vertically.

SECTION 1 What Are Waves?

DISCOVER ················· ACTIVITY

How Do Waves Travel?

1. Fill a shallow pan with about 3 centimeters of water.
2. With a pencil, touch the surface of the water at one end of the pan twice each second for about a minute.
3. Describe the pattern the waves make. Sketch a rough diagram of what you see.
4. Float a cork on the water. How do you think the cork will move if there are waves? Repeat Step 2 to find out.

Think It Over

Observing What happened to the cork in Step 4? How is the cork's movement similar to the wave's movement? How is it different? Draw a diagram of what you see. Use arrows to show the movement of the cork.

GUIDE FOR READING

- ◆ What causes waves?
- ◆ What are the three main types of waves?

Reading Tip Before you read, think of what comes to mind when you hear the word *wave*. As you read, write a definition of wave.

Far out to sea, the wind disturbs the calm surface of the water. A ripple forms. As the wind continues to blow, the ripple grows into a powerful wave that can travel a great distance. Near the beach, surfers wait eagerly. They quickly paddle into deeper water to catch the monstrous wave. Surfers enjoy the power of nature as they ride the wave to the shore.

What are waves? How can they travel so far? Why are some waves more powerful than others? In this section, you will explore how waves begin and how they move.

Waves and Energy

Waves crashing on a beach show the tremendous energy waves can carry. A **wave** is a disturbance that transfers energy from place to place. In science, **energy** is defined as the ability to do work. To understand waves, think of a boat out on the ocean. If a wave disturbs the surface of the water, it will cause anything floating on the water to be disturbed, too. The energy carried by a wave can lift even a large ship as it passes.

The disturbance caused by a wave is temporary. After the wave has passed, the water is calm again.

◀ A surfer riding a wave

14 ◆ O

READING STRATEGIES

Reading Tip Before students read the section, encourage them to create visual representations of waves they are familiar with. Some students may draw ocean waves. Others may use gestures or pieces of rope or string to demonstrate wave patterns.

Vocabulary As students read, have them list each boldfaced vocabulary term and write a definition of the term in their own words.

Study and Comprehension Have students write brief summaries of the information under each heading. Remind students to include only main ideas and key details in their summaries. Students can then use the summaries as study guides for the section.

What Carries Waves? Many waves require something to travel through. Water waves travel along the surface of the water, and sound waves travel through air. You can even make a wave travel along a rope. The material through which a wave travels is called a **medium**. Gases (such as air), liquids (such as water), and solids (such as ropes) all act as mediums. Waves that require a medium through which to travel are called **mechanical waves**.

Although waves travel through a medium, they do not carry the medium itself with them. Look at the duck in Figure 1. When a wave moves under the duck, the duck moves up and down. It does not move along the surface of the water. After the wave passes, the water and the duck return to where they started.

Breaking waves at a beach behave a little differently. When waves hit a beach, the water does move along with the wave. This happens because the ocean floor near the beach slopes upward. As the water at the bottom of the wave hits the slope, it moves up toward the top of the wave. The top of the wave gets bigger and continues to move forward. Eventually it topples over, turning white and frothy.

Not all waves require a medium to carry them along. Light from the sun, for example, can travel through empty space. Light is an example of an electromagnetic wave. You will learn more about electromagnetic waves in Chapter 3.

What Causes Waves? You can create waves by dipping your finger in water. **Waves are created when a source of energy causes a medium to vibrate.** A **vibration** is a repeated back-and-forth or up-and-down motion. This motion is the wave.

A moving object has energy. The moving object can transfer energy to a nearby medium, creating a wave. For example, as the propellers of a motorboat turn, they disturb the calm water surface. The boat's propeller transfers energy to the water. The propeller produces a wave that travels through the water. As the boat moves through the water, it also causes waves.

☑ *Checkpoint* *What are mechanical waves?*

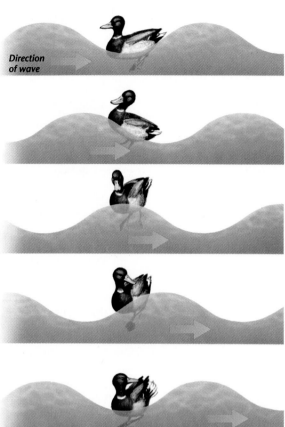

Direction of wave

Figure 1 Waves travel through water, but they do not carry the water with them. The duck moves up and down as a wave passes under it. The duck does not travel along with the wave.
Interpreting Diagrams If you add a sixth sketch to the diagram, which stage should it most resemble?

Waves and Energy

Demonstration

Materials *2-m long cord, colored ribbon*
Time 10 minutes

Tie one end of the cord to a doorknob or piece of furniture at about waist height. Tie one end of the ribbon to the middle of the cord. Hold the cord almost taut and parallel to the floor, then flick the end of the cord so that a wave travels along the cord. To help students distinguish between the wave and the medium, ask: **Which way did the wave move?** *(Along the cord)* **The ribbon?** *(Up and down)* Challenge students to explain what this tells them about the relationship between the wave and the medium. *(Sample: The wave moves through the medium but does not carry the medium along with it.)* **learning modality: visual**

Using the Visuals: Figure 1

Have students point to the top of each wave in the figure. Then ask: **What happens to the top of the wave over time?** *(It moves to the right of the picture.)* Have students compare and contrast this movement to the motion of the duck. *(The duck moves up and down while the wave moves to the right.)* Challenge students to infer what the duck's motion would be like if the wave moved twice as fast. *(The duck would move up and down twice as fast.)* **learning modality: visual**

Answers to Self-Assessment
Caption Question
Figure 1 A sixth sketch would resemble the second stage of the visual.
☑ *Checkpoint*
Mechanical waves are waves that require a medium through which to travel.

Program Resources

◆ **Teaching Resources** 1-1 Lesson Plan, p. 13; 1-1 Section Summary, p. 14
◆ **Guided Study Workbook** Section 1-1

Ongoing Assessment

Oral Presentation Ask students to describe what happens when a pebble is dropped into a pond using the terms *medium* and *wave*. *(Sample: When a pebble is dropped into a pond, it causes a disturbance in the medium, and a wave travels through the water.)*

Types of Waves

Using the Visuals: Figure 2

Challenge students to sketch similar drawings, making the crests closer together, farther apart, taller, and shorter. Encourage them to label the crests and troughs. **learning modality: visual** Students can save their sketches in their portfolios.

Including All Students

Materials *spring toy, colored ribbon*
Time 10 minutes

This activity will help students who need additional help to understand the concept of longitudinal waves. Have two volunteers hold opposite ends of a spring toy. Tie a brightly colored ribbon onto one coil of the spring. Encourage one volunteer to begin a wave by pushing one end of the spring toy toward the other end without letting go. Students can observe the behavior of the ribbon at points of compression and rarefaction along the wave. Ask students to compare this motion with the motion of a transverse wave. Ask: **What do these two motions have in common?** (*Samples: Both are caused by a disturbance in a medium; both are repeated motion.*)
limited English proficiency

Building Inquiry Skills: Comparing and Contrasting

Ask a volunteer to draw a transverse wave on the board. Invite students to point in the direction of the wave motion. Then ask them to point in the direction that the particles of the medium move. (*Students' arms should be perpendicular to the original position.*) Then draw, or challenge a volunteer to draw, a longitudinal wave. Ask students to point first in the direction of the wave motion, then in the direction of the medium's motion. (*Students should point in the same direction both times.*)
learning modality: kinesthetic

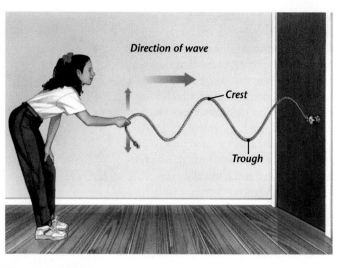

Figure 2 As she moves the free end of a rope up and down, the girl transfers energy to the rope. The energy travels along the rope, creating a transverse wave.

Types of Waves

Different types of waves travel through mediums in different ways. **Waves are classified according to how they move. The three types of waves are transverse waves, longitudinal waves, and surface waves.**

Transverse Waves When you make a wave on a rope, the wave moves from one end of the rope to the other. The rope itself, however, moves up and down or from side to side. Waves that move the medium at right angles to the direction in which the waves are traveling are called **transverse waves.** Transverse means "across." As a transverse wave moves in one direction, the particles of the medium move across the direction of the wave. Figure 2 shows that some parts of the rope are very high while some are very low. The highest parts of the wave are called **crests,** and the lowest parts are called **troughs** (trawfs).

Figure 3 The coils in the spring toy move back and forth parallel to the motion of the wave. This is a longitudinal wave. *Comparing and Contrasting How does this wave compare with waves on a rope?*

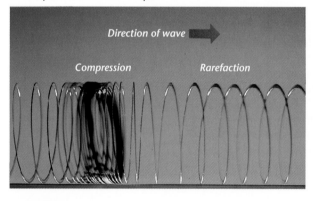

Longitudinal Waves Figure 3 shows a different kind of wave. If you stretch out a spring toy and push and pull one end, you can produce a longitudinal wave. **Longitudinal waves** (lawn juh TOO duh nul) move the particles of the medium parallel to the direction in which the waves are traveling. The coils in the spring move back and forth parallel to the wave motion.

Notice in Figure 3 that in some parts of the spring the coils are close together.

Background

Integrating Science Massive disturbances from underwater earthquakes or volcanoes can form deadly tsunamis. The word *tsunami* comes from a Japanese word meaning "harbor wave." Tsunamis usually occur as a series of surface waves and can travel as fast as 1,000 km/hour. As a tsunami approaches shore, its velocity slows and its height increases. The result is a huge wall of water.

In July 1998, a deadly tsunami struck the northern shore of Papua New Guinea. The waves, which were up to 15 m high, were triggered by a 7.0 magnitude earthquake only 30 km off the coast. Two entire villages were washed away. Many people who were near the coastline were swept out to sea or tossed into the nearby jungle by the force of the waves. More than 2,000 people died.

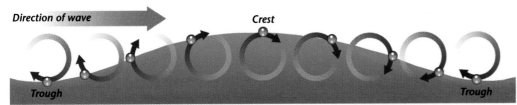

Direction of wave

Crest

Trough   **Trough**

In other parts, the coils are more spread out. The parts where the coils are close together are called **compressions** (kum PRESH uns). The parts where the coils are spread out, or rarefied, are called **rarefactions** (rair uh FAK shunz).

As compressions and rarefactions travel along the spring toy, each coil moves slightly forward and then back. The energy travels from one end of the spring to the other, creating a wave. After the wave passes, each part of the spring returns to the position where it started.

Combinations of Waves **Surface waves** are combinations of transverse and longitudinal waves. These waves occur at the surface between two mediums, such as water and air. When a wave passes through water, the water (and anything on it) moves up and down, like a transverse wave on a rope. The water also moves back and forth slightly in the direction that the wave is traveling, like the coils of the spring. But unlike the coils of a spring, water does not compress. The up-and-down and back-and-forth movements combine to make each particle of water move in a circle. Figure 4 shows the circular motion of surface waves.

Figure 4 In a surface wave, up-and-down motion combines with back-and-forth motion. The combination produces circular motion.

Section 1 Review

1. Where do waves get their energy?
2. Name the three types of waves. Give an example of each type.
3. When a wave passes a ship at sea, how does the wave affect the ship?
4. **Thinking Critically** **Applying Concepts** The vibrations produced by a jackhammer are used to break up pavement. What type of waves do you think the jackhammer produces in the ground? Explain.

Check Your Progress
CHAPTER PROJECT 1
Find and list as many examples of periodic motion as you can. Look for cycles and patterns that repeat in only a few seconds and others that take hours or days to repeat. Try to find examples that continue day after day, such as the rising and setting of the sun. Don't limit your search to your home or school. Look at the world around you and at the solar system for ideas. Describe and sketch each example you find.

Program Resources

◆ **Teaching Resources** 1-1 Review and Reinforce, p. 15; 1-1 Enrich, p. 16

Media and Technology

 Transparencies "Transverse Wave," Transparency 2; "Longitudinal Wave," Transparency 3

Answers to Self-Assessment

Caption Question

Figure 3 This wave is longitudinal, which means the particles of the medium move parallel to the direction that the waves are traveling. The waves on a rope are transverse, which means the particles of the medium move across the direction of the wave.

---

3 Assess

Section 1 Review Answers

1. Waves get their energy from the source of a vibration or disturbance.
2. Transverse—wave on a rope; longitudinal—compression wave on a spring toy; surface—wave on the surface of water
3. The wave makes the ship move up and down.
4. Answers may vary. Students may say that the jackhammer produces surface waves, because the jackhammer moves the ground up and down similar to creating up and down vibrations on the surface of water. Students may also say that the jackhammer produces longitudinal waves that travel down into the ground.

Check Your Progress
CHAPTER PROJECT 1
Students' lists should include at least ten different periodic motions or events. Remind students that they are looking for patterns or repeated events. Make sure students record detailed information about each event, including the duration of the event, how frequently it repeats, and any other measurable qualities about the event (e.g., how high a swing travels or how wide a pendulum swings). Encourage students to continue to look for periodic events around them.

Performance Assessment

Drawing Have students diagram a transverse wave and a longitudinal wave, including arrows showing the directions of motion of the waves and of the particles.

 Portfolio Students can save their diagrams in their portfolios.

O ◆ 17

Objectives

After completing the lesson, students will be able to
♦ list and describe the basic properties of waves;
♦ describe how a wave's speed is related to its wavelength and frequency and calculate a wave's speed.

Key Terms amplitude, wavelength, frequency, hertz (Hz)

1 Engage/Explore

Activating Prior Knowledge

Invite students to list examples of waves or wavelike motion. *(Samples: ocean waves, the motion of a snake, ripples on the water)* Ask students to describe different speeds or sizes of waves they have seen.

⸻⸻ DISCOVER ⸻⸻

Skills Focus predicting
Materials *medium-weight rope about 3 m long*
Time 10 minutes
Tips Caution students not to flick the rope at one another. If classroom space is not available, students may be able to perform the activity in the hall. Make sure students work quietly and do not block walkways or emergency exits. Before the activity, you may wish to introduce the term *wavelength* to help students describe their experiences.
Expected Outcome The observer will see transverse waves travel down the rope.
Think It Over The wavelength grew shorter when the rope was flicked more often. The waves will become longer if the partner flicks the rope less often.

DISCOVER ⸻⸻⸻⸻⸻⸻⸻⸻ ACTIVITY

How Can You Change a Wave?

1. Lay a rope about 3 meters long on a smooth floor. Securely hold one end. Have a partner hold the other end.

2. Flick the end of the rope left and right about once per second to make a series of waves travel down the rope. Observe the waves as they travel toward your partner.

3. Now flick the end of the rope more often—about two times per second. Again, observe the waves.

4. Switch roles with your partner and repeat Steps 2 and 3.

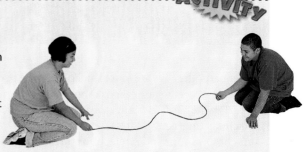

Think It Over
Predicting What happened to the waves when you flicked the rope more often? How will the wave change if you flick the rope less often than once per second? Try it.

GUIDE FOR READING

♦ What are the basic properties of waves?

♦ How is a wave's speed related to its wavelength and frequency?

Reading Tip As you read, make a list of the properties of waves. Write a sentence that describes each property.

Rhythmic gymnastics ▶

One of the most elegant and graceful Olympic sports is rhythmic gymnastics. A ribbon dancer flicks a stick attached to a ribbon, making waves travel down the ribbon. Some of the waves are long, while others are shorter. The rate at which the gymnast flicks her hands affects the length and shape of the waves in the ribbon.

There are many different kinds of waves. Waves can carry a little energy or a lot. They can be short or long. They can be rare or frequent. They can travel fast or slow. All waves, however, share certain properties. **The basic properties of waves are amplitude, wavelength, frequency, and speed.**

Wave Diagrams

To understand the properties of waves, it helps to represent a wave on a diagram. Transverse waves like those on a rope are easy to draw. You can draw a transverse wave as shown in Figure 5. Think of the horizontal line as the position of the rope before it is disturbed. This is its rest position. As the wave passes, the rope goes above or below the rest position. Remember that the crests and the troughs are the highest and lowest points on the wave.

READING STRATEGIES

Reading Tip Suggest that pairs of students discuss the information in the section before writing sentences describing the properties of waves. Encourage students to paraphrase their descriptions. Remind them that to paraphrase a sentence or paragraph means to restate it in their own words.

Study and Comprehension Before students begin reading, have them preview the section by reading the headings and boldfaced sentences and terms. Discuss with students what they already know about properties of waves. Then have students look at the pictures and read the captions. Encourage students to jot down questions and try to answer them as they read.

To draw longitudinal waves, think of the compressions in the spring toy as being similar to the crests of a transverse wave. The rarefactions in the spring toy are like the troughs of a transverse wave. By treating compressions as crests and rarefactions as troughs, you can draw longitudinal waves in the same way as transverse waves.

☑ *Checkpoint* Which part of a longitudinal wave is similar to the crest of a transverse wave?

Amplitude

Some waves are very high, while others are barely noticeable. The distance the medium rises depends on the amplitude of the wave that passes through it. **Amplitude** is the maximum distance the particles of the medium carrying the wave move away from their rest positions. The amplitude is a measure of how much a particle in the medium moves when disturbed by the wave. The amplitude of a water wave is the maximum distance a water particle moves above or below the surface level of calm water.

You know that waves are produced by something vibrating. The farther the medium moves as it vibrates, the larger the amplitude of the resulting waves. You can increase the amplitude of the waves on a rope by moving your hand up and down a greater distance. To do this, you have to use more energy. This greater amount of energy is then transferred to the rope. Thus, the amplitude of a wave is a direct measure of its energy.

Amplitude of Transverse Waves Compare the two transverse waves in Figure 6. You can see that wave A goes up and down a greater distance than wave B. The amplitude of a transverse wave is the maximum distance the medium moves up or down from its rest position. You can find the amplitude of a transverse wave by measuring the distance from the rest position to a crest or to a trough.

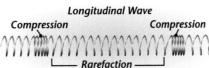

Figure 5 The crests and troughs of a transverse wave are the points at which the medium is farthest from the rest position. The compressions of a longitudinal wave correspond to the crests of a transverse wave.

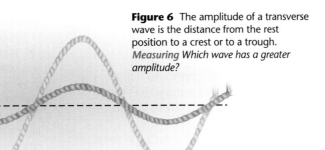

Figure 6 The amplitude of a transverse wave is the distance from the rest position to a crest or to a trough. *Measuring Which wave has a greater amplitude?*

Wave Diagrams

Inquiry Challenge

Materials *masking tape, 2-m rope, meter stick*
Time 20 minutes

Direct students to closely examine Figure 5. Have students work in small groups. Students should first place a long piece of masking tape along the floor to indicate the rest position. Two students can use the rope to generate transverse waves, and others can mark and measure the crests and troughs. Finally, challenge students to use their data to draw the transverse wave. **cooperative learning**

Portfolio　Students can save their wave diagrams in their portfolios.

Amplitude

Building Inquiry Skills: Controlling Variables

Materials *bed sheet or similar length of fabric*
Time 10 minutes

Fold the sheet or fabric to about 1 m in width. Position a student at each end, holding the sheet parallel to the floor with both hands. Have one student use a rhythmic motion to raise and lower his or her end. The waves should move toward the stationary student. Then have the student creating the wave use a larger or smaller range of motion. Ask: **What is the manipulated variable?** (*Amplitude*) Challenge students to explain how amplitude is related to energy. (*Waves with higher amplitudes have more energy.*) **learning modality: kinesthetic**

Ongoing Assessment

Drawing Have students draw two longitudinal waves with different amplitudes.

Program Resources

◆ **Teaching Resources** 1-2 Lesson Plan, p. 17; 1-2 Section Summary, p. 18
◆ **Guided Study Workbook** Section 1-2

Media and Technology

Exploring Physical Science Videodisc Unit 6, Side 2, "A Wave Is a Wave Is a Wave"

Chapter 2

Answers to Self-Assessment

Caption Question
Figure 6 Wave A has the larger amplitude.

☑ *Checkpoint*
A compression of a longitudinal wave is similar to the crest of a transverse wave.

Wavy Motions

Preparing for Inquiry

Key Concept Transverse and longitudinal waves demonstrate wave properties such as wavelength, amplitude, and frequency.

Skills Objectives Students will be able to
◆ observe properties of waves;
◆ compare and contrast transverse and longitudinal waves.

Time 40 minutes

Alternative Materials Coiled springs that can be stretched to about 3 m work better than shorter lengths. You can also use two plastic toy springs joined end to end with PVC cement. Some students may be able to see the waves more clearly in the brightly colored plastic coils.

Guiding Inquiry

Invitation

Ask students to describe how they could use the spring toy to model waves. Demonstrate with a volunteer the motions students will perform in the lab.

Troubleshooting the Experiment

◆ Caution students not to overstretch the spring because it may lose its shape.
◆ Make sure students hold onto the ends of the spring toys firmly. Released springs can cause injury.

Analyze and Conclude

1. In Steps 1–5, students should describe transverse waves. In Steps 6–7, students should describe longitudinal waves.
2. Transverse; the movement of the medium is at right angles to the direction the wave is traveling.
3. The wave is reflected back along the spring, but it is inverted so that the crest of the reflected wave is on the opposite side of the spring from the crest of the original wave.
4. Longitudinal; the movement of the medium is in the same direction as the wave is traveling.
5. As rate increases, frequency increases and wavelength decreases.
6. Moving your hand a greater distance will increase the amplitude of the wave.

Figure 7 If the compressions of a longitudinal wave are very crowded, the wave has a large amplitude.
Interpreting Diagrams Which longitudinal wave shown has the larger amplitude?

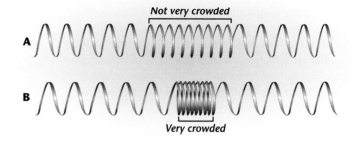

Amplitude of Longitudinal Waves The amplitude of a longitudinal wave is a measure of how compressed or rarefied the medium becomes. High-energy vibrations cause the compressions to be very crowded. This makes the rarefactions quite loose. Crowded compressions and uncrowded rarefactions are like high crests and low troughs. They mean that the longitudinal wave has a large amplitude.

Skills Lab

Observing

Wavy Motions

N ow it's your turn to make some waves on a spring toy. In this lab, you will observe some properties of waves.

Problem

How do waves travel in a spring toy?

Materials

spring toy   meter stick

Procedure

1. On a smooth floor, stretch the spring to about 3 meters. Hold one end while your partner holds the other end. Do not overstretch the spring toy.
2. Pull a few coils of the spring toy to one side near one end of the spring.
3. Release the coils and observe the motion of the spring. What happens when the disturbance reaches your partner? Draw what you observe.
4. Have your partner move one end of the spring toy to the left and then to the right on the floor. Be certain that both ends of the spring are held securely. Draw a diagram of the wave you observe.
5. Repeat Step 4, increasing the rate at which you move the spring toy left and right. Record your observations.
6. Squeeze together several coils of the spring toy, making a compression.
7. Release the compressed section of the spring toy and observe the disturbance as it moves down the spring. Record your observations. Draw and label what you see.

7. Students' drawings and explanations should describe the wave moving through the medium; while the particles in the medium move parallel to the direction of the wave.

Extending the Inquiry

More to Explore

Waves will travel at different speeds in different spring toys. The wavelength, frequency, and amplitude will also vary. Different sizes of springs and different materials determine how wave properties will change. Different spring toys have different masses and require different amounts of force to stretch.

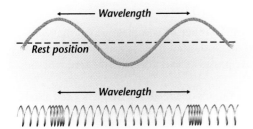

Figure 8 The wavelength of a transverse wave is the distance from crest to crest. The wavelength of a longitudinal wave is the distance from compression to compression.

Wavelength
Rest position
Wavelength

Wavelength

A wave travels a certain distance before it starts to repeat. The distance between two corresponding parts of a wave is its **wavelength.** You can find the wavelength of a transverse wave by measuring the distance from crest to crest or from trough to trough. You can find the wavelength of a longitudinal wave by measuring the distance from one compression to the next.

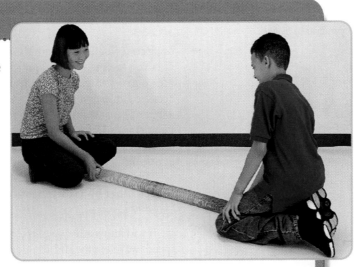

Analyze and Conclude

1. Compare the waves generated in Steps 1–5 with the waves generated in Steps 6–7.
2. Were the waves generated in Steps 1–5 transverse or longitudinal? Explain your answer.
3. In Step 3 of the procedure, compare the original wave to the wave that came back.
4. Were the waves generated in Steps 6 and 7 transverse or longitudinal? Explain your answer.
5. What happened to the wavelength and frequency when you increased the rate at which the spring toy moved left and right?
6. How did you change the amplitude of the waves you made?
7. **Think About It** Based on your observations, describe two ways that waves move through a spring toy. Use drawings and written explanations.

More to Explore

Obtain a wide variety of spring toys. Look for different sizes and materials, such as metal and plastic. Explore the differences among the waves you can produce on each spring. What accounts for these differences?

 21

Answers to Self-Assessment

Caption Question

Figure 7 Wave B has the larger amplitude.

Media and Technology

Lab Activity Videotape
Sound and Light, 1

Amplitude, continued

Using the Visuals: Figure 7

Ask students: **Which wave has more energy?** *(The one with the greater compression)* **How can you tell?** *(The compression is the amplitude of the wave, and the amplitude is a measure of the energy.)* **learning modality: visual**

Wavelength

Building Inquiry Skills: Interpreting Diagrams

Refer students to the diagrams in Figure 8. Ask them to predict the distance between the trough shown and the next trough. *(The distance will be the same as the distance between the crests.)* Have students draw a transverse wave. Then challenge them to draw a wave that is identical except that it has a wavelength equal to half the wavelength in the first drawing. Repeat for the longitudinal wave shown in the diagram. **learning modality: visual**

Inquiry Challenge

Materials *spring toy, tub of water*
Time 15 minutes
Tips Since space is limited, the distance the spring is stretched will be short.

Encourage students to predict the effect of water on the speed of transverse and longitudinal waves. Then allow students to choose a partner and challenge them to design an experiment to test their predictions using a spring toy and a tub of water. *(Because water is more dense than air, more energy will be required to produce the same movement. The waves will slow down in the water.)* **learning modality: kinesthetic**

Frequency

Demonstration

Materials *pencil, watch or clock with second hand*
Time 5 minutes

This demonstration allows students to observe how a frequency can increase or decrease. Tap a pencil on a table with a consistent beat for five seconds. Then ask: **How would you increase the frequency?** (*Tap the table more often in the five seconds.*) **How would you decrease the frequency?** (*Tap the table less often in the five seconds.*) Summarize by describing frequency as the number of vibrations or waves per second.
learning modality: kinesthetic

Speed

Math TOOLBOX

Ask students to identify the units used to measure frequency. (*Hertz, or Hz*) Then challenge the students to calculate the speed of a wave that has a wavelength of 0.5 m and a frequency of 4 waves per second. (*2 m/s*)
learning modality: logical/mathematical

Building Inquiry Skills: Inferring

As students examine the equation for speed, ask them to infer how two waves traveling at the same speed could have different frequencies. (*The waves would have different wavelengths.*) Then choose two pairs of students to check their inferences by demonstrating this comparison. Give each pair of students a rope about 3 m long. Each student should face their partner from a comfortable distance, holding the rope so it has a little slack. The students should stand so that the ropes are parallel to each other. (*Students in both pairs should work together to create waves with the same speed but different wavelengths. They should time the waves to determine the frequencies of both.*)
learning modality: kinesthetic

Math TOOLBOX

Calculating With Units

When calculating with quantities that include units, treat the units as you do the numbers.

For example, if an object travels 6 m in 2 s, here is how you find its speed:

$$\text{Speed} = \frac{\text{Distance}}{\text{Time}}$$
$$= \frac{6 \text{ m}}{2 \text{ s}}$$
$$= 3 \text{ m/s}$$

A wave on a lake has a wavelength of 0.5 m and a frequency of 2 Hz (2 Hz = 2 per second, or 2/s). To find the speed of the wave, use this formula:

$$\text{Speed} = \text{Wavelength} \times \text{Frequency}$$

Substitute and simplify:

$$\text{Speed} = 0.5 \text{ m} \times 2 \text{ Hz}$$
$$= 0.5 \text{ m} \times 2/\text{s}$$
$$= 1 \text{ m/s}$$

The speed of the wave is 1 m/s. Note that the answer is in meters per second, which is a correct unit for speed.

Frequency

Wave **frequency** is the number of complete waves that pass a given point in a certain amount of time. If you make waves on a rope so that one wave passes by every second, the frequency is 1 wave per second.

Since waves are vibrations of a medium, frequency can also be described as the number of vibrations per second. To increase the frequency of the waves on a rope, you can make more vibrations by moving your hand up and down more often, perhaps two or three times per second. To decrease the frequency, you move your hand less often, perhaps once every two or three seconds.

Frequency is measured in units called **hertz (Hz)**. A wave or vibration that occurs every second has a frequency of 1 Hz. If two waves pass you every second, then the frequency of the wave is 2 per second, or 2 hertz. The hertz was named after the German scientist Heinrich Hertz, who first produced radio waves in an experimental situation.

☑ *Checkpoint* *How can you increase the frequency of rope waves?*

Speed

Imagine watching a distant thunderstorm on a hot summer day. First you see the flash of lightning. A few seconds later you hear the roll of thunder. Even though the lightning and thunder occurred at the same instant, they reach you seconds apart. This happens because sound and light travel at very different speeds. Light travels much faster than sound. Different waves travel at different speeds. The speed of a wave is how far the wave travels in one unit of time, or distance divided by time.

The speed, wavelength, and frequency of a wave are related to each other by a mathematical formula.

$$\text{Speed} = \text{Wavelength} \times \text{Frequency}$$

If you know any two of the quantities in the speed formula—speed, wavelength, and frequency—you can calculate the third quantity. For example, if you know the speed and the wavelength of a wave, you can calculate the frequency. If you know the speed and the frequency, you can calculate the wavelength.

$$\text{Frequency} = \frac{\text{Speed}}{\text{Wavelength}} \qquad \text{Wavelength} = \frac{\text{Speed}}{\text{Frequency}}$$

Waves in different mediums travel at different speeds. In a given medium and under the same conditions, the speed of a wave is constant. For example, all sound waves traveling through the air at the same pressure and at the same temperature travel

---

Background

History of Science Heinrich Hertz (1857–1894) was a German physicist who pioneered the technology that led to radar, radio, and television.

Hertz wanted to find physical evidence that electromagnetic waves exist. To do this, he built an electromagnetic wave transmitter and receiver from polished brass rods and looped wire. He successfully demonstrated his device, which caused a spark to travel from an oscillator to a receiver, in his classroom in Berlin. The demonstration showed that electromagnetic waves exist and travel at the speed of light.

Soon after Hertz's experiments, a young Italian scientist, Guglielmo Marconi (1874–1937), developed the first wireless communication system.

at the same speed. If the temperature or pressure changes, the sound waves will travel at a different speed.

If one type of wave travels at a constant speed in one medium, what do you think will happen if the frequency changes? When you multiply the wavelength and frequency after the change, you should get the same speed as before the change. Therefore, if you increase the frequency of a wave, the wavelength must decrease.

Sample Problem

The speed of a wave on a rope is 50 cm/s and its wavelength is 10 cm. What is the frequency?

Analyze.	You know speed and wavelength. You want to find frequency.
Write the formula.	$\text{Frequency} = \dfrac{\text{Speed}}{\text{Wavelength}}$
Substitute and solve.	$\text{Frequency} = \dfrac{50 \text{ cm/s}}{10 \text{ cm}}$
	$\text{Frequency} = \dfrac{50 \text{ /s}}{10}$
	Frequency = 5 /s (5 per second) or 5 Hz.
Think about it.	If you move your hand as often as 5 times a second, then fairly short waves, only 10 cm long, will move down the rope.
Practice Problems	1. A wave has a wavelength of 5 mm and a frequency of 2 Hz. At what speed does the wave travel?
	2. The speed of a wave on a guitar string is 100 m/s and the frequency is 1,000 Hz. What is the wavelength of the wave?

Section 2 Review

1. List the four basic properties of waves. Describe each property.
2. How are the speed, wavelength, and frequency of a wave related?
3. Can two waves have the same wavelength but different amplitudes? Explain.
4. **Thinking Critically** **Inferring** When you increase the tension on a piece of wire, the speed of waves on it increases, but the wavelength stays constant. What happens to the frequency of the waves as the tension on the wire is increased?

Check Your Progress

CHAPTER PROJECT 1

Observe the amplitude, wavelength, frequency, and speed of one of the periodic motions on your list. How many complete repetitions of each periodic motion occur in a given amount of time? How long does it take for a periodic event to finish and start again? Compare the highest and lowest position or the nearest and farthest position of the object showing periodic motion. Record your observations in your notebook.

Chapter 1   O ◆ **23**

Encourage students to phrase the problem and solution in sentences using their own words. *(Sample: If a wave can move 50 cm in 1 s, how many 10-cm waves will there be in 1 s?)*

Answers
1. (5 mm)(2 Hz) = 10 mm/s
2. (100 m/s) ÷ (1000 Hz) = 0.1 m

3 Assess

Section 2 Review Answers

1. Amplitude—distance from rest position to the crest or trough; wavelength—distance from crest to crest or trough to trough; frequency—number of waves that pass a given point each second; speed—distance traveled in a given time
2. Speed = wavelength × frequency
3. Two waves can have the same wavelength but different amplitudes if they have the same frequency but different amounts of energy.
4. The frequency increases.

Check Your Progress

CHAPTER PROJECT 1

Students should be able to explain their methods for determining the amplitude, wavelength, and frequency of the chosen event. For example, to determine frequency, students should measure the sun's motion from the same point each day. Encourage students to graph at least one periodic event and label its amplitude, wavelength, and frequency.

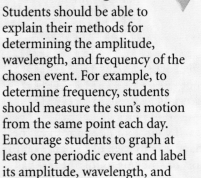

Media and Technology

Exploring Earth Science Videodisc
Unit 2, Side 2, "The Wave"

Chapter 4

Answers to Self-Assessment

☑ *Checkpoint*

Increase the number of vibrations per second on the rope by moving your hand more often.

Performance Assessment

Skills Check Have students draw on graph paper a diagram of a wave with a wavelength of 3 cm and an amplitude of 2 cm. Instruct them to calculate the speed of such a wave if its frequency is 10 Hz. *(30 cm/s)*

Objectives

After completing the lesson, students will be able to
◆ identify and compare reflection, refraction, and diffraction;
◆ describe the two types of interference of waves;
◆ identify and describe standing waves and resonance.

Key Terms reflection, angle of incidence, angle of reflection, refraction, diffraction, interference, constructive interference, destructive interference, standing wave, node, antinode, resonance

1 Engage/Explore

Activating Prior Knowledge

Use a hand-held mirror, or hang a mirror in the classroom. Ask students: **If you can see someone's eyes in a mirror, does that mean they can also see you?** Challenge students to discover whether their answer was correct. *(Students should discover that, as long as they are looking at the mirror, the other person can always see them in the mirror.)*

•••••••• **DISCOVER** ••••••••

Skills Focus developing hypotheses
Materials *ball, meter stick, water*
Time 10 minutes
Tips If your floor does not show the moisture path well, place paper on the floor for students to roll the wet ball along.
Think It Over Students should say that the ball bounced back from the wall at the same angle that it hit the wall.

DISCOVER •••••••••••••••••••••••••••••••• **ACTIVITY**

How Does a Ball Bounce?

1. Choose a spot at the base of a wall. From a distance of 1 m, roll a wet ball along the floor straight at the spot you chose. Watch the angle at which the ball bounces back by looking at the path of moisture on the floor.

2. Wet the ball again. From a different position, roll the ball at the same spot, but at an angle to the wall. Again, observe the angle at which the ball bounces back.

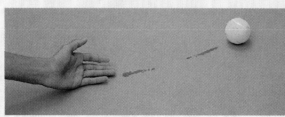

Think It Over

Developing Hypotheses How do you think the angle at which the ball hits the wall is related to the angle at which the ball bounces back? To test your hypothesis, roll the ball from several different positions toward the same spot on the wall.

GUIDE FOR READING

◆ What happens when waves hit a surface?
◆ How do waves bend?
◆ How do waves interact with each other?

Reading Tip Before you read, preview *Exploring Interactions of Waves* on pages 28–29. Make a list of any unfamiliar words. As you read, write a definition for each word on your list.

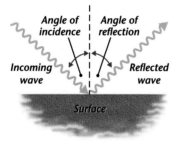

Angle of incidence | Angle of reflection
Incoming wave | Reflected wave
Surface

Figure 9 The angle of reflection is equal to the angle of incidence.

It is a hot, sunny day. You are the first person to enter the calm water of the swimming pool. To test the temperature of the water, you dip one foot in first. Your foot causes a series of ripples to travel across the water to the far wall of the pool. As each ripple hits the wall, it bounces off the wall and travels back toward you.

Reflection

When water waves hit the side of a swimming pool, they bounce back. **When an object or wave hits a surface through which it cannot pass, it bounces back.** This is called **reflection.**

To show reflection of a wave, draw a line to represent a surface. Draw another line to show a wave moving toward the surface at an angle. Now imagine a line perpendicular to the surface. The **angle of incidence** is the angle between the incoming wave and the imaginary perpendicular line. The **angle of reflection** is the angle between the reflected wave and the imaginary line. The law of reflection states that the angle of reflection equals the angle of incidence. All waves obey the law of reflection.

There are many examples of reflection in your everyday life. A ball that hits a wall bounces back, or is reflected. When you look in a mirror, you use reflected light to see yourself. An echo is an example of reflected sound.

READING STRATEGIES

Reading Tip After students prepare their lists, encourage them to draw a simple sketch to demonstrate the meaning of each unfamiliar word, using labels as needed. Next, allow students to choose a partner and take turns explaining their diagrams.

Study and Comprehension As students read the section, have them write definitions for the boldfaced terms. Then instruct them to work in small groups to create worksheets based on the terms. Offer suggestions such as matching activities or fill-in-the-blank activities. Then have each group compose the worksheet and an answer key. Direct groups to exchange worksheets and complete them. Then have students check their answers against the answer keys.

Refraction

Have you ever pushed a shopping cart that had a stiff wheel? If so, you know how difficult it is to control the direction of the cart. This is because the stiff wheel can't turn as fast as the other wheels. As you push the cart, it tends to veer to the side of the sticky wheel and so changes direction. Waves sometimes change direction when they enter a new medium. If a wave enters the new medium at an angle, one side changes speed before the other side. **When a wave moves from one medium into another medium at an angle, it changes speed as it enters the second medium, which causes it to bend.** The bending of waves due to a change in speed is called **refraction.**

Though all waves change speed when they enter a new medium, they don't always bend. Bending occurs only when one side of the wave enters the new medium before the other side of the wave. The side of the wave that enters the new medium first changes speed first. The other side is still traveling at its original speed. The bending occurs because the two sides of the wave are traveling at different speeds.

☑ *Checkpoint* What is refraction?

Diffraction

Sometimes waves can bend around an obstacle in their path. For example, waves can pass through a narrow entrance to a harbor and then spread out inside the harbor. Figure 10 shows water waves diffracting as they enter a harbor.

When a wave passes a barrier or moves through a hole in a barrier, it bends and spreads out. The bending of waves

Observing
ACTIVITY

Here is how you can simulate what happens as waves move from one medium to another.
1. Roll a drinking straw from a smooth tabletop straight onto a thin piece of terry cloth or a paper towel. Describe how the straw's motion changes as it leaves the smooth surface.
2. Repeat Step 1, but roll the straw at an angle to the cloth or paper. Describe what happens as each side of the straw hits the cloth or paper. How are your results similar to what happens when waves are refracted?

Figure 10 Waves from the ocean enter the harbor and spread out. This is an example of diffraction. *Predicting How do you think the waves in the harbor would change if the opening were wider?*

Reflection

Inquiry Challenge
Materials *flashlight, small mirror*

Time 20 minutes

🅚 Challenge small groups of students to plan how to use a mirror to project the beam of a flashlight around a corner. Students' plans should include drawings that show how the light will be reflected. Allow students to try their plans. Ask: **How did you decide where to place the mirror?** *(Because the angle of incidence is equal to the angle of reflection, the mirror should be placed so that light will hit it at a 45° angle.)* **cooperative learning**

Refraction

Sharpen your Skills

Observing

Materials *straw, piece of terry cloth or towel, paper*

Time 10 minutes
Tips Demonstrate rolling the straw along the tabletop. Push or blow on the straw so that it rolls by itself.
Expected Outcome The side of the straw that hits the cloth first slows down and the straw turns. Waves also slow down and change direction when they pass from one medium to another.
Extend Students can experiment with different materials to determine which cause the greatest refraction of the rolling straw. **learning modality: visual**

Answers to Self-Assessment
Caption Question
Figure 10 If the opening were wider, the waves would not diffract as much.
☑ *Checkpoint*
Refraction is the bending of waves due to a change in speed when the waves enter a new medium.

Ongoing Assessment

Oral Presentation Ask students to explain the difference between reflection and refraction.

Diffraction

Demonstration

Materials *shallow glass baking pan, overhead projector, wooden block*
Time 15 minutes

To show how waves bend around obstacles, place the pan on the projector, and half fill it with water. Generate waves at one end of the pan. Have students draw what they see. Put the block against one side of the pan, approximately in the middle of the pan. Ask students: **What will happen to the waves when they meet the block?** *(The waves will bend around the edges of the block.)* Generate waves as before, and have students draw what they see.
learning modality: visual

Interference

Inquiry Challenge

Materials *yarn, tape, straight drinking straws*
Time 15 minutes

Group students in teams of four, and challenge each group to create patterns of constructive and destructive interference using these materials. First, tape the ends of the yarn down about 80 cm apart on a flat surface. Have each student direct a straw toward the yarn and blow gently. Ask: **How can you show constructive interference?** *(At least two students must create waves from the same side of the yarn.)* Then ask: **How can you show destructive interference?** *(At least two students must create waves from opposite sides of the yarn. The waves should cancel if two students blow from opposite sides with equal strength toward the same point.)* Encourage each group to create a variety of interesting waveforms.
cooperative learning

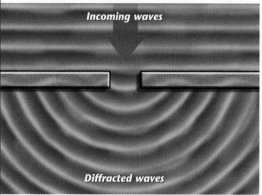
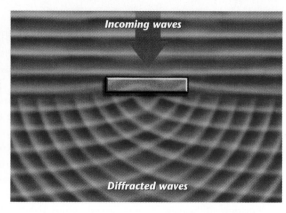

Figure 11 The diagram shows how waves diffract. A wave can go through a hole in a barrier and spread out (left). Or it can bend around a barrier (right).

around the edge of a barrier is known as **diffraction.** Figure 11 shows a water wave passing through a hole in a barrier and another bending around a barrier. In each case, you see the wave diffracting on the other side of the barrier.

✓ *Checkpoint* **What is diffraction?**

Interference

Suppose that you and a friend are each holding one end of a rope. If you both flick the ends at the same time, you send two waves toward each other. What will happen when those two waves meet?

When two or more waves meet, they have an effect on each other. This interaction is called **interference.** There are two types of interference: constructive and destructive.

Constructive Interference **Constructive interference** occurs whenever two waves combine to make a wave with a larger amplitude. You can think of constructive interference as waves "helping each other" to give a stronger result, or combining energy.

Figure 12A shows two identical waves (same amplitude, same wavelength) traveling in the same direction at the same time. If the two waves travel along the same path at the same time, they will behave as one. What will the combined wave look like? The crests of the first wave will occur at the same place as the crests of the second wave. The energy from the two waves will combine. Thus the amplitude of the new wave will be twice the amplitude of either of the original waves.

If the waves have the same wavelength but different amplitudes, the crests will still occur at the same place and add together. The resulting amplitude will be the sum of the two original amplitudes. Similarly, the troughs will occur together, making a deeper trough than either wave alone.

Background

History of Science In 1927, U.S. physicist Clinton J. Davisson and Lester H. Germer, working at Bell Telephone Laboratories in New York City, demonstrated that invisible particles, called *electrons*, undergo diffraction when they are reflected from a surface. To show this, they bombarded a nickel crystal with a stream of electrons. Analysis of the reflected electrons revealed that the electrons interfered with each other, producing a pattern of diffraction.

Similar work was done by George P. Thomson, an English physicist at the University of Aberdeen. Thomson showed that electrons also undergo diffraction after passing through a very thin crystal.

In 1937, Davisson and Thomson shared the Nobel Prize in physics for their discovery, which led to new ways to identify substances and study the properties of materials.

Figure 12 The diagrams show how identical waves can combine.

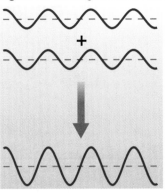
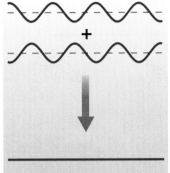
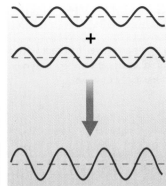

A. When the crests align, the waves add together and produce a wave with twice the original amplitude.

B. When the crests of one wave align with the troughs of another, they cancel each other out.

C. If one wave travels a little behind the other, they combine both constructively and destructively at different places.

Destructive Interference When the amplitudes of two waves combine with each other producing a smaller amplitude, the result is called **destructive interference.** What happens if the crests don't meet at the same place? In this case, one wave comes after the other. Figure 12B shows what happens when the crests of the first wave occur at the same place as the troughs of the second wave. The amplitude of the first wave cancels out the amplitude of the second wave. This type of interference produces a wave with an amplitude of zero. The original waves seem to be destroyed. If the two waves have different amplitudes, they will not cancel each other out but will combine to produce a wave with a smaller amplitude.

Two identical waves can travel along the same path, one a little behind the other. When this happens, the waves combine constructively in some places and destructively in others.

Standing Waves

If you tie a rope to a doorknob and continuously shake the free end, waves will travel down the rope, reflect at the end, and come back. The reflected waves will collide with the incoming waves. When the waves meet, interference occurs. After they pass each other, they carry on as if the interference had never occurred.

If the incoming wave and the reflected wave combine at the right places, the combined wave appears to be standing still. A **standing wave** is a wave that appears to stand in one place, even though it is really two waves interfering as they pass through each other. If you make a standing wave on a rope, the wave looks as though it is standing still. But in fact, waves are traveling along the rope in both directions.

Standing Waves

Here's how you can make a standing wave.

1. Tie a piece of elastic cord about 3 m long to a fixed, solid object. Hold the cord securely and pull it tight.

2. Slowly move the end of the cord up and down until you produce a standing wave.

3. Now move the cord up and down twice as fast to double the frequency. What happens?

Predicting What do you think will happen if you triple the original frequency? Try it. Be careful to keep a good grip on the cord.

Have students lay a ruler perpendicular to the crest of the top wave in Figure 12A. Ask: **What part of the second wave is directly beneath the first wave's crest?** (*The crest*) Then ask: **What happens to the amplitude of the combined wave?** (*It doubles.*) Repeat this procedure for each diagram. Ask: **Why don't the waves in Figure 12C combine to form a straight line?** (*The crests and troughs don't align.*)
learning modality: visual

Standing Waves

Skills Focus predicting
Materials *3-m elastic cord; fixed, solid object, such as a doorknob*
Time 10 minutes
Tips Students may need practice to develop waves that appear to stand in one place.
Expected Outcome In Step 3, the cord will have two standing waves.
Predicting Students should predict that there will be three standing waves.
Extend Challenge students to make standing waves of different amplitudes.
learning modality: kinesthetic

Answers to Self-Assessment

✓ *Checkpoint*

Diffraction is the bending of waves around the edge of a barrier.

Ongoing Assessment

Writing Have students describe constructive interference and destructive interference between waves of different amplitudes. (*Constructive interference—waves combine so that the resulting amplitude is equal to the sum of the original amplitudes. Destructive interference—waves combine to form a wave with a smaller or zero amplitude.*)

EXPLORING

Interactions of Waves

As students look at each section, have them draw a quick sketch of the waves. Sketches should indicate if the waves change direction, amplitude, or shape. For future reference, students can label their sketches as reflection, refraction, diffraction, or interference.
Extend Challenge students to build models of the scene in the visual using a pan of water and common objects. Then have them demonstrate wave reflection, refraction, or interference on their models. **learning modality: visual**

Using the Visuals: Figure 13

As students trace the path of each wave with one finger, have them compare the energy of the wave at each antinode to the energy at the other points on the wave. *(Students should realize that the energy is greatest at the antinodes.)*
limited English proficiency

Demonstration

Materials *thin crystal drinking glass, water*
Time 10 minutes

Pour a small amount of water into the glass. Wet your index finger and begin to move your finger around the rim of the glass. Ask students to predict what will happen. *(Some students may predict that the glass will begin to "sing.")* When your finger is moving at the correct speed, the glass will begin to make a distinctive "singing" sound. Explain that the glass is vibrating at the same frequency as your finger; when you move your finger so that the glass vibrates at its natural frequency, the resonance causes the glass to produce sounds. Allowed supervised students to try to reproduce the sound. **learning modality: kinesthetic**

EXPLORING Interactions of Waves

When waves interact with solid objects or with each other, they behave in a variety of ways.

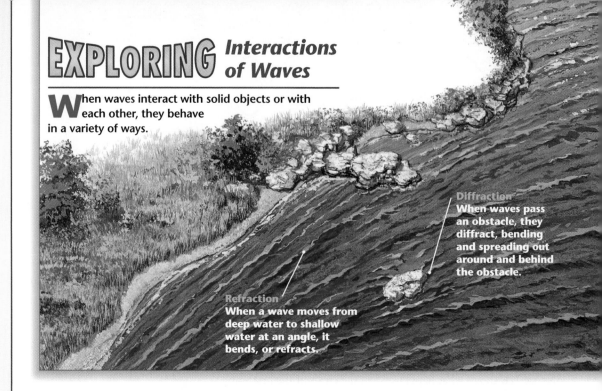

Diffraction
When waves pass an obstacle, they diffract, bending and spreading out around and behind the obstacle.

Refraction
When a wave moves from deep water to shallow water at an angle, it bends, or refracts.

Figure 13 A standing wave is set up when the reflected wave interacts with the incoming wave. The nodes are the points of zero amplitude. The antinodes are the points of maximum amplitude.

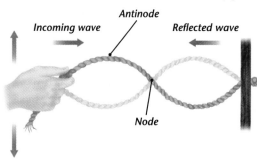

Incoming wave   Antinode   Reflected wave

Node

Nodes and Antinodes At certain points, destructive interference causes the two waves to combine to produce an amplitude of zero, as in Figure 13. These points are called **nodes.** The nodes always occur at the same place on the rope. The diagram also shows how the amplitudes of the two waves combine to produce amplitudes greater than zero. The crests and troughs of the standing wave are called **antinodes.** These are the points of maximum energy.

Resonance Have you ever pushed a child on a swing? At first, it is difficult to push the swing. But once you get it going, you need only push gently to keep it going. When an object is vibrating at a certain frequency, it takes very little energy to maintain or increase the amplitude of the wave.

Most objects have a natural frequency of vibration. Their particles vibrate naturally at a certain frequency. **Resonance** occurs when vibrations traveling through an object match the object's natural frequency. If vibrations of the same frequency are added, the amplitude of the object's vibrations increases.

Background

Facts and Figures Earthquakes cause seismic waves that vibrate at a variety of frequencies. When these waves pass underground, they cause the structures on top of the ground to shake and sway. How a building responds to an earthquake depends on many factors, including the height of the building, the materials from which it is made, and the frequency of the seismic waves. If a building shares the same natural frequency as a passing seismic wave, the whole structure may vibrate violently.

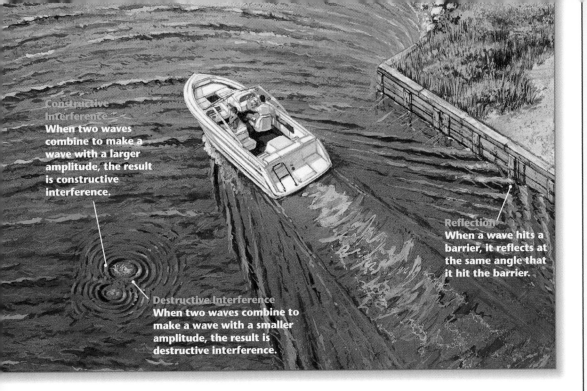

Constructive Interference When two waves combine to make a wave with a larger amplitude, the result is constructive interference.

Destructive Interference When two waves combine to make a wave with a smaller amplitude, the result is destructive interference.

Reflection When a wave hits a barrier, it reflects at the same angle that it hit the barrier.

An object that is vibrating at its natural frequency absorbs energy from objects that vibrate at the same frequency. Resonance occurs in music and adds a distinct quality to the sound.

If an object is not very flexible, resonance can cause it to shatter. For this reason, marching troops are told to break step as they cross a bridge. If they all march across the bridge in perfect step, it is possible that the pounding could match the natural frequency of the bridge. The increased vibration could cause the bridge to collapse.

 Section 3 Review

1. What is the law of reflection?
2. What causes refraction?
3. Describe the difference between constructive and destructive interference.
4. What causes a standing wave?
5. **Thinking Critically Predicting** Two water waves have the same wavelength. The crests of one occur at the same place as the crests of the second. If one wave has twice the amplitude of the other, will the waves interfere constructively or destructively? Explain.

Science at Home

With your parent's permission, fill the kitchen sink with water to a depth of about 10 cm. Dip your finger in the water repeatedly to make waves. Demonstrate reflection and interference to your family members. Try to think of ways to demonstrate refraction and diffraction as well.

Program Resources

◆ **Teaching Resources** 1-3 Review and Reinforce, p. 23; 1-3 Enrich, p. 24

Media and Technology

 Transparencies Exploring Interactions of Waves," Transparency 4

3 Assess

Section 3 Review Answers

1. The law of reflection states that the angle of reflection is equal to the angle of incidence.

2. Refraction occurs when a wave moves from one medium to another at an angle. The wave changes direction because one side changes speed before the other side.

3. In constructive interference, the amplitude of two waves add to produce a wave of greater amplitude. In destructive interference, two waves combine to produce a wave with less amplitude.

4. If two waves travel toward each other in the same medium and combine in the right places, the combined waves will appear as a standing wave.

5. Since the crests of the two waves are aligned, the waves will interfere constructively.

 **Science at Home**

Materials *sink, water, bath toy*

Suggest students first use a floating bath toy to show the difference between the wave and the medium. Students can then describe a wave interaction, such as reflection, before demonstrating it to family members. If there is enough class time, allow students to demonstrate the methods they used to show different wave interactions.

Performance Assessment

Writing Have students describe the following interactions of waves: reflection, refraction, diffraction, constructive interference, destructive interference.

O ◆ 29

Making Waves

Preparing for Inquiry

Key Concept Wave phenomena and interactions such as reflection, refraction, diffraction, and interference can be modeled with water waves using a ripple tank.

Skills Objectives Students will be able to
- model the behavior of waves in a harbor;
- observe water waves under varying conditions;
- control variables to produce waves of different amplitude, frequency, and wavelength;
- interpret data and draw conclusions about wave behavior.

Time 25 minutes

Advance Planning Prepare the ripple tanks. Have modeling clay, corks, droppers, paper towels, and rulers on hand.

Alternative Materials This activity may be performed as a demonstration using a commercial ripple tank. Ripple tanks that allow images to be projected onto the tabletop, ceiling, or other flat surface work best. Use a bulb-type turkey baster to adjust water levels if students choose to study that as a variable.

Guiding Inquiry

Invitation

Show a video featuring water waves during a storm, or have the class discuss waves they have seen in ponds, lakes, or swimming pools. Encourage students to describe waves of different sizes and to explain what happened when waves interacted.

Introducing the Procedure

Have students perform several practice trials to determine the best way to observe the waves in the tank. Some students may be able to watch the reflection of the waves in the mirror. Other groups may prefer to adjust the position of the ripple tank or use a lamp so that light reflected off the mirror projects the images of the waves onto the ceiling.

Making Waves

Making Waves

In this lab, you will use a model to investigate wave behavior.

Problem

How do water waves interact with each other and with solid objects in their paths?

Materials

water	plastic dropper
metric ruler	paper towels
modeling clay	

cork or other small floating object
ripple tank (aluminum foil lasagna pan with mirror at the bottom)

Procedure

1. Fill the pan with water to a depth of 1.5 cm. Let the water come to rest. Make a data table like the one shown in your text.
2. Fill a plastic dropper with water. Then release a drop of water from a height of about 10 cm above the center of the ripple tank. Observe the reflection of the waves that form and record your observations.
3. Predict how placing a paper towel across one end of the ripple tank will affect the reflection of the waves. Record your prediction in your notebook.
4. Drape a paper towel across one end of the ripple tank so it hangs in the water. Repeat Step 2, and record your observations of the waves.
5. Remove the paper towel and place a stick of modeling clay in the water near the center of the ripple tank.
6. From a height of about 10 cm, release a drop of water into the ripple tank halfway between the clay and one of the short walls. Record your observations.
7. Place the clay in a different position so that the waves strike it at an angle. Then repeat Step 6.

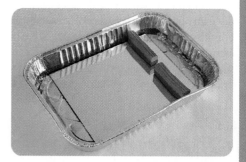

DATA TABLE		
Type of Barrier	Observations Without Cork	Observations With Cork

Troubleshooting the Experiment

- Point out weaker reflected waves to the students so that they will know what to look for.
- Make sure students can correctly identify crests and troughs of waves.
- Caution students to be careful with ripple tanks, and remind them to clean up all spills immediately. Do not allow students to handle wet mirrors.

Expected Outcome

Students should be able to control wave amplitude, frequency, and wavelength by changing the methods they use to produce the waves. Students should observe and describe reflection, refraction, diffraction, and wave interference.

8. Place two sticks of clay end-to-end across the width of the tank. Adjust the clay so that there is a gap of about 2 cm between the ends of the two pieces. Repeat Step 6. Now change the angle of the barrier in the tank. Again repeat Step 6, and watch to see if the waves interact with the barrier any differently.

9. Cut the two pieces of clay in half. Use the pieces to make a barrier with three 2-cm gaps. Then repeat Step 6.

10. Remove all the clay and add a small floating object, such as a cork, to the water. Then repeat Steps 2–9 with the floating object. Observe and record what happens to the cork in each step.

11. Once you have finished all of the trials, clean and dry your work area.

Analyze and Conclude

1. How are waves affected by the paper towel hanging in the water?
2. What happens when waves strike a barrier head on? When they strike it at an angle?
3. What happens when waves strike a barrier with a gap in it? With three gaps in it?
4. **Think About It** How does the behavior of waves in your model compare to the behavior of waves in a harbor?

Design an Experiment

Predict what would happen if you could send a steady train of uniform waves the length of the tank for an extended time. Use a plastic bottle with a pinhole in the bottom to make a model that will help to test your prediction. Get permission from your teacher to try out your dropper device.

Program Resources

◆ **Teaching Resources** Skills Lab blackline masters, pp. 31–33
◆ **Inquiry Skills Activity Book** Provides teaching and review of all inquiry skills

Media and Technology

 Lab Activity Videotape
Sound and Light, 2

Analyze and Conclude

1. The waves made by rocking the tank have a greater amplitude than do waves made with a dropper, and do not curve or radiate out from a single point. Waves made with the dropper are large, curved ripples followed by smaller and smaller ripples.
2. As the height increases, the amplitude of the waves increases. Above a certain height, the drops cause the water to splash. The first drop produces waves, and the splashed drops also produce waves when they fall into the water.
3. The wet paper towel absorbs the wave's energy. Either there is no reflected wave, or the reflected wave is much weaker than the original wave.
4. No matter the angle at which they strike the barrier, the waves are reflected at an angle equal to the angle of incidence.
5. Diffraction occurs when a wave hits a barrier with a gap in it, and part of the wave passes through the gap and spreads throughout the water on the other side of the barrier. The rest of the wave front is reflected back. When a wave hits a barrier with two gaps, two sections of the incoming wave pass through. Two small waves grow wider and wider until they overlap and interfere.
6. The behavior of waves in the model is similar to the behavior of waves in a harbor. The waves in a harbor, however, would have more complex interactions.

Extending the Inquiry

Design an Experiment A plastic bottle can be used to deliver a steady stream of waves across the ripple tank by simply poking a hole in the bottom of the bottle with a pin and filling the bottle one-third full of water. You can regulate the frequency of the drops by changing the amount of water in the bottle. Hold the bottle over the surface of the ripple tank with a clamp and ring stand. Once a steady stream of waves is maintained in the tank, students can more closely study refraction and diffraction of waves. Challenge students to work together to calculate wave speed and frequency by timing a wave's movement between two marks. When speed and frequency are known, wavelength can be calculated.

SECTION 4 — Seismic Waves

Objectives

After completing the lesson, students will be able to
◆ describe what creates seismic waves;
◆ identify the different types of seismic waves;
◆ explain how a seismograph works.

Key Terms seismic wave, primary wave, secondary wave, tsunami, seismograph

1 Engage/Explore

Activating Prior Knowledge

Show students a video clip or photographs that depict damage done by earthquakes. Ask: **What causes the buildings and roads to break apart and collapse?** (*The vibrations of Earth's surface*)

DISCOVER

Skills Focus inferring
Materials *5 empty plastic film canisters, sand, modeling clay*
Time 10 minutes
Tips Caution students not to pound the table so hard that they hurt their hands or damage property. Remind students to fasten the lid on the canister of sand tightly.
Expected Outcome When the canisters are not stuck, the canister of sand moves less than the other canisters when someone pounds the table. When the canisters are stuck to the table with clay, none of the canisters move.
Think It Over The canister that contains the sand is heavier, so it does not move as easily as the empty canisters.

SECTION 4 — Seismic Waves

DISCOVER ··· ACTIVITY

Can You Find the Sand?

1. Fill a plastic film canister with sand and replace the lid tightly.

2. Place the canister on a table with four other identical but empty canisters. Mix them around so that a classmate does not know which can is which.

3. With your fist, pound on the table a few times. Have your classmate try to figure out which canister contains the sand.

4. Stick each canister to the table with some modeling clay. Pound on the table again. Now can your classmate figure out which canister contains the sand?

Think It Over
Inferring Pounding on a table makes waves. Why might the canister containing the sand respond differently from the empty canisters?

GUIDE FOR READING

◆ **What happens when rock beneath Earth's surface moves?**

◆ **What are the different types of seismic waves?**

◆ **How does a seismograph work?**

Reading Tip As you read, make a table comparing primary, secondary, and surface waves.

Some of the most dramatic waves originate deep inside Earth. On August 27, 1883, the eruption of Krakatau volcano in Indonesia caused a series of earthquakes. Vibrations from the earthquakes formed waves that traveled from the island through the surrounding water. On the open ocean, the waves were only about 1 meter high. As they entered shallower water, near land, the waves traveled more slowly. This caused the waves at the back to catch up to the front and to pile on top. The first wave grew into a wall of water over 35 meters high. People on ships far out at sea could not even tell when the waves went by. But on the islands of Java and Sumatra thousands of people were killed as the enormous waves crashed onto the land.

Figure 14 This illustration shows a giant wave reaching the coast of Java. The wave was caused by earthquakes related to the eruption of Krakatau volcano 40 kilometers away.

READING STRATEGIES

Reading Tip Suggest students use a table such as the following to compare primary waves and secondary waves.

Primary (P) Waves	Secondary (S) Waves
• are longitudinal	• are transverse
• have compressions and rarefactions	• have crests and troughs
• travel through all parts of Earth	• do not travel through the liquid part in Earth's center

Concept Mapping Have students create flowcharts that show how seismic waves are produced by earthquakes.

Study and Comprehension After students read the section, have them outline the information. Suggest that they use the major headings and subheadings as topics and subtopics of the outline. Then have them use key details as numbered items under the subtopics.

Types of Seismic Waves

An earthquake occurs when rock beneath Earth's surface moves. The movement of Earth's plates creates stress in the rock. **When the stress in the rock builds up enough, the rock breaks or changes shape, releasing energy in the form of waves or vibrations.** The waves produced by earthquakes are known as **seismic waves.** (The word *seismic* comes from the Greek word *seismos,* meaning "earthquake.")

Seismic waves ripple out in all directions from the point where the earthquake occurred. As the waves move, they carry the energy through Earth. The waves can travel from one side of Earth to the other. **Seismic waves include primary waves, secondary waves, and surface waves.**

Primary Waves Some seismic waves are longitudinal waves. Longitudinal seismic waves are known as **primary waves,** or P waves. They are called primary waves because they move faster than other seismic waves and so arrive at distant points before other seismic waves. Primary waves are made up of compressions and rarefactions of rock inside Earth.

Secondary Waves Other seismic waves are transverse waves with crests and troughs. Transverse seismic waves are known as **secondary waves,** or S waves. Secondary waves cannot travel through liquids. Since part of Earth's core is liquid, S waves do not travel directly through Earth and cannot be detected on the side of Earth opposite an earthquake. Because of this, scientists on the side of Earth opposite the earthquake detect mainly P waves.

Surface Waves When P waves and S waves reach Earth's surface, some of them are transformed into surface waves similar to waves on the surface of water. Recall that surface waves are a combination of longitudinal and transverse waves. Even though surface waves travel more slowly than either P or S waves, they produce the most severe ground movements.

Earthquakes that occur underwater can cause huge surface waves on the ocean called **tsunamis** (tsoo NAH meez). Tsunamis can cause great damage when they reach land.

Checkpoint *How are P waves different from S waves?*

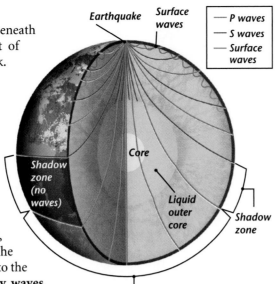

Figure 15 P waves travel through all parts of Earth. S waves do not travel through Earth's core. Surface waves travel only along Earth's surface. The shadow zone is where there are no seismic waves. *Applying Concepts Why don't S waves travel through Earth's core?*

---

2 Facilitate

Types of Seismic Waves

Using the Visuals: Figure 15

Have students trace the path of P waves across the figure. Then ask students to trace the motion of the S waves. *(Students should move their fingers in an up-and-down motion as they trace a path outward from the epicenter. They should stop tracing the waves at the liquid core of the Earth.)* Finally, have students infer where the strongest surface waves would occur. *(Near the epicenter, where the P waves and S waves have the most energy.)* **learning modality: visual**

Social Studies Connection

Tell students that, on average, one very large earthquake occurs somewhere on Earth each year.

◆ In 1755, an earthquake off the coast of Lisbon, Portugal, caused damage 1,000 km away in Algiers, the capital of Algeria. The quake produced a tsunami whose waves hit the island of Martinique in the eastern Caribbean 10 hours later.

◆ Between 1811 and 1812, three earthquakes occurred in the state of Missouri, near New Madrid. The quakes produced waves that destroyed chimneys in Cincinnati, Ohio.

◆ In 1964, an earthquake in Alaska shook 1,300,000 square km. Damage from the resulting tsunami was reported in Crescent City, California.

Challenge students to determine the distances between the origins of these earthquakes and their effects using a globe. **learning modality: logical/ mathematical**

Answers to Self-Assessment

Caption Question

Figure 15 S waves do not travel through Earth's core because part of Earth's core is liquid, and S waves cannot travel through liquids.

Checkpoint

P waves are longitudinal and move faster than S waves; S waves cannot travel through liquids.

Ongoing Assessment

Writing Have students list the three types of seismic waves.

Detecting Seismic Waves

3 Assess

Section 4 Review Answers

1. When the rock beneath Earth's surface breaks or moves due to built-up stress, it releases energy in the form of seismic waves.

2. P waves are longitudinal; S waves are transverse; surface waves are a combination of P and S waves.

3. By measuring the time between the arrival of the P waves and of the S waves, scientists can tell how far away the earthquake was. By comparing measurements from at least three seismographs at different locations, they can tell where it occurred.

4. S waves do not travel through liquids. If S waves can travel through the core of the moon, then the moon's core must be solid.

Science at Home

Materials *spoon, table*

ACTIVITY

Suggest that students try gently tapping a variety of surfaces, such as wood, glass, and metal. They should record their observations in a table and share what they learned with the class. *(The tapping sounds louder with your ear on the surface. The sound is loudest through metal, less loud through glass, and least loud through wood.)*

Performance Assessment

Organizing Information Have students create Venn diagrams that compare and contrast primary, secondary, and surface waves.

Figure 16 A scientist studies the printout from a seismograph.

Detecting Seismic Waves

If you did the Discover activity, you saw how waves can affect different masses by different amounts. To detect and measure earthquake waves, scientists use instruments called **seismographs** (SYZ muh grafs). **A seismograph records the ground movements caused by seismic waves as they move through Earth.**

The frame of the seismograph is attached to the ground, so the frame shakes when seismic waves arrive at the seismograph's location. Seismographs used to have pens attached to the frame that made wiggly lines on a roll of paper as the ground shook. Now scientists use electronic seismographs that use computers to record data about Earth's motion.

Since P waves travel through Earth faster than S waves, P waves arrive at seismographs before S waves. By measuring the time between the arrival of the P waves and the arrival of the S waves, scientists can tell how far away the earthquake was. By comparing readings from at least three seismographs at different places on Earth, scientists can tell where the earthquake occurred.

INTEGRATING TECHNOLOGY Oil, water, minerals, and other valuable substances are hidden under Earth's surface. To find out what is under the ground, geologists may set off explosives to produce a small earthquake. The seismic waves from the explosion reflect from structures deep underground to seismographs located around the site of the explosion. The readings help geologists to locate mineral resources underground.

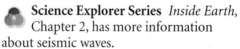 **Section 4 Review**

1. What causes seismic waves?
2. Describe the different types of seismic waves.
3. How do seismographs help scientists determine where an earthquake occurred?
4. **Thinking Critically Inferring** S waves can travel from one side of the moon, through the core, to the other side. What does this tell you about the center of the moon? Explain.

 Science at Home

Find out how disturbances travel through different solids. Have a family member or friend tap one end of the table with a spoon. Now put your ear down on the other side of the table and listen to the tapping again. What difference do you notice? Repeat the tapping on various surfaces around your home. What observations have you made?

Program Resources

Science Explorer Series *Inside Earth,* Chapter 2, has more information about seismic waves.
◆ **Teaching Resources** 1-4 Review and Reinforce, p. 27; 1-4 Enrich, p. 28

Media and Technology

Exploring Earth Science Videodisc Unit 2, Side 2, "Waves in the Earth"; Unit 3, Side 1, "Rock and Roll"

Chapter 2   Chapter 9

SECTION 1 — What Are Waves?

Key Ideas

◆ Waves are created when a source of energy causes a medium to vibrate.

◆ The three types of waves are transverse waves, longitudinal waves, and surface waves.

Key Terms

wave	vibration	longitudinal
energy	transverse	wave
medium	wave	compression
mechanical	crest	rarefaction
wave	trough	surface wave

SECTION 2 — Properties of Waves

Key Ideas

◆ The basic properties of waves are amplitude, wavelength, frequency, and speed.

◆ The speed, frequency, and wavelength of a wave are related to each other by a mathematical formula.

Speed = Wavelength × Frequency

Key Terms

amplitude	frequency
wavelength	hertz (Hz)

SECTION 3 — Interactions of Waves

Key Ideas

◆ When an object or wave hits a surface through which it cannot pass, it bounces back.

◆ When a wave moves from one medium into another medium at an angle, it changes speed as it enters the second medium and bends.

◆ When a wave passes a barrier or moves through a hole in a barrier, it bends and spreads out.

Key Terms

reflection	constructive interference
angle of incidence	destructive interference
angle of reflection	standing wave
refraction	node
diffraction	antinode
interference	resonance

SECTION 4 — Seismic Waves

INTEGRATING EARTH SCIENCE

Key Ideas

◆ When stress in the rock beneath Earth's surface builds up enough, the rock breaks or changes shape, releasing energy in the form of seismic waves.

◆ Seismic waves include primary waves, secondary waves, and surface waves.

◆ A seismograph records the ground movements caused by seismic waves as they move through Earth.

Key Terms

seismic wave	tsunami
primary wave	seismograph
secondary wave	

Organizing Information

Concept Map Copy the concept map about waves onto a separate sheet of paper. Then complete it and add a title. (For more on concept maps, see the Skills Handbook.)

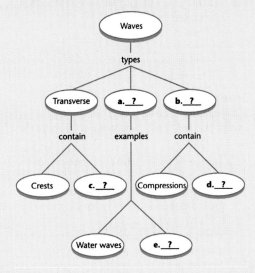

Organizing Information

Concept Map Sample title: *Waves*;
a. surface **b.** longitudinal **c.** troughs
d. rarefactions **e.** some seismic waves

Media and Technology

Interactive Student Tutorial CD-ROM O-1

Computer Test Bank *Sound and Light*, Chapter 1 Test

Program Resources

◆ **Teaching Resources** Chapter 1 Project Scoring Rubric, p. 12; Chapter 1 Performance Assessment Teacher Notes, pp. 138–139; Chapter 1 Performance Assessment Student Worksheet, p. 140; Chapter 1 Test, pp. 141–144

Reviewing Content
Multiple Choice
1. a **2.** b **3.** d **4.** d **5.** b

True or False
6. longitudinal **7.** true **8.** refraction
9. standing **10.** primary

Checking Concepts

11. In a transverse wave, the particles of the medium move at right angles to the direction of the wave's travel. In a longitudinal wave, the particles of the medium travel in the same direction as the wave. Drawings should show the directions of travel.

12. by measuring how compressed or rarefied the medium becomes

13. Speed = wavelength $\times$ frequency

14. In constructive interference, the amplitudes of the waves add to create a wave with a greater amplitude. In destructive interference, amplitudes cancel out or decrease.

15. The frame of a seismograph is attached to the ground. Electronic equipment records movement of the frame caused by seismic waves as they move through Earth.

16. Students' articles should include a description of a typical "wave" and how the wave travels around the stadium. Students should realize that people represent the particles in the medium.

Thinking Critically

17. In constructive interference, the amplitudes add, so the resulting wave will have an amplitude $1\frac{1}{2}$ times that of the higher wave. Destructive interference between waves of equal amplitudes creates a resulting wave with an amplitude of zero.

18. Frequency = speed/wavelength = (10 m/s)/2 m = 5 Hz; Frequency = speed/wavelength = 2 (10 m/s)/2 m = 10 Hz

19. Students' models should demonstrate that, when a wave enters a new medium at an angle, one side slows down before the other, causing the wave to bend.

20. The water itself does not move across the lake. Only the wave moves across the lake.

Reviewing Content

 For more review of key concepts, see the Interactive Student Tutorial CD-ROM.

Multiple Choice
Choose the letter of the best answer.

1. A wave carries
   a. energy.   **b.** matter.
   c. water.   **d.** air.

2. The distance between one crest and the next crest is the wave's
   a. amplitude.   **b.** wavelength.
   c. frequency.   **d.** speed.

3. In a given medium, if the frequency of a wave increases, its
   a. wavelength increases.
   b. speed increases.
   c. amplitude decreases.
   d. wavelength decreases.

4. The bending of a wave due to a change in its speed is
   a. interference.
   b. diffraction.
   c. reflection.
   d. refraction.

5. Seismic waves that do *not* travel through liquids are
   a. P waves.
   b. S waves.
   c. surface waves.
   d. tsunamis.

True or False
If the statement is true, write true. If it is false, change the underlined word or words to make the statement true.

6. <u>Transverse</u> waves have compressions and rarefactions.

7. When the particles of a medium move a great distance as the wave passes, the wave has a large <u>amplitude</u>.

8. When a wave changes speed as it enters a new medium at an angle, it undergoes <u>diffraction</u>.

9. Nodes and antinodes occur in <u>longitudinal</u> waves.

10. <u>Secondary</u> waves arrive at distant points before other seismic waves.

Applying Skills

21. a surface wave or a tsunami

22. 0.3 m; 200 m/s; frequency = speed ÷ wavelength = (200 m/s) ÷ (200,000 m) = 0.001 Hz

23. If a huge water wave hits a coastal town, it can do great damage to buildings and can endanger lives. The amount of damage depends on the energy carried by the wave, which in turn depends on the amplitude.

Checking Concepts

11. Explain the difference between transverse and longitudinal waves. Use diagrams to illustrate your explanation.

12. How can you find the amplitude of a longitudinal wave?

13. How are a wave's speed, wavelength, and frequency related?

14. Describe the difference between constructive and destructive interference.

15. Explain how seismographs work.

16. **Writing to Learn** Suppose you are a sportswriter with a background in science. While at a baseball game, you notice that at various times, entire sections of people stand up and sit down again. This "wave" travels around the stadium. Write a short newspaper article that describes what the crowd is doing. Be sure to use terms such as amplitude, frequency, wavelength, and speed in your description. Give your article a title.

Thinking Critically

17. **Comparing and Contrasting** One wave has half the amplitude of a second wave. The two waves interfere constructively. Draw a diagram and describe the resulting wave. Describe the resulting wave if two waves of equal amplitude interfere destructively.

18. **Calculating** A wave travels at 10 m/s and has a wavelength of 2 m. What is the frequency of the wave? If the speed of the wave doubles but the wavelength remains the same, what is the new frequency? Show your work.

19. **Making Models** Describe a way to model refraction of a wave as it enters a new medium.

20. **Applying Concepts** Suppose a wave moves from one side of a lake to the other. Does the water move across the lake? Explain.

24. Time = distance ÷ speed; 5,000 km = 5,000,000 m; time = 5,000,000 m ÷ (200 m/s) = 25,000 s or about 417 minutes or 7 hours

Applying Skills

The wave in the illustration is a giant ocean wave produced by an underwater earthquake. Use the illustration to answer Questions 21–24.

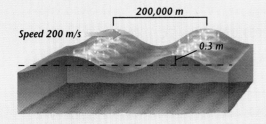

200,000 m

Speed 200 m/s

0.3 m

21. **Classifying** What kind of wave is shown in the above diagram?
22. **Interpreting Diagrams** What is the amplitude of the wave shown? What is its speed? Find the frequency of the wave. Show your work.

23. **Predicting** What could happen if this wave hits a coastal city? What property of a wave determines how much damage it could do?
24. **Calculating** How long would it take this wave to travel 5,000 km?

Performance **Assessment**

Project Wrap Up Share your examples of periodic events and patterns with your classmates. On your display, highlight the repeating patterns and the frequency of each example. Which periodic events involve the transmission of waves through the vibrations of a medium?

Reflect and Record In your journal, describe the common or unusual events in your life that repeat periodically. Did you and your classmates observe the same things, or did your classmates surprise you with the examples they found?

Test Preparation

Use these questions to prepare for standardized tests.

Use the diagram to answer Questions 25–29.

25. What type of waves did you create by throwing the stone?
   a. transverse   **b.** longitudinal
   c. surface   **d.** seismic

26. What is the medium for the waves?
   a. stone   **b.** water
   c. leaf   **d.** air

27. What was transferred by the waves?
   a. water   **b.** energy
   c. floating objects   **d.** air

28. When the leaf was raised to its highest position by the wave, it was at the wave's
   a. trough.   **b.** compression.
   c. crest.   **d.** rarefaction.

29. What two factors do you need to know to determine a wave's speed?
   a. amplitude and frequency
   b. amplitude and wavelength
   c. angle of incidence and angle of reflection
   d. wavelength and frequency

Performance **Assessment**

Project Wrap Up After all presentations have been made, lead a class discussion in which students compare their observations. During the discussion, have students classify the waves involved in their events as transverse, longitudinal, and surface waves. Make sure they identify the medium through which the waves traveled.

Reflect and Record Students should realize that periodic events are fairly common, although they may comment that there are many events that do not repeat periodically. Students should discuss whether they and their classmates identified the same events.

Test Preparation

25. c   26. b   27. b   28. c   29. d

Program Resources

◆ **Inquiry Skills Activity Book** Provides teaching and review of all inquiry skills
◆ **Standardized Test Preparation Book** Provides standardized test practice
◆ **Reading in the Content Area** Provides strategies to improve science reading skills
◆ **Teacher's ELL Handbook** Provides multiple strategies for English language learners

Sections	Time	Student Edition Activities	Other Activities
CHAPTER PROJECT 2 **Music to Your Ears** p. 039	Ongoing (3 weeks)	Check Your Progress, pp. 051, 059, 070 Project Wrap Up, p. 073	TE Chapter 2 Project Notes, pp. 038–39
1 The Nature of Sound pp. 040–45 ◆ 2.1.1 Define sound and explain how it travels. ◆ 2.1.2 Identify the factors that affect the speed of sound. ◆ 2.1.3 Describe what happens when an object moves faster than the speed of sound.	3 periods/ $1\frac{1}{2}$ blocks	**Discover** What Is Sound?, p. 040 **Sharpen Your Skills** Graphing, p. 043 **Science at Home** p. 044 **Skills Lab: Measuring** The Speed of Sound, p. 045	TE Building Inquiry Skills: Observing, p. 041; Making Models, p. 042 TE Including All Students, p. 041 TE Integrating Life Science, p. 041 TE Including All Students, p. 043 ISLM 0-2, "Tuning Forks"
2 Properties of Sound pp. 046–51 ◆ 2.2.1 Explain how intensity and loudness are related. ◆ 2.2.2 Explain the relationship between frequency and pitch. ◆ 2.2.3 Describe the apparent change in frequency observed in the Doppler effect.	3 periods/ $1\frac{1}{2}$ blocks	**Discover** How Does Amplitude Affect Loudness?, p.046 **Try This** The Short Straw, p. 048 **Try This** Pipe Sounds, p. 050	TE Inquiry Challenge, p. 049 TE Demonstration, p. 049 TE Demonstration, p. 051
3 Combining Sound Waves pp. 052–61 ◆ 2.3.1 Identify timbre and tone and state the difference between noise and music. ◆ 2.3.2 Describe what happens when two or more sound waves interact.	5 periods/ $2\frac{1}{2}$ blocks	**Discover** How Can You Produce Patterns of Sound?, p. 052 **Try This** Plucking Rubber Bands, p. 054 **Real-World Lab: How It Works** Musical Notes, pp. 060–61	TE Building Inquiry Skills: Comparing and Contrasting, p. 053; Forming Operational Definitions, p. 055; Applying Concepts, p. 056 TE Real-Life Learning, p. 057 TE Inquiry Challenge, p. 058
4 *INTEGRATING LIFE SCIENCE* **How You Hear Sound** pp. 062–65 ◆ 2.4.1 Explain how the body interprets sound waves. ◆ 2.4.2 Identify causes of hearing loss and ways that hearing loss can be prevented.	4 periods/ 2 blocks	**Discover** Where Is the Sound Coming From?, p. 062 **Try This** Listen to Sounds, p. 063	TE Integrating Health, p. 064
5 Applications of Sound pp. 066–70 ◆ 2.5.1 Explain how sonar and bats use reflection of sound waves to locate objects. ◆ 2.5.2 Define ultrasound and give examples of its application.	$2\frac{1}{2}$ periods/ 1–2 blocks	**Discover** How Can You Use Time to Measure Distance?, p. 066 **Sharpen Your Skills** Designing Experiments, p. 067	TE Including All Students, p. 067 TE Building Inquiry Skills: Making Models, p. 068 TE Demonstration, p. 069 TE Real-Life Learning, p. 069
Study Guide/Assessment pp. 071–73	1 period/ $\frac{1}{2}$ block		ISAB Provides teaching and review of all inquiry skills

 For Standard or Block Schedule The Resource Pro® CD-ROM gives you maximum flexibility for planning your instruction for any type of schedule. Resource Pro® contains Planning Express®, an advanced scheduling program, as well as the entire contents of the Teaching Resources and the Computer Test Bank.

Key: **SE** Student Edition
PLM Probeware Lab Manual
ISAB Inquiry Skills Activity Book

CHAPTER PLANNING GUIDE

Program Resources	Assessment Strategies	Media and Technology
TR Chapter 2 Project Teacher Notes, pp. 034–35 **TR** Chapter 2 Project Overview and Worksheets, pp. 036–39	**TE** Check Your Progress, pp. 051, 059, 070 **TE** Performance Assessment: Chapter 2 Project Wrap Up, p. 073 **TR** Chapter 2 Project Scoring Rubric, p. 040	Science Explorer Internet Site Audio CDs and Audiotapes, English-Spanish Section Summaries
TR 2-1 Lesson Plan, p. 041 **TR** 2-1 Section Summary, p. 042 **TR** 2-1 Review and Reinforce, p. 043 **TR** 2-1 Enrich, p. 044 **TR** Skills Lab blackline masters, pp. 061–62 **SES** Book D, *Human Biology and Health,* Chapter 7	**SE** Section 1 Review, p. 044 **SE** Analyze and Conclude, p. 045 **TE** Ongoing Assessment, pp. 041, 043 **TE** Performance Assessment, p. 044	Lab Activity Videotape, *Sound and Light,* 3 Exploring Physical Science Videodisc, Unit 6 Side 2, "Rollin' Thunder" Transparency 6, "How a Drum Makes Sound Waves"
TR 2-2 Lesson Plan, p. 045 **TR** 2-2 Section Summary, p. 046 **TR** 2-2 Review and Reinforce, p. 047 **TR** 2-2 Enrich, p. 048	**SE** Section 2 Review, p. 051 **TE** Ongoing Assessment, pp. 047, 049 **TE** Performance Assessment, p. 051	Exploring Physical Science Videodisc, Unit 6 Side 2, "Watching Sound" Transparency 7, "The Doppler Effect"
TR 2-3 Lesson Plan, p. 049 **TR** 2-3 Section Summary, p. 050 **TR** 2-3 Review and Reinforce, p. 051 **TR** 2-3 Enrich, p. 052 **TR** Real-World Lab blackline masters, pp. 063–65	**SE** Section 3 Review, p. 059 **SE** Analyze and Conclude, p. 061 **TE** Ongoing Assessment, pp. 053, 055, 057 **TE** Performance Assessment, p. 059	Lab Activity Videotape, *Sound and Light,* 4
TR 2-4 Lesson Plan, p. 053 **TR** 2-4 Section Summary, p. 054 **TR** 2-4 Review and Reinforce, p. 055 **TR** 2-4 Enrich, p. 056 **SES** Book D, *Human Biology and Health,* Chapter 7	**SE** Section 4 Review, p. 064 **TE** Ongoing Assessment, p. 063 **TE** Performance Assessment, p. 064	Exploring Physical Science Videodisc, Unit 6 Side 2, "Making Silence" Transparency 8, "The Ear"
TR 2-5 Lesson Plan, p. 057 **TR** 2-5 Section Summary, p. 058 **TR** 2-5 Review and Reinforce, p. 059 **TR** 2-5 Enrich, p. 060 **SES** Book B, *Animals,* Chapter 4 **SES** Book D, *Human Biology and Health,* Chapter 8	**SE** Section 5 Review, p. 070 **TE** Ongoing Assessment, pp. 067, 069 **TE** Performance Assessment, p. 070	Exploring Physical Science Videodisc, Unit 6 Side 2, "Blind as a Bat" Transparency 9, "Sonar"
GSW Provides worksheets to promote student comprehension of content **RCA** Provides strategies to improve science reading skills **ELL** Provides multiple strategies for English language learners	**SE** Study Guide/Assessment, pp. 071–73 **TR** Performance Assessment, pp. 0145–147 **TR** Chapter 2 Test, pp. 0148–151 **CTB** *Sound and Light,* Chapter 2 Test **STP** Provides standardized test practice	Computer Test Bank, *Sound and Light,* Chapter 2 Test Interactive Student Tutorial CD-ROM, 0-2

TE Teacher's Edition
RCA Reading in the Content Area
GSW Guided Study Workbook

TR Teaching Resources
ISLM Integrated Science Laboratory Manual
ELL Teacher's ELL Handbook

CTB Computer Test Bank
STP Standardized Test Preparation Book
SES Science Explorer Series Text

Meeting the National Science Education Standards and AAAS Benchmarks

National Science Education Standards	Benchmarks for Science Literacy	Unifying Themes
Science as Inquiry (Content Standard A) ◆ **Design and conduct a scientific investigation** Students make measurements and control variables as they measure the speed of sound and produce musical tones. *(Skills Lab, Real-World Lab)* **Life Science** (Content Standard D) ◆ **Structure and function in living systems** The human ear converts sound waves into nerve impulses. *(Section 4)* ◆ **Regulation and behavior** Some animals use infrasonic and ultrasonic waves to communicate and make sense of their environment. *(Section 5)* **Science and Technology** (Content Standard E) ◆ **Design a solution or product** Students design and build a musical instrument. *(Chapter Project)* **Science in Personal and Social Perspectives** (Content Standard F) ◆ **Personal health** Exposure to extremely loud sounds for long periods of time can cause permanent hearing damage. *(Section 4)* ◆ **Risks and benefits** Students consider the causes and effects of noise pollution. *(Section 4; Science and Society)* ◆ **Science and technology in society** Ultrasonic and sonar devices allow scientists to locate objects within the body and beneath the sea. *(Section 5)*	**2C Mathematical Inquiry** Sonar devices determine the location of objects based on the time it takes for a sound wave to reflect back to the device and the speed of sound in water. *(Section 5)* **3C Issues in Technology** Noise pollution is mainly caused by transportation systems; students debate how noise pollution can be controlled. *(Science and Society)* Technological devices that use ultrasonic waves include sonar machines, sonograms, ultrasonic toothbrushes, jewelry cleaners, and auto-focus cameras. *(Section 5)* **4F Motion** Sound travels in longitudinal waves from a vibrating source. The speed of a sound wave is affected by properties of the medium through which the wave moves. *(Section 1; Skills Lab)* Sound waves can be characterized by their pitch and loudness. *(Section 2)* Sound waves reflect off objects. *(Section 5)* **6C Basic Functions** The structure of the human ear allows it to transmit vibrations from sound waves. Nerve cells in the cochlea of the inner ear change vibrations into impulses that the brain interprets. *(Section 4)* **11A Systems** Musical instruments are systems that transform the vibration of a string, an air column, or the instrument itself into sound of a pleasing timbre. The quality of sound is determined by the fundamental tones and overtones. *(Sections 2, 3; Real-World Lab; Chapter Project)*	◆ **Energy** Sound is produced by vibrations that give energy to the particles of a medium. Sound is a form of energy that travels as a longitudinal wave. *(Section 1)* ◆ **Patterns of Change** The speed of sound is determined by the properties of the medium through which it travels. *(Section 1, Skills Lab)* ◆ **Scale and Structure** The speed at which sound waves travel is determined by the elasticity, temperature, and density of the medium through which the waves are moving. *(Section 1; Skills Lab)* The properties of sound waves include intensity, frequency, and timbre. *(Sections 2, 3)* The outer ear captures sound waves, the middle ear transmits the waves as vibrations, and the inner ear transmits vibrations to nerve signals to allow humans to hear. *(Section 4)* ◆ **Systems and Interactions** Musical instruments have vibrating strings or columns of air that produce sounds of a pleasing timbre. *(Section 3; Real-World Lab; Chapter Project)* Infrasonic and ultrasonic waves can be bounced off objects and used to detect objects or communicate. *(Section 5)*

Take It to the Net

 Interactive text at www.phschool.com

Science Explorer comes alive with iText.

- **Complete student text** is accessible from any computer with a browser.
- **Animations, simulations, and videos** enhance student understanding and retention of concepts.
- **Self-tests and online study tools** assess student understanding.
- **Teacher management tools** help you make the most of this valuable resource.

STAY CURRENT with **SCIENCE NEWS**®

Find out the latest research and information about how sound waves are used at: **www.phschool.com**

Go to **www.phschool.com** and click on the Science icon. Then click on Science Explorer under PH@school.

ACTIVITY	Time (minutes)	Materials Quantities for one work group	Skills
Section 1			
Discover, p. 40	10	**Consumable** water **Nonconsumable** bowl, tuning fork	Observing
Sharpen Your Skills, p. 43	15	**Consumable** graph paper **Nonconsumable** pencil	Graphing
Science at Home, p. 44	home	**Nonconsumable** long metal water pipe (or metal railing)	Observing, Drawing Conclusions
Skills Lab, p. 45	50	**Nonconsumable** metric tape measure, drum and drumstick (or empty coffee can and metal spoon), digital stopwatch, thermometer	Measuring
Section 2			
Discover, p. 46	10	**Nonconsumable** guitar string attached to nails in wooden board	Forming Operational Definitions
Try This, p. 48	10	**Consumable** drinking straw **Nonconsumable** scissors	Predicting
Try This, p. 50	10	**Nonconsumable** vacuum cleaner tube or tube toy, piece of cloth	Observing
Section 3			
Discover, p. 52	15	**Consumable** glue **Nonconsumable** coffee can, latex glove, small mirror tile, flashlight, spoon	Inferring
Try This, p. 54	15	**Nonconsumable** 2 rubber bands of different thicknesses, 30 cm ruler, pencil	Drawing Conclusions
Real-World Lab, pp. 60–61	45	**Consumable** water, masking tape **Nonconsumable** 3 identical glass bottles, marking pen, pencil	Predicting, Observing, Inferring
Section 4			
Discover, p. 62	10	No special materials are required.	Observing
Try This, p. 63	15	**Consumable** string **Nonconsumable** metal spoon	Inferring
Science at Home, p. 64	home	No special materials are required.	Observing, Communicating
Section 5			
Discover, p. 66	10	**Consumable** masking tape **Nonconsumable** meter stick, soft ball, stopwatch	Inferring
Sharpen Your Skills, p. 67	15	**Consumable** square piece of cardboard, 2 empty paper towel or aluminum foil tubes **Nonconsumable** metric ruler, ticking watch	Designing Experiments

A list of all materials required for the Student Edition activities can be found beginning on page T15. You can obtain information about ordering materials by calling 1-800-848-9500 or by accessing the Science Explorer Internet site at: **www.phschool.com**

Music to Your Ears

Students often associate music and musical instruments more with art than with science. However, all sound produced by musical instruments follows the laws of physics, and a knowledge of these laws is helpful both in designing instruments and in playing them.

Purpose In this project, students apply the concepts they learn in this chapter to the design, construction, and performance of a simple musical instrument.

Skills Focus After completing the Chapter 2 Project, students will be able to
- apply concepts from the chapter to design simple musical instruments;
- control variables as they construct and modify their instruments according to scientific principles;
- communicate the processes they went through and play their instruments.

Project Time Line This project will take approximately two and a half weeks. On the first day, have a class discussion in which students describe and compare different types of instruments. Students should spend the next two days beginning to formulate designs and compiling lists of materials. Allow a week for students to design and construct their instruments. Students should test and modify their instruments while they learn a simple tune. On the final day or two, allow students to perform and present their designs. Before beginning the project, see Chapter 2 Project Teacher Notes on pages 34–35 in Teaching Resources for more details on carrying out the project. Also distribute to students the Chapter 1 Project Overview, Worksheet, and Scoring Rubric on pages 36–40 in Teaching Resources.

Suggested Shortcuts To save time, allow students to work in small groups.

Possible Materials Students will need drawing paper during the planning and design phases of the project. The materials students need will vary depending on the type of instrument they want to design. You may give students a list of available materials and have them design instruments using only

WEB ACTIVITY www.phschool.com

SECTION 1 The Nature of Sound	SECTION 2 Properties of Sound	SECTION 3 Combining Sound Waves
Discover **What Is Sound?**	Discover **How Does Amplitude Affect Loudness?**	Discover **How Can You Produce Patterns of Sound?**
Sharpen Your Skills **Graphing**	Try This **The Short Straw**	Try This **Plucking Rubber Bands**
Skills Lab **The Speed of Sound**	Try This **Pipe Sounds**	Real-World Lab **Musical Notes**

38 ◆ O

those materials, or you may try to accommodate different designs by providing a wide variety of materials or allowing students to provide their own. A materials list could include
- rubber bands of different lengths or thicknesses
- cardboard boxes
- cardboard or PVC tubes of different lengths
- string
- wooden craft sticks or tongue depressors
- drinking straws
- bottles

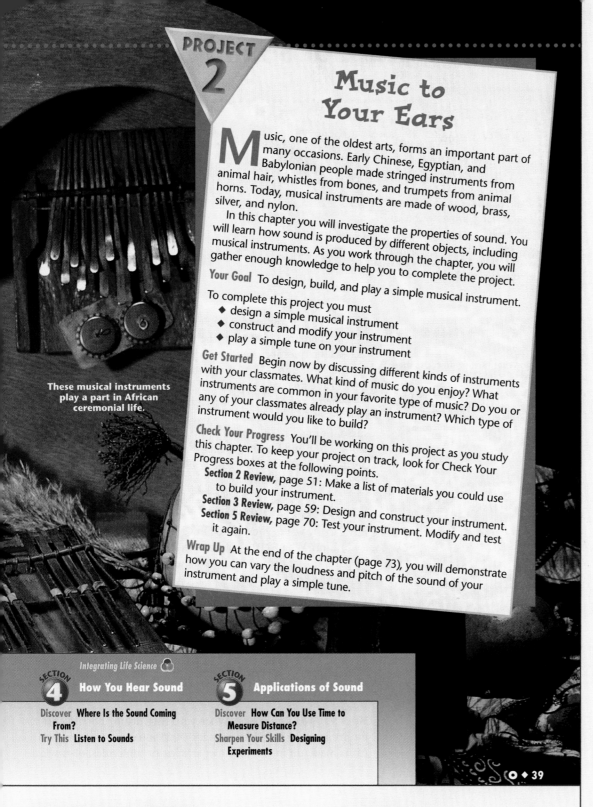

PROJECT 2

Music to Your Ears

Music, one of the oldest arts, forms an important part of many occasions. Early Chinese, Egyptian, and Babylonian people made stringed instruments from animal hair, whistles from bones, and trumpets from animal horns. Today, musical instruments are made of wood, brass, silver, and nylon.

In this chapter you will investigate the properties of sound. You will learn how sound is produced by different objects, including musical instruments. As you work through the chapter, you will gather enough knowledge to help you to complete the project.

Your Goal To design, build, and play a simple musical instrument.

To complete this project you must
◆ design a simple musical instrument
◆ construct and modify your instrument
◆ play a simple tune on your instrument

Get Started Begin now by discussing different kinds of instruments with your classmates. What kind of music do you enjoy? What instruments are common in your favorite type of music? Do you or any of your classmates already play an instrument? Which type of instrument would you like to build?

Check Your Progress You'll be working on this project as you study this chapter. To keep your project on track, look for Check Your Progress boxes at the following points.

Section 2 Review, page 51: Make a list of materials you could use to build your instrument.

Section 3 Review, page 59: Design and construct your instrument.

Section 5 Review, page 70: Test your instrument. Modify and test it again.

Wrap Up At the end of the chapter (page 73), you will demonstrate how you can vary the loudness and pitch of the sound of your instrument and play a simple tune.

These musical instruments play a part in African ceremonial life.

SECTION 4 *Integrating Life Science* 🌐
How You Hear Sound

Discover Where Is the Sound Coming From?
Try This Listen to Sounds

SECTION 5
Applications of Sound

Discover How Can You Use Time to Measure Distance?
Sharpen Your Skills Designing Experiments

O ◆ 39

Program Resources

◆ **Teaching Resources** Chapter 2 Project Teacher Notes, pp. 34–35; Chapter 2 Project Overview and Worksheets, pp. 36–39; Chapter 2 Project Scoring Rubric, p. 40

Media and Technology

 Audio CDs and **Audiotapes**
English-Spanish Section Summaries

WEB ACTIVITY  www.phschool.com

You will find an Internet activity, chapter self-tests for students, and links to other chapter topics at this site.

Launching the Project To introduce the project, play a recording or a video tape of people playing interesting or unusual instruments. Have students discuss the sounds produced by the instruments and compare them to other instruments they know about. Encourage students to discuss different styles of music and the instruments that are used to create them.

Allow time for students to read the description of the project in their text and the Chapter 2 Project Overview and Worksheets. Have students brainstorm a list of instrument types they could create in this project.

Performance Assessment

The Chapter 2 Project Scoring Rubric on page 40 of Teaching Resources will help you evaluate how well students complete the Chapter 2 Project. Students will be assessed on
◆ the thoroughness of their designs and how well they planned their constructions;
◆ whether they used chapter concepts in the design, construction, and modification of their instruments;
◆ how well they modified their instruments based on the results of their tests;
◆ the clarity and completeness of their presentations and how well their instruments are able to produce a tune.

By sharing the Chapter 2 Scoring Rubric with students at the beginning of the project, you will make it clear to them what they are expected to do.

The Nature of Sound

Objectives

After completing the lesson, students will be able to

◆ define sound and explain how it travels;

◆ identify the factors that affect the speed of sound;

◆ describe what happens when an object moves faster than the speed of sound.

Key Terms larynx, elasticity, density

1 Engage/Explore

Activating Prior Knowledge

Direct students to make a sound using their hands. Most students will clap or snap their fingers. Ask: **What caused the sound that you heard?** *(The impact created by the hands or fingers causes the sound. Some students may say the impact causes the air to vibrate, thereby producing sound.)*

········ DISCOVER ········

Skills Focus observing
Materials *bowl, water, tuning fork*

Time 10 minutes
Tips If you have tuning forks of different frequencies, students can trade them and compare observations. Lower frequency tuning forks make waves that are more easily seen. Make sure students understand what the word *prong* refers to.
Expected Outcome Students will see tiny ripples in the water when the vibrating prong is dipped in the bowl. When they hold the vibrating tuning fork up to their ears, they will hear the sound of the tuning fork.
Think It Over The ripples in the water are caused by the vibrations from the tuning fork that pass into the water. Different sizes of tuning forks will produce different waves. For example, a tuning fork with a higher frequency will produce water ripples that have a higher frequency and a shorter wavelength.

The Nature of Sound

DISCOVER ·············· ACTIVITY····

What Is Sound?

1. Fill a bowl with water.
2. Tap a tuning fork against the sole of your shoe. Place the tip of one of the prongs in the water. What do you see?
3. Tap the tuning fork again. Predict what will happen when you hold it near your ear. What do you hear?

Think It Over
Observing How do you think your observations are related to the sound you hear? What might change if you use a tuning fork of a different size? What would change in the sound you hear?

GUIDE FOR READING

◆ What is sound?
◆ What factors affect the speed of sound?

Reading Tip Before you read, preview the headings in the section. Record the headings in outline form, leaving room to add notes.

H ere is an old riddle: If a tree falls in a forest and no one is there to hear it, does the tree make a sound? To answer the question, you must decide how to define the word "sound." If sound is something that a person must hear with his or her ears, then you might say that the tree makes no sound.

When a tree crashes down, the energy with which it strikes the forest floor is transmitted through the ground and the surrounding air. This energy causes the ground and the air to vibrate. If sound is a disturbance that travels through the ground or the air, then sound is created even if no one is around. So the tree does make a sound.

Sound and Longitudinal Waves

Just like the waves you studied in Chapter 1, sound begins with a vibration. When a tree crashes to the ground, the surrounding air particles are disturbed. This disturbance causes other vibrations in nearby particles.

How Sound Travels Like all waves, sound waves carry energy through a medium without the particles of the medium traveling along. A common medium for sound is air. Each molecule in the air moves back and forth as the disturbance goes by. **Sound is a disturbance that travels through a medium as a longitudinal wave.** When the disturbance in the air reaches your ears, you hear the sound.

How Sounds Are Made When you beat a drum, the surface of the drum begins to vibrate so quickly that you cannot see it move. Air is made up mostly of tiny particles, or molecules, of gases.

READING STRATEGIES

Reading Tip After students write the outline headings, have a volunteer read aloud the information under the first major heading. Then, as a class, outline the information, adding notes to these headings:
I. Sound and Longitudinal Waves
   A. How Sound Travels
   B. How Sounds Are Made
   C. Sound in Solids and Liquids
   D. How Sound Bends

Study and Comprehension After students read the section, have them use the information in their outline notes to write question-and-answer flashcards. Instruct them to write a question on one side of a note card and the answer on the other side of the card. Then have partners use the flashcards to quiz each other on the nature of sound. Encourage students to save their flashcards to use as study guides for the section.

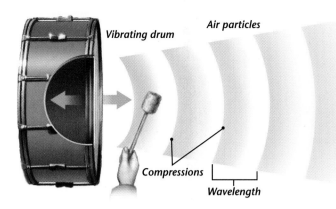

Vibrating drum

Air particles

Compressions

Wavelength

Figure 1 As the drum vibrates back and forth, it creates compressions and rarefactions in the air. *Classifying What type of wave does a drum make?*

Figure 1 shows how the vibration of a drum creates a disturbance in the molecules in the air near it. When the drumhead moves to the right, it pushes the molecules together, creating a compression. When the drumhead moves to the left, the molecules move farther apart, creating a rarefaction.

When you pluck a guitar string, it vibrates back and forth, creating compressions and rarefactions. These compressions and rarefactions travel through the air as longitudinal waves similar to the longitudinal waves that you saw travel along a spring.

INTEGRATING LIFE SCIENCE Your vocal cords act like vibrating guitar strings. Whenever you speak or sing, you force air from your lungs up through your voice box, or **larynx.** Your larynx consists of two folds of tissue called vocal cords, shown in Figure 2. The forced air rushes by your vocal cords, making them vibrate. As your vocal cords move toward each other, the air between them is compressed. As they move apart, the air spreads out, or is rarefied. Like vibrating guitar strings, your vocal cords produce compressions and rarefactions in the air. The air carries these longitudinal waves to other people's ears as well as to your own.

To mouth

Vocal cords

Trachea

Lungs

Figure 2 When a person speaks or sings, the vocal cords vibrate. The vibrations produce longitudinal sound waves in the air.

Sound in Solids and Liquids

Sound can also travel through solids and liquids. When you knock on a door, the particles of the door vibrate. The vibration creates sound waves that travel through the door. When the sound waves reach the other side of the door, they make sound waves in the air on the far side. In old western movies, you may see someone put an ear to a railway track to tell if a train is on the way.

Sound and Longitudinal Waves

Building Inquiry Skills: Observing

Materials *small drum (or bowl covered with a rubber balloon), iron filings, pencil*
Time 15 minutes

ACTIVITY

Have students sprinkle iron filings on the head of the drum. Ask them to predict what will happen to the filings when the drum is struck. Have students test their predictions by striking the drum gently with the eraser end of a pencil. Ask: **How are the iron filings similar to molecules in the air near the drumhead?** *(Both move when the drumhead vibrates.)* **learning modality: visual**

Including All Students

Materials *guitar*
Time 10 minutes

ACTIVITY

Allow hearing and visually-impaired students to place one hand on the body of the guitar and pluck the strings with the opposite hand. Ask: **What do you feel?** *(The guitar vibrates.)* Then ask: **How do people hear these vibrations?** *(The vibrations create longitudinal waves that travel to people's ears.)* **learning modality: kinesthetic**

 Integrating Life Science

Time 5 minutes

ACTIVITY

Direct students to gently place their fingers on their larynxes. Then have them softly sing the "Star-Spangled Banner." Ask: **What happens to the larynx as you sing?** *(It vibrates.)* Have students compare what they feel when they sing the high notes, when they sing the low notes, and when they whisper. **learning modality: kinesthetic**

Ongoing Assessment

Drawing Have students draw pictures to show how sound waves move through the air when a person claps.

Program Resources

◆ **Teaching Resources** 2-1 Lesson Plan, p. 41; 2-1 Section Summary, p. 42
◆ **Guided Study Workbook** Section 2-1

Media and Technology

 Transparencies "How a Drum Makes Sound Waves," Transparency 6

Answers to Self-Assessment

Caption Question

Figure 1 A drum makes a longitudinal wave.

Sound and Longitudinal Waves, continued

Building Inquiry Skills: Making Models

Materials *3 m string, nail, hammer, 2 empty cans*

Time 15 minutes

Before the activity, prepare the cans by carefully puncturing the bottom of each can using a hammer and nail. Have pairs of students tie a can to each end of the string by inserting the string into the hole and making a knot. Then have partners hold one can and stretch the string until it is taut. Direct students to take turns whispering to one another and listening for sounds through the cans. Ask: **How does this demonstrate sound traveling through a solid?** (*The sound waves are transmitted through the air to the string, and then through the string to the other can.*) **learning modality: kinesthetic**

Building Inquiry Skills: Interpreting Illustrations

Have students describe how the sound in Figure 3 travels when it passes through the open door. (*The sound waves spread out and fill the room.*) To help students contrast the behavior of sound waves and light, ask: **Imagine that the dog were holding a flashlight. Would the light shine on the cat? Why or why not?** (*No. The light would not bend and would not reach into the corners of the room to shine on the cat.*) **learning modality: visual**

The Speed of Sound

Using the Visuals: Figure 4

Challenge students to calculate how long it would take to hear thunder that occurs 1.7 km away. Students should assume that the temperature is 20°C. (*1.7 km = 1,700 m; 1,700 m ÷ 340 m/s = 5 s*) **learning modality: logical/mathematical**

Figure 3 When sound waves enter a room through an open door, they spread out. This is called diffraction.

Figure 4 The speed of sound depends upon the medium through which it is traveling. *Making Generalizations In general, does sound travel faster in solids, liquids, or gases?*

Speed of Sound	
Medium	**Speed (m/s)**
Gases	
Air (0°C)	330
Air (20°C)	342
Liquids	
Fresh water	1,490
Salt water	1,530
Solids (25°C)	
Lead	1,210
Plastic	1,800
Silver	2,680
Copper	3,100
Gold	3,240
Brick	3,650
Hard wood	4,000
Glass	4,540
Iron	5,100
Steel	5,200

The sound of the train travels easily through the steel tracks. If you put your ear to the ground, you might hear distant traffic. Sound waves from the traffic are traveling through the ground as well as through the air.

Sound can travel only if there is a medium to transmit the compressions and rarefactions. In outer space, there are no molecules to compress or rarefy. The energy of the original vibrations has nothing through which to travel. So sound does not travel through outer space.

How Sound Bends When sound waves hit a barrier with a small hole in it, some of the waves pass through the hole. Just as diffraction causes water waves to spread out in a harbor, the sound waves spread out, or diffract, as they go through the hole. When sound waves go through a doorway, they spread out. Even if you are off to the side of the room, you may still hear sound from outside. If you are outside the room and not too far from the doorway, you can hear sound coming from inside the room.

Because of diffraction, you can also hear sounds from around corners. Waves passing a corner spread out as they pass.

The Speed of Sound

If you have ever seen a live band perform, you've noticed that the sounds produced by the different instruments and singers all reach your ears at the same time. If they did not travel at the same speed, the sounds that were played together would reach you at different times and would not sound very pleasant.

The speed of sound depends on the properties of the medium it travels through. At room temperature, about 20°C, sound travels at about 342 m/s. This is much faster than most jet airplanes travel through the air. Figure 4 shows the speed of sound through some common materials.

Background

History of Science In the seventeenth century, scientists began the attempt to measure the speed of sound through air. One of the first to make a scientific measurement was a Frenchman, Pierre Gassendi. He compared the difference between the time it took to see the flash of gunpowder from a gun with the time it took to hear the gunshot. Gassendi calculated a value—just over 478 m/s—which was much higher than the actual speed of sound. At about the same time, two Italian physicists used the same technique but got a more accurate measurement of 350 m/s. In 1738, scientists obtained a fairly accurate speed of sound—332 m/s. Another value, 331.45 m/s, was obtained in 1942, and was amended in 1986 to 331.29 m/s at a temperature of 0°C.

As the properties of a medium change, so too does the speed of the sound that travels through it. **The speed of sound depends on the elasticity, density, and temperature of the medium.**

Elasticity Since sound is a transfer of energy, its speed depends on how well the particles in the medium bounce back after being disturbed. If you stretch a rubber band and then let it go, it returns to its original shape. However, when you stretch modeling clay and then let it go, it stays stretched. Rubber bands are more elastic than modeling clay. **Elasticity** is the ability of a material to bounce back after being disturbed. If a medium is very elastic, its particles easily go back to their original positions. Sound travels more quickly in mediums that have a high degree of elasticity because when the particles are compressed, they quickly spread out again.

Solid materials are usually more elastic than liquids or gases, so compressions and rarefactions travel very well in solids. The particles of a solid do not move very far, so they bounce back and forth quickly as the compressions and rarefactions of the sound waves go by. Most liquids are not very elastic. Sound is not transmitted as well in liquids as it is in solids. Gases are generally very inelastic and are the poorest transmitters of sound.

Density The speed of sound also depends on how close together the particles of the substance are. The **density** of a medium is how much matter, or mass, there is in a given amount of space, or volume.

In materials in the same state of matter—solid, liquid, or gas—sound travels more slowly in denser mediums. The denser the medium, the more mass it has in a given volume. The particles of a dense material do not move as quickly as those of a less-dense material. Sound travels more slowly in dense metals, such as lead or silver, than in iron or steel.

Temperature In a given medium, sound travels more slowly at lower temperatures and faster at higher temperatures. At a low temperature, the particles of a medium are more sluggish. They are more difficult to move and return to their original positions more slowly.

At 20°C, the speed of sound in air is about 342 m/s. At 0°C, the speed is about 330 m/s. At higher altitudes the air is colder, so sound travels more slowly at higher altitudes.

☑ *Checkpoint* *How does elasticity affect the speed of sound?*

Figure 5 Some substances are more elastic than others. Sponges and rubber bands are more elastic than modeling clay. *Predicting Is sound likely to travel faster through a sponge, a rubber band, or a piece of modeling clay?*

Sharpen your Skills

Graphing ACTIVITY

Graph the following data, to show how the speed of sound through air changes with temperature. Show temperature from –20°C to 30°C on the horizontal axis. (*Note:* Negative numbers are less than zero.) Plot speed from 300 m/s to 400 m/s on the vertical axis.

Air Temperature (°C)	Speed (m/s)
–20	318
–10	324
0	330
10	336
20	342
30	348

How does air temperature affect the speed of sound?

Program Resources

Science Explorer Series *Human Biology and Health*, Chapter 7, contains information on hearing.

Media and Technology

Exploring Physical Science Videodisc
Unit 6, Side 2, "Rollin' Thunder"
Chapter 3

Answers to Self-Assessment

Caption Questions

Figure 4 Sound travels faster in solids.
Figure 5 Sound travels faster through a rubber band.

☑ *Checkpoint*

Increasing elasticity increases the speed of sound.

Including All Students

Materials *slice of bread* ACTIVITY
Time 5 minutes

To help students who are still mastering English to understand density, give students a slice of bread. Explain that the bread is not very dense. Then have them squash the bread into a ball. Ask: **What happened to the particles in the bread when you squashed it?** (*The particles got closer together.*) Point out that the amount of bread did not change, but the bread's density increased. **limited English proficiency**

Sharpen your Skills

Graphing

Materials *graph paper, pencil* ACTIVITY
Time 15 minutes
Tips Suggest that students use intervals of 5°C on the horizontal axis and 10 m/s on the vertical axis, starting at 300 m/s.
Expected Outcome Students' graphs should indicate that the speed of sound increases as temperature increases.
Extend Provide research materials students can use to find the temperatures of the different layers of Earth's atmosphere. They should determine the approximate speed of sound at each layer. **learning modality: logical/ mathematical**

Ongoing Assessment

Oral Presentation Ask students to describe how increasing the density and temperature of air affects the speed of sound.

O ◆ 43

Moving Faster Than Sound

Language Arts Connection

Have students write brief newspaper articles with headlines explaining Chuck Yeager's or Andy Green's accomplishment. Articles should explain how temperature affected when and where the events took place. **learning modality: visual**

 Students can save their articles in their portfolios.

3 Assess

Section 1 Review Answers

1. A vibration creates compressions and rarefactions in the medium near the source of the sound. This results in a longitudinal wave.
2. Greater elasticity, less density, and higher temperatures cause the speed of sound to increase in a given medium.
3. Because there are no air particles in outer space, there is nothing for a longitudinal wave to pass through.
4. Gold; sound travels faster through solids that are less dense.

Science at Home

Materials *long metal pipe* **ACTIVITY**

The effect will be most noticeable if the pipe is at least 25 m long. Students will hear the sound first through the metal of the pipe and a little later through the air. Sound travels faster in metal than in air because the metal is more elastic and more dense.

Performance Assessment

Drawing Have students create illustrations that show how sound is produced. Their illustrations should show a source for the sound, such as a dog barking, and then how sound travels through a particular medium. Students should label their illustrations and include a short description of how sound waves travel and bend.

Figure 6 On October 14, 1947, Captain Chuck Yeager became the first person to fly a plane faster than the speed of sound (top). On October 15, 1997, Andy Green officially became the first person to drive a land vehicle faster than the speed of sound (bottom).

Moving Faster Than Sound

The supersonic age began with a bang on October 14, 1947. Far above the California desert, Captain Chuck Yeager of the United States Air Force had just "broken the sound barrier." Captain Yeager was at an altitude of 12,000 meters and just about out of fuel. He had used much of his fuel to get to a higher altitude because the speed of sound is slower higher up. Wide open throttles accelerated his plane to over 293 meters per second, the speed of sound at that altitude. Thus, when he hit 294 meters per second, he exceeded the speed of sound at that altitude. At a lower altitude, the speed of sound is much faster and he would not have had the power or speed to exceed it. Yeager's team chose to go high in part because the temperature there is lower and the speed of sound is slower. Each pilot today who "goes supersonic" owes Chuck Yeager a debt of gratitude.

Fifty years later, Andy Green stood poised on Nevada's Black Rock desert. He had traveled all the way from Great Britain to go supersonic—on the ground! He chose the desert because it is flat, wide open, and cold in the morning. All of these factors were important to the attempt. On October 15, 1997, at the coolest time of the day, Green blasted off in his jet-powered car, *Thrust.* A short time later he traveled a measured distance at an average speed of 339 meters per second—7 meters per second faster than the speed of sound at that altitude. Andy Green was the first person to break the sound barrier on the ground.

Section 1 Review

1. How does sound travel through a medium?
2. How do elasticity, density, and temperature affect the speed of sound through a medium?
3. Explain why sound cannot travel through outer space.
4. **Thinking Critically** **Applying Concepts** Sound travels faster through glass than through gold. Based on this information, which material would you say is more dense? Explain.

44 ◆ O

Science at Home

Find a long metal railing or water pipe. **CAUTION:** *Beware of sharp edges and rust.* Put one ear to the pipe while a family member taps on the pipe some distance away. Do you hear the sound first with the ear touching the pipe or with your other ear? Compare the sound you hear through the metal with the sound coming through the air. What accounts for the difference?

Program Resources

◆ **Teaching Resources** 2-1 Review and Reinforce, p. 43; 2-1 Enrich, p. 44
◆ **Integrated Science Laboratory Manual** O-2, "Tuning Forks"

44 ◆ O

Measuring

The Speed of Sound

Sound travels at different speeds through different materials. In this lab, you will measure the speed of sound in air.

Problem

How fast does sound travel in air?

Materials

metric tape measure

drum and drumstick (or empty coffee can and metal spoon)

digital stopwatch

thermometer

Procedure

1. With the approval of your teacher, select an outdoor area such as a football field.
2. Record the outdoor air temperature in °C.
3. Measure a distance of 100 meters in a straight line. How long do you think it should take for a sound to travel the 100 m?
4. Stand at one end of this measured distance with the drum. Have two teammates go to the other end with a stopwatch. One teammate, the "watcher," should watch you and the drum. The other, the "listener," should face away from the drum and listen for the sound.
5. Make a short, loud noise by striking the drum.
6. As you strike the drum, the watcher should start the stopwatch. When the listener hears the sound, he or she should immediately say "stop." Then the watcher stops the watch. Record the time to one tenth of a second.
7. Repeat Steps 4–6 five times. How consistent are your times? What might account for any differences?
8. Now switch roles. Repeat Steps 4–6 with different students beating the drum, watching, and listening.

Analyze and Conclude

1. How far did the sound travel? How long did it take? (Calculate the average of the five measured times.)
2. To calculate the speed of sound in air, use this formula:

$$Speed = \frac{Distance}{Time}$$

3. How well does your result compare with the prediction you made in Step 3? Make a list of reasons to account for any differences. What could you do to improve the accuracy of your measurements?
4. **Think About It** Another way to measure the speed of sound would be to stand near a tall building, shout, and wait to hear the echo. To use the echo method, what adjustments would you have to make to the procedure in this lab?

Design an Experiment

How could you find out the effect of changing air temperature on the speed of sound? Write a set of procedures you could use to conduct such an experiment.

---

3. Answers will vary. Differences could be caused by wind speed or air temperature. To improve the accuracy, the experiment could be done over a longer distance.

4. The time measured would be the time taken for the sound to travel to the wall and back. Students should divide the time by two.

Program Resources

◆ **Teaching Resources** Skills Lab blackline masters, pp. 61-62

Media and Technology

 Lab Activity Videotape
Sound and Light, 3

Extending the Inquiry

Design an Experiment Students could repeat the procedure once per week for a semester, or repeat the procedure at different times of day. Sound travels faster on hot days than on cold ones.

The Speed of Sound

Preparing for Inquiry

Key Concept Students will measure how fast sound travels in air.

Skills Objectives Students will be able to
◆ measure a large distance;
◆ observe how long it takes a sound to be heard;
◆ calculate the speed of sound;
◆ design experiments to find out the effect of changing air temperature on the speed of sound.

Time 50 minutes

Advance Planning Choose an appropriate outdoor location. Obtain the drums or make alternative noisemakers.

Alternative Materials Use any instrument that makes a short, loud noise. Examples: an empty coffee can and metal spoon, or two boards that will be slapped together.

Guiding Inquiry

Invitation Review the concept of speed. Provide examples of the speed of animals and vehicles to demonstrate the concept.

Introducing the Procedure

◆ Have students read the procedure before going outdoors.
◆ If distance is measured in meters and time in seconds, speed will be expressed in terms of m/s.

Troubleshooting the Experiment

The times will be very short (0.3 s) so the error in measurement will be relatively large.

Expected Outcome

◆ Students' data should show that sound travels 100 m in about 0.3 s.
◆ Answers will vary depending on wind speed, air temperature, and human error.

Analyze and Conclude

1. 100 m. Students' data should show times near 0.3 s.
2. Accept answers between 200 m/s and 500 m/s.

SECTION 2 Properties of Sound

Objectives

After completing the lesson, students will be able to

- explain how intensity and loudness are related;
- explain the relationship between frequency and pitch;
- describe the apparent change in frequency observed in the Doppler effect.

Key Terms intensity, loudness, decibel (dB), ultrasound, infrasound, pitch, Doppler effect

1 Engage/Explore

Activating Prior Knowledge

Ask students who play musical instruments to describe how they vary the sounds produced by the instruments. Encourage students to describe how they change the notes produced and how they vary how loudly they play. Volunteers may want to demonstrate for the class.

•••••••• DISCOVER ••••••••

Skills Focus forming operational definitions

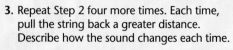

Materials *guitar string attached to nails in wooden board*

Time 10 minutes

Tips Assemble materials before the activity. Make sure the string is taut and wrapped securely around the nails. Students may also use a stringed guitar. Have students use graph paper or prepare a sheet of paper marked in centimeters to measure amplitude.

Expected Outcome The farther the string is pulled, the louder the sound.

Think It Over The amplitude of a vibration is the distance that the string moves to either side. You can change the amplitude by pulling the string back a different distance. The greater the amplitude, the louder the sound.

SECTION 2 Properties of Sound

DISCOVER ••••••••••••••••••••••••••••••• ACTIVITY

How Does Amplitude Affect Loudness?

1. Your teacher will give you a wooden board with two nails in it. Fasten a guitar string to the board by wrapping each end tightly around a nail.

2. Hold the string near the middle. Pull it about 1 cm to one side. This distance is the amplitude of vibration. Let it go. How far does the string move to the other side? Describe the sound you hear.

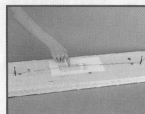

3. Repeat Step 2 four more times. Each time, pull the string back a greater distance. Describe how the sound changes each time.

Think It Over
Forming Operational Definitions How would you define the amplitude of the vibration? How did you change the amplitude each time? What effect did changing the amplitude have on the sound?

GUIDE FOR READING

- How are sound intensity and loudness related?
- How are frequency and pitch related?
- What causes the Doppler effect?

Reading Tip As you read, use your own words to write a phrase or sentence describing each boldfaced word.

Suppose you and a friend are standing next to each other. You are talking in your normal speaking voice. After you say good-bye and your friend has walked away, you realize you have forgotten to tell your friend something important. How do you get your friend's attention? You will need to shout to be heard. When you shout, you take a deep breath and exhale very fast, and your voice sounds louder.

Intensity and Loudness

Compare the sound of a whisper to that of a hearty shout. The sounds are different because the amount of energy carried by the sound waves is different. The sound waves caused by a shout carry much more energy than those of a whisper.

Intensity You have seen how you can change the amplitude of a wave along a rope. If you move the rope a greater distance, you give it more energy as you shake it. When a sound wave carries a larger amount of energy, the molecules of the medium move a greater distance as the waves pass by, and the sound wave has a greater amplitude. The **intensity** of a sound wave is the amount of energy the wave carries per second through a unit area. Intensity is measured in watts per square meter (W/m^2).

Loudness If you did the Discover activity with the guitar string, you noticed how pulling the string back different distances affected the loudness of the sound you heard. You changed the

READING STRATEGIES

Reading Tip Suggest students write their descriptive phrases or sentences in a journal or on note cards. Students can then use the information as a study guide, adding more information and images or symbols, as necessary. Invite volunteers to read aloud the information they wrote for each boldfaced word.

Vocabulary Pair students and have them use dictionaries to explore other words with the prefixes *ultra-* and *infra-*. Challenge students to identify words with these prefixes, such as *ultramodern* and *infrastructure*.

Study and Comprehension After students read the section, have them write summaries of the relationship between sound intensity and loudness, and between frequency and pitch. Also have them describe the Doppler effect.

amplitude of vibration of the string. Sound waves of higher amplitude have a greater intensity because they carry more energy per second through a given area. The greater the intensity of a sound wave, the louder it is. **Loudness** describes what you actually hear. **A sound wave of greater intensity generally sounds louder.**

To increase the loudness of the music coming from a CD player, you adjust the volume control. Loudspeakers or head-phones give off sound by vibrating a cone of material. Figure 7 shows how the vibrations make compressions and rarefactions in the air, just like a vibrating drumhead. As you turn up the volume, the cone vibrates with a greater amplitude and the sound you hear is louder.

Loudness, or sound level, is measured in **decibels (dB).** Figure 8 shows the loudness of some familiar sounds. The loud-ness of a sound you can barely hear is about 0 dB. Each 10 dB increase in sound level represents a tenfold increase in intensity. For example, a sound at 30 dB is ten times more intense than a sound at 20 dB. Sounds louder than 100 dB can cause damage to your ears, especially if you listen to those sounds for long peri-ods of time. Sounds louder than 120 dB can cause pain and sometimes permanent hearing loss.

☑ *Checkpoint* How does amplitude affect the loudness of a sound?

Figure 7 A loudspeaker gives out sound by vibrating cones of material. The greater the ampli-tude of vibration, the greater the volume, or loudness, of the sound.

Loudness of Sounds		
Sound	**Loudness (dB)**	**Hearing Damage**
Threshold of human hearing	0	None
Rustling leaves	10	
Whisper	20	
Very soft music	30	
Classroom	35	
Average home	40–50	
Loud conversation	60–70	
Heavy street traffic	70	
Loud music	90–100	After long exposure
Subway train	100	
Rock concert	115–120	Progressive
Jackhammer	120	Threshold of pain
Jet engine	120–170	
Space shuttle engine	200	Immediate and irreversible

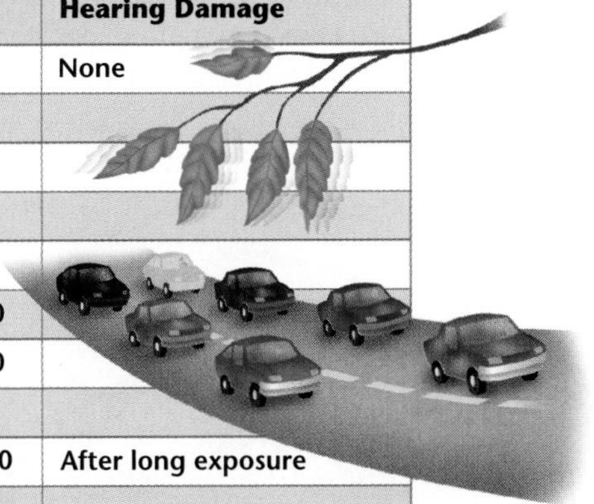

Figure 8 Some sounds are so soft, you can barely hear them. Others are so loud that they can damage your ears. *Applying Concepts How is the sound of a space shuttle engine different from that of a whisper?*

Program Resources

◆ **Teaching Resources** 2-2 Lesson Plan, p. 45; 2-2 Section Summary, p. 46
◆ **Guided Study Workbook** Section 2-2

Answers to Self-Assessment

Caption Question

Figure 8 The sound made by a space shuttle engine is much louder than the sound of a whisper and can cause immediate and irreversible hearing damage.

☑ *Checkpoint*

Sound waves of greater amplitude produce louder sounds.

2 *Facilitate*

Intensity and Loudness

Using the Visuals: Figure 8

Have students look at Figure 8. Point out that a whisper is 10 decibels louder than rustling leaves. Ask: **What does an increase of 10 decibels mean in terms of loudness when you compare a whisper and rustling leaves?** *(A whisper is 10 times as loud as rustling leaves.)* Ask students if they can tell by looking at the table why some rock musicians have hearing loss. *(Hearing damage occurs after long exposure to loud music.)* **learning modality: visual**

Health Connection

Many students use headphones to listen to music. Tell students that researchers have noted an increase in hearing damage among young people, and they think one cause is listening to loud music through headphones. The first symptom of hearing damage is sometimes a ringing in the ears, a condition known as *tinnitus.* Scientists have recently discovered that tinnitus is caused by signals from the part of the brain responsible for hearing. They theorize that the brain is trying to compensate for damage to the nerves and structures of the ear. Encourage students to find out the decibel level that corresponds to each volume setting when they use headphones. **learning modality: verbal**

Ongoing Assessment

Writing Ask students to explain the relation between intensity and loudness of sound. *(Intensity refers to the amount of energy carried by a sound wave, loudness describes what you actually hear. A sound wave of greater intensity sounds louder.)*

Frequency and Pitch

TRY THIS

The Short Straw

Try this activity to see how the length of a straw affects the sound it makes when you blow through it.

1. Flatten one end of a drinking straw and cut the end to form a point.
2. Blow through the straw. Describe what you hear.

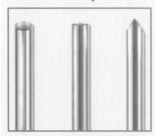

Predicting What changes would you hear if you shortened the straw by cutting off some of the straight end? Test your prediction.

Frequency and Pitch

A barbershop quartet consists of four singers with very different voices. When all four people sing together, the different voices combine to make a pleasing sound.

Frequency When a person sings, muscles in the throat stretch and relax the vocal cords. This changes the frequency of the sound waves. When the vocal cords are stretched, they vibrate more often as the air rushes past them. This creates higher-frequency sound waves. When the vocal cords are relaxed, they vibrate less often and produce lower-frequency sound waves. The frequency of a sound wave is the number of vibrations that occur per second. A frequency of 50 Hz means fifty vibrations per second. A bass singer can produce a range of frequencies from about 80 Hz to about 260 Hz. A trained soprano voice can produce frequencies higher than 1,000 Hz.

Most people can hear sounds with frequencies between 20 Hz and 20,000 Hz. Sound waves with frequencies above the normal human range of hearing are called **ultrasound**. The prefix *ultra-* means "above." Sounds with frequencies below the normal human range of hearing are called **infrasound**. The prefix *infra-* means "below."

Pitch Before a barbershop quartet begins to sing, one member plays a note on a pitch pipe. This gives the lead singer the correct starting note. The **pitch** of a sound is a description of how high or low the sound seems to a person. **The pitch of a sound that you hear depends on the frequency of the sound wave.** Sound waves of high frequency have a high pitch, while sound waves of low frequency have a low pitch.

Figure 9 A barbershop quartet consists of four singers, whose voices sound good together. *Comparing and Contrasting In what way are the four voices different?*

Background

Figure 10 The key farthest to the left on a piano is attached to the longest string. This key plays the note with the lowest pitch. *Developing Hypotheses Why do longer strings generally produce lower notes than shorter strings?*

When a string vibrates, the pitch of the sound depends on the length and thickness of the string, the material it is made from, and how tightly it is stretched. You can change the pitch of a sound by changing the properties of the string that produces it. For example, violinists and guitarists tune their instruments by turning knobs that stretch the strings. A tighter string produces a higher frequency. You hear the higher frequency as a sound with higher pitch.

Different lengths of string produce different frequencies, too. In general, a short string produces a higher pitch than a long string under the same tension. Consider the range of notes you can play on a piano. The key farthest to the left on a piano keyboard produces the note with the lowest pitch. It is attached to the longest string, which vibrates at a frequency of about 27 Hz. The key farthest to the right on a piano keyboard produces the note with the highest pitch. It is attached to the shortest string, which vibrates at a frequency of 4,186 Hz.

✓ *Checkpoint* How are frequency and pitch related?

Resonance Have you ever heard of an opera singer who could shatter a glass with a sustained high note? How can that happen? All objects vibrate naturally. The vibrations are so frequent that you usually cannot see them. The frequency of the vibrations depends on the type and shape of the object. If the frequency of sound waves exactly matches the natural frequency of an object, the sound waves can add to the object's vibrations. Resonance occurs when the frequency of the sound waves and the natural frequency of the object are the same.

Suppose a note has the same frequency as the natural vibration of a crystal glass. If the note is played steadily, the sound waves can add to the amplitude of vibration of the glass. If the note is played loudly enough and for long enough, the amplitude of vibration can increase so much that the glass shatters.

Figure 11 Some musical instruments can produce notes with vibrations that match the natural frequency of a crystal glass. If the note is sustained, the amplitude of vibration can cause the glass to shatter.

Answers to Self-Assessment

Caption Questions

Figure 9 The voices are of different pitches.

Figure 10 Long strings vibrate at a lower frequency, so they produce lower notes.

✓ *Checkpoint*

The higher the frequency, the higher the pitch.

Inquiry Challenge

Materials *scissors, fishing line, metric ruler, thumb tacks, piece of cork or bulletin board* **ACTIVITY**
Time 30 minutes

 Challenge student groups to design experiments that address the following question: **How does the length of a piece of fishing line affect the pitch of the sound the line produces when it vibrates?** Assign individual tasks such as assembling materials, conducting the experiment, and evaluating the pitch. Check plans before allowing students to carry out their designs. Encourage them to predict the outcome of the experiment. After they are finished, ask: **How well did your predictions match the actual outcome?** *(Answers may vary. Students should find that longer pieces of line produce lower pitches.)* **cooperative learning**

Demonstration

Materials *test tube rack, 2 tuning forks with the same pitch, 1 with a different pitch, tuning fork mallet* **ACTIVITY**
Time 15 minutes

Place two unmatched tuning forks in a test tube rack and hold the other in your hand. Tell students that the tuning fork you are holding vibrates at the same pitch as one of the others in the stand. Ask students to predict what will happen if you strike the tuning fork in your hand and move it close to each of the other tuning forks. Test student predictions. Ask: **Which tuning fork has the same frequency as the one that was struck?** *(The tuning fork that began to vibrate.)* **learning modality: visual**

Frequency and Pitch,
continued

TRY THIS

Skills Focus observing
Materials *vacuum cleaner tube or tube toy, piece of cloth*
Time 10 minutes
Tips Tubes may be found at a vacuum supply store, or you may use small tubes that are sold as noise-making toys. These are about 30 cm long and less than 2.5 cm in diameter. Warn students not to stand near one another and not to swing the tubes wildly.
Observing The sound was produced by vibrations of air particles at the end of the tube. As the speed of the tube increases, the pitch becomes higher. If the end of the tube is plugged, the air particles cannot vibrate when it swings; therefore, little sound is produced.
Extend Have students compare the pitch of tubes of different lengths.
learning modality: kinesthetic

The Doppler Effect

Using the Visuals: Figure 12

Have students compare the distances between the sound waves received by the observer on the left and the observer on the right. Ask: **What do you observe about the distance between the sound waves as the car moves away from the observer on the left?** *(The sound waves are farther apart.)* Then ask: **What about the sound waves as the car moves toward the observer on the right?** *(The sound waves are closer together.)*
learning modality: visual

Pipe Sounds

Try this activity to see how a single pipe can produce different pitches.

1. Find an open space where there are no objects or people near you.
2. Hold the end of a flexible plastic tube firmly (a vacuum cleaner hose works well) and swing it over your head until it produces a sound. Try to swing the tube by moving only your wrist.
3. Now slowly increase the speed of the tube. Then slow it down. Use varying speeds. Describe what you hear as you change the speed of the whirling tube.

Observing How was the sound produced? How did the pitch change with an increase in speed? What happens if you plug the far end of the tube with a cloth? Explain.

The Doppler Effect

Even though a sound may have a constant frequency, it does not always sound that way to a listener. Have you ever heard a police car speed by with its siren on? If you listen carefully you will notice something surprising. As the car moves toward you, the pitch of the siren is higher. As the car goes by and moves away, the pitch drops. But the frequency of the siren is not really changing. If you were riding in the police car, you would hear the same pitch all the time. The apparent change in frequency as a wave source moves in relation to the listener is called the **Doppler effect.** If the waves are sound waves, the change in frequency is heard as a change in pitch.

The Doppler Demonstration The Doppler effect was named after Christian Doppler, an Austrian scientist who described it about 150 years ago. To demonstrate the effect, Doppler put a musical band on an open flatcar of a train. He stood on the ground nearby. As the train approached him, the notes the musicians played seemed to be a higher pitch. As the train passed, the notes seemed to drop in pitch. Doppler repeated the experiment, but this time he stood on the train and had the musicians play while they were seated on the ground. Doppler heard the same changes in pitch as the train he rode approached and passed the band. The effect was the same regardless of who was moving, the band or Doppler.

Changing Pitch To understand what causes this apparent change in pitch, imagine you are standing still and throwing tennis balls at a wall about 5 meters in front of you. If you throw one ball each second, the balls hit the wall at a rate of one per second. The frequency is 1 per second, or 1 Hz. Now suppose you walk toward the wall, still throwing one ball per second.

Figure 12 As the police car speeds by, the pitch of the siren seems to change. Ahead of the car, the sound waves are piling up, so the pitch is higher. Behind the car the waves spread out, so the pitch is lower.

Background

Integrating Science Weather forecasters use the Doppler effect to make observations about weather patterns. A form of radar, called Doppler radar, provides information about the movement of heavy winds, such as those that occur in tornadoes and hazardous frontal systems. Traditional weather radar, which uses radio waves, identifies where rainfall is taking place and how severe the rainfall is. Doppler radar measures the speed of the rain, sleet, or snow as it is blown by the wind. When precipitation is moving, Doppler radar shows where the radar waves bunch up and where they spread apart. This helps forecasters understand how winds will move in a weather system. Using data from Doppler radar, the National Weather Service's Nexrad system produces maps of weather patterns that are easy for untrained viewers to interpret.

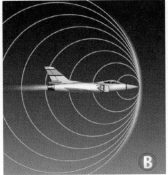

Because each ball has a shorter distance to travel than the one before, it takes less time to get there. The balls hit the wall more often than one per second, or with a higher frequency than before. Similarly, if you throw balls at the wall as you back away, the balls will hit the wall with lower frequency. Each ball has farther to travel before it hits the wall, so it takes longer to get there.

Figure 12 shows how sound waves from a moving source behave. **As a sound source moves toward the listener, the waves reach the listener with a higher frequency. The pitch appears to increase because of the Doppler effect.**

This piling up of sound waves has a spectacular effect in the air. Figures 13A and B show how as a plane travels almost as fast as the speed of sound, the sound waves pile up in front of the plane. This pile-up is the "sound barrier." When the plane flies faster than the speed of sound, it breaks through the barrier. When the sound barrier is broken, as in Figure 13C, a huge amount of energy is released in the form of a shock wave. People on the ground nearby hear a loud noise called a sonic boom.

Figure 13 When a plane approaches the speed of sound, waves pile up to form the sound barrier. When the plane exceeds the speed of sound, it moves through this barrier, causing the shock wave that we hear as a sonic boom.

 Section 2 Review

1. What makes some sounds louder than others?
2. Explain the relationship between frequency and pitch.
3. How can you change the pitch produced by a vibrating string?
4. Explain how resonance can cause a crystal glass to shatter.
5. What is the Doppler effect?
6. **Thinking Critically Relating Cause and Effect** If you are riding in a fire truck with the siren blaring, you do not hear the Doppler effect. Explain.

Check Your Progress

CHAPTER PROJECT 2

Think about the design of your instrument and how it will produce sounds. Consider how you will vary the sound produced by your instrument. Make a list of the materials you could use to build your instrument. Begin to collect your materials.

Program Resources

◆ **Teaching Resources** 2-2 Review and Reinforce, p. 47; 2-2 Enrich, p. 48

Media and Technology

Transparencies "The Doppler Effect," Transparency 7

Demonstration

Materials *large pan, water, tuning fork*
Time 15 minutes

Allow students to see how the Doppler effect takes place with waves from a tuning fork. Fill the pan with water. Strike a tuning fork and place one prong in the water about 10 cm from the edge. Slowly bring the prong toward the edge of the pan. Ask: **What do you observe about the waves made by the tuning fork?** (*The waves bunch up as they get closer to the side of the pan.*) **learning modality: visual**

3 Assess

Section 2 Review Answers

1. Sound waves that have larger amplitudes sound louder.
2. Higher frequency produces higher pitch.
3. By changing the length, tension, or thickness of the string
4. The sound waves increase the amplitude of vibration of the crystal glass. If the amplitude of the vibrations increases enough, the glass can shatter.
5. The apparent change in frequency as a wave source moves in relation to a listener.
6. Since you are moving with the source of the sound, the siren sounds the same all the time.

Check Your Progress

CHAPTER PROJECT 2

Have students devise several methods to vary the pitch of the sounds produced by their instruments. Encourage students to apply the concepts of frequency and pitch to predict what effect each modification will have on their designs.

Performance Assessment

Skills Check Have students demonstrate the effects on sound waves when the amplitude and frequency of the waves in a tightened string are changed.

SECTION 3 Combining Sound Waves

Objectives

After completing the lesson, students will be able to
- identify timbre and tone and state the difference between noise and music;
- describe what happens when two or more sound waves interact.

Key Terms timbre, music, noise, dissonance, acoustics, beats

1 Engage/Explore

Activating Prior Knowledge

Ask students to describe what happens when a band or an orchestra "tunes up." Ask them to compare what music sounds like when all the instruments are in tune to the sounds produced, when some of the instruments are out of tune.

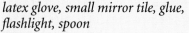

DISCOVER

Skills Focus inferring
Materials *coffee can, latex glove, small mirror tile, glue, flashlight, spoon*
Time 15 minutes
Tips Caution students not to cut themselves on the inside edge of the can. You can replace the small mirror tile with a piece of flattened aluminum foil. Darken the room to make the reflections easier to see.
Expected Outcome As the spoon is tapped on the can, the light patterns on the wall will flicker. Their frequency will change as the frequency of the tapping changes.
Think It Over The vibrations from the tapping are transmitted to the latex. As the latex vibrates, the mirror reflects light to different places on the wall. As the frequency of the tapping increases, the mirror moves at a higher frequency, the reflections on the wall also move at a higher frequency.

SECTION 3 Combining Sound Waves

DISCOVER ⟡ ACTIVITY

How Can You Produce Patterns of Sound?

1. Obtain an empty coffee can.
2. Stretch the palm area of a latex glove over the open end. Glue a small mirror tile in the center of the glove.
3. Shine a flashlight so that the light reflects off the mirror and onto a wall.
4. Ask a classmate to continuously tap a spoon on the closed end of the can. Make sure you keep the light shining on the mirror. Observe the light patterns that are reflected on the wall. What do the patterns look like? Draw and label what you observe.
5. Have your classmate change the frequency of the tapping. Draw what you observe.

Think It Over
Inferring What causes the moving patterns on the wall? What happens when you change the frequency of the tapping? Explain.

GUIDE FOR READING

- What is sound quality?
- How are music and noise different?
- What happens when two or more sound waves interact?

Reading Tip Before you read, list as many musical instruments as you can. Write a short description of how you think each one works. Revise your list as you read.

Imagine you are waiting for a train at a busy station. In the middle of all the hustle and bustle, you notice lots of different sounds. A baby wails while a teenager listens to a favorite radio station. Then the train rolls in. Why are some sounds pleasing to hear while others make you want to cover your ears? The answer is in the way sound waves combine.

Busy train station ▶

READING STRATEGIES

Reading Tip Suggest students create charts on which to list the musical instruments, describe how they think the instruments work, and then write what they learned after reading the section. Have students write these column headings on a sheet of paper: *What I Know, What I Want to Know, What I Learned.* Instruct students to fill in the first two columns before they read, and the last column after they read the section.

Study and Comprehension After students read the section, have them write eight fill-in-the-blank questions about combining sound waves, as in the examples shown. Then have partners exchange questions and answer them.
- Timbre describes the ___ of the sound you hear. *(quality)*
- Repeated changes in loudness are called ___. *(beats)*

Sound Quality

Think of all the different sounds you hear on a given day. Some sounds are pleasant, such as your favorite kind of music, a babbling brook, or a baby cooing. Other sounds are unpleasant, such as loud power tools, fingernails scratching on a chalkboard, or a constant drip of water from a tap. Your ears hear all kinds of sounds—some that you like and some that you don't.

To understand the quality of sound, consider the example of a violin string. As the string vibrates, waves travel along the string and then reflect back, setting up a standing wave. Figure 14 shows how a string vibrates with different frequencies. The frequency at which a standing wave occurs is the string's resonant frequency. Every object, including musical instruments, has its own resonant frequency.

The resonant frequency produces a pitch called the fundamental tone. However, most of the sounds you hear are not pure tones. Although a tuning fork or pitch pipe produces a single tone, more complex instruments produce several tones at once. For example, a string can vibrate at several frequencies at the same time. The higher frequencies produce sounds heard as having higher pitch. The higher pitches, or overtones, have frequencies of two, three, or four times the frequency of the fundamental tone.

Timbre (TAM bur) describes the quality of the sound you hear. Overtones can be weak, strong, or missing. The timbre of a sound depends on which overtones are present. **The blending of the fundamental tone and the overtones makes up the characteristic sound quality, or timbre, of a particular sound.**

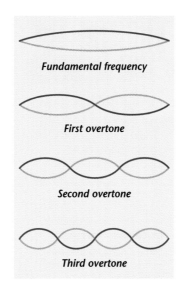

Sounds produced by different instruments have different timbres. The sound of a note played on a trumpet has a different timbre from the same note played on a violin or flute. The trumpet, the violin, and the flute produce different overtones. The size, shape, and materials used also affect the timbre of an instrument.

☑ *Checkpoint* *What factors affect the quality of a sound?*

Fundamental frequency

First overtone

Second overtone

Third overtone

Figure 14 When half a wave takes up the whole string, a fundamental tone is produced (top). Waves half, one third, one fourth, and so on, as long as the fundamental wave produces overtones. *Inferring How does the pitch of each overtone compare with the pitch of the fundamental tone?*

Answers to Self-Assessment

Caption Question

Figure 14 The pitch of each overtone is higher than the pitch of the fundamental tone.

☑ *Checkpoint*

The quality of a sound is affected by the blending of the fundamental tone and the overtones.

---

2 Facilitate

Sound Quality

Using the Visuals: Figure 14

Direct students to count the number of crests shown in the fundamental frequency. *(one)* Then ask: **How many crests do you count in the first overtone?** *(two)* Ask students to infer what a fourth overtone might look like. *(It would have five crests.)* **learning modality: visual**

Building Inquiry Skills: Comparing and Contrasting

Materials *tuning fork, recorder or other simple wind instrument*

Time 10 minutes

Allow students to listen to the tone produced by a tuning fork and one produced by a simple wind instrument, such as a recorder. Ask: **How is the sound produced by the tuning fork different from the tone of the recorder?** *(The tuning fork produces a sound wave of one frequency. The recorder produces several tones—the fundamental frequency and overtones.)* **learning modality: kinesthetic**

Ongoing Assessment

Writing Have students explain why the song "Happy Birthday to You" sounds different when played on a violin and a piano. *(The timbre of the instruments is different because they produce different blends of the fundamental frequencies and overtones.)*

Making Music

Skills Focus
drawing conclusions

Materials *2 rubber bands of different thicknesses, 30 cm ruler, pencil*

Time 15 minutes

Tips Rubber bands that are too thick will not stretch enough. Caution students not to launch bands with rulers. Students should explain that the sounds are caused by vibrations in the air caused by vibrations in the rubber bands. Because they are different thicknesses, the bands should produce sounds of different pitches.

Drawing Conclusions In Step 4, the part of the rubber band that is vibrating is shorter so the pitch is higher.

Extend Provide additional rulers and then ask students to arrange several elastic bands so that the bands increase in pitch. **learning modality: verbal**

Cultural Diversity

Point out that the definition of which combinations of tones are pleasing varies from place to place, as well as from time to time. Tell students that music from different cultures can often sound like it is out of tune because it is based on a different system of fundamental frequencies and overtones. Allow students to hear samples of music from India, the Middle East, the Caribbean, Africa, and the Far East. As they listen, challenge students to identify combinations of tones and kinds of instruments that are different from those used in Western music. **learning modality: kinesthetic**

Plucking Rubber Bands

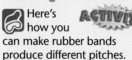 Here's how you can make rubber bands produce different pitches.

1. Wrap two rubber bands of different thickness lengthwise around a 30-cm ruler. The bands should not touch each other.

2. Place a pencil under the bands at about the 5-cm mark.

3. Pluck one band and then the other. What causes the sounds? How are the sounds from the two bands different?

4. With one finger, hold down one of the bands between 5 cm and 30 cm. Pluck the band again.

Drawing Conclusions How is the sound the rubber band made in Step 4 different from the sound it made in Step 3? What caused this difference?

Figure 15 Violins are stringed instruments, flutes and clarinets are woodwinds, and trumpets are brass instruments. *Making Generalizations What do all these musical instruments have in common?*

Making Music

If the combination of the fundamental tone and the overtones results in a sound with a pleasing timbre and a clear pitch, the sound is considered **music.** Most music contains only a few fundamental tones and their overtones. **Music is a set of tones combined in ways that are pleasing to the ear.** The design of a musical instrument affects the overtones it produces when a note is played. All musical instruments produce vibrations when played. The material that vibrates varies. The major groups of instruments are strings, brass, woodwinds, and percussion.

Strings Stringed instruments have strings that vibrate when plucked, struck, or rubbed with a bow. A short string vibrates at a higher frequency and so produces a higher-pitched sound than a long string. As they play, musicians place their fingers on different places along the string to vary the pitch. The material, thickness, and tightness of a string also affects the pitch it produces. Instruments such as guitars, violins, and cellos also have a box, or sounding board. The box improves the quality of the sound produced by the strings. Larger stringed instruments, such as the cello and the double bass, produce lower pitches.

Brass and Woodwinds Brass instruments, such as trumpets and trombones, produce sound when the player's lips vibrate against the mouthpiece. This vibration causes the air column inside the instrument to vibrate. The musician adjusts the length of the air column by pressing valves or moving slides.

Background

History of Science Musicologists who study early music and ancient instruments blend both scientific practices and artistic talent. One of the most renowned musicologists was a German, Curt Sachs (1881–1959). Sachs created a classification system for instruments based on the way the instruments produced sound. He identified four classes of musical instruments. Idiophones and membranophones produce sound by percussion (cymbals, drums, kazoos); chordophones produce sound by the vibration of strings (pianos, guitars, harps); and aerophones produce sound by the vibration of a column of air (harmonica, recorder, trumpets). Sach's classification system is still used today, with the addition of the electrophones, instruments that produce sound by electrical, electromechanical, or electronic means.

Many woodwind instruments, such as clarinets and oboes, have a thin, flexible strip of material called a reed. When the player blows into the mouthpiece, the reed vibrates along with the column of air. The longer the column of air, the lower the pitch. Larger woodwind and brass instruments, such as the bassoon and the tuba, produce lower pitches.

Percussion Percussion instruments, such as drums, bells, cymbals, and xylophones, vibrate when struck. The sound they produce depends on the material from which they are made. It also depends on the size of the instrument, and the part of the instrument that is played. For example, larger drums produce lower pitches.

Figure 16 Percussion instruments vibrate when struck.
Predicting Describe the sound produced by a large drum compared with that of a small drum of the same material.

☑ *Checkpoint* *What are the main groups of musical instruments?*

Noise

You are sitting comfortably in your classroom chair, watching a classmate write on the board. Suddenly, you hear the accidental scratch of fingernails as the chalk flies from your friend's grasp. The sound makes you wince.

Why is the squeak of fingernails on a chalkboard so unpleasant? One answer is that the squeak is noise. **Noise** is a mixture of sound waves that do not sound pleasing together. **Noise has no pleasing timbre and no identifiable pitch.** Consider the noise of chalk squeaking on a chalkboard or the noise of a jackhammer working in the street. The vibrations that produce these sounds are random. Even if an engine produces a hum that has a fundamental tone and overtones, the lack of rhythm in the sound makes us call it noise instead of music.

Sounds that are music to some people are noise to others. Some rock bands and orchestras play compositions with tones that seem to have no musical relationship. The sound produced when these notes are played together is called **dissonance.** Dissonance is music to the ears of people who enjoy the sound.

Music CONNECTION

One of the most widely known compositions of Sergei Prokofiev, a Russian composer who lived from 1891 to 1953, is *Peter and the Wolf.* In this work, each instrument, or group of instruments, represents a character in the story.

In Your Journal

Listen to a recording of *Peter and the Wolf.* Write a review of this work. Do you agree with how Prokofiev matched instruments with characters? Which instrument would you have chosen to represent each character?

Music CONNECTION

Before students listen to the recording of *Peter and the Wolf,* have a class discussion about how different tones or styles of music can express different moods. For example, ask students to describe music that is "happy," or "sad," or "scary." Point out that music has been used to express many emotions and ideas for thousands of years.

In Your Journal Students may describe being amused, frightened, or irritated by the portrayals of the different characters. Students' suggestions should include descriptions of why they think their changes would be more convincing.

Noise

Building Inquiry Skills: Forming Operational Definitions

Materials *audio tape, audio cassette recorder with microphone*
Time 20 minutes

Guide students in defining music and noise. Have them record a variety of sounds around the school and on the school grounds. As students listen to each sound, have them categorize the sound as a single tone or set of tones and as pleasant or unpleasant. Have them determine which sounds were musical and which were noise. Conclude by asking: **What distinguishes musical sounds from those that are noise?** *(Musical sounds are pleasant to hear and have more than one tone. Sounds that are noise are unpleasant to hear.)* **learning modality: logical/mathematical**

Ongoing Assessment

Oral Presentation Have students name five musical sounds and five sounds that are noise.

Answers to Self-Assessment

Caption Questions

Figure 15 All musical instruments produce vibrations when played.
Figure 16 It will have a lower pitch.

☑ *Checkpoint*
Strings, brass and woodwinds, and percussion

EXPLORING
Making Music

If possible, make arrangements with your school's band or music instructor for students to examine several of the instruments shown, such as a violin, clarinet, French horn and electronic keyboard. As students read the paragraphs, they should locate the structures and materials on the actual instruments. Allow students to draw the bow across the violin's strings so they can see how the strings vibrate. Students can also take turns playing the electronic keyboard. Prevent students from placing their mouths on the wind instruments for health reasons. After examining the instruments, ask students to name the part of each instrument that vibrates. *(Violin—strings; harp—strings; clarinet—reed and air column; electronic keyboard—speaker cone; French horn— lips and air column)*

Extend Ask students to closely examine a percussion instrument, such as a xylophone, and determine how it produces music. Remind students to indicate what materials it is made out of and how the musician controls the sound it produces. **learning modality: visual**

Building Inquiry Skills: Applying Concepts

Materials *metal or plastic whistle*
Time 15 minutes

Have students apply their knowledge about musical instruments as they examine a metal or plastic whistle. Allow students to blow into the whistle and evaluate its pitch. Ask: **Does it make sound waves with a high or low frequency? How can you tell?** *(It has a high pitch, so it makes sound waves with a high frequency.)* Ask students to determine to what group of instruments the whistle belongs. Students should explain their answer. *(A whistle is a wind instrument, since movement of air through or across the mouthpiece causes the air inside the whistle to vibrate.)* **learning modality: logical/mathematical**

EXPLORING Making Music

The sound produced by a musical instrument depends on the instrument's size and shape. The material from which the instrument is made and the way it is played also affect the timbre of the sound.

Violin
The violin is a carefully crafted wooden box with strings. The strings are attached to tuning pegs, which can be turned to adjust the tension. When the strings are rubbed with a bow, they vibrate. The violinist controls the pitch by placing the fingers at different positions along the string.

Harp
The harp consists of a row of strings, each one a different length. The harpist gracefully plucks the strings with the fingers to produce music. The short strings produce higher pitches than the long strings do.

Background

Facts and Figures The first piano was adapted from the harpsichord by an Italian, Bartolomeo Cristofori, in 1709. Unlike the harpsichord, which has strings to pluck, the piano has keys attached to hammers. The hammers strike the strings and fall back, leaving the strings to vibrate. The use of the hammers enables the player to partially control the loudness of the sound by controlling how hard the keys are struck.

Cristofori's invention was described as a harpsichord with *piano e forte*, which means "soft and loud" in Italian. The words *pianoforte* and *piano* come from this.

The modern piano comes directly from Cristofori's piano. When the wire strings are struck by the hammers, they vibrate. This vibration is transmitted to a soundboard by a bridge under the strings. The soundboard amplifies the sound and changes its quality.

Clarinet
The clarinet is a woodwind instrument. It has a single reed that vibrates when the player blows into the mouthpiece. The vibrations set up resonance in the air column. The player changes the pitch by pressing on the keys.

Electronic keyboard
A keyboard is a common name for an electronic music maker. It uses a computer chip to reproduce the sound of many different instruments by matching the tones and overtones that the individual instruments produce.

French horn
The French horn is a brass instrument. When the musician's lips vibrate in the mouthpiece, a column of air vibrates in the horn. The player changes the length of the air column by pressing and releasing keys. This changes the pitch of the notes produced.

Including All Students

Students who need an additional challenge can find out how musical notation works. Ask these students to prepare presentations that show how musical notation, such as that shown in the background of the Exploring, describes different musical notes. Allow students to present their findings to the class. **learning modality: visual**

Portfolio Students can save their presentation materials in their portfolios.

Real-Life Learning

Materials *musical instrument*
Time Time will vary.

Many students may show an interest in learning to play musical instruments. Encourage these students to pursue their interests through the school music or band programs. If some students in class already play musical instruments, invite them to display their skills to the class. Allow these students to work with others to prepare a musical presentation for the class. This could be a short, easy-to-learn song, or you may want to have them create a song using information relevant to the chapter. If some students are more accomplished using their instruments, allow them to share their expertise with those who are still learning basic skills. **cooperative learning**

Ongoing Assessment

Skills Check Ask students to list the different types of musical instruments and describe how each produces different pitches.

Interference of Sound Waves

Including All Students

If students have difficulty understanding how sound waves interact, draw sample diagrams on the board. Show two waves with compressions in the same location. Indicate that the resulting wave has compressions of greater amplitude. Then draw two waves in which the compressions are not aligned. Ask: **What happens when the compression of the first wave meets the rarefaction of the second wave?** *(The resulting wave has no amplitude.)* **learning modality: visual**

Inquiry Challenge

Materials (per group) *small cassette recorder, box with lid, plastic foam pellets, 2 blank cassette tapes*

ACTIVITY

Time 30 minutes

Challenge students to design experiments to determine whether air or plastic foam is a better soundproofing material. Ask students: **What variables must you control?** *(The volume of the sound played outside the box, the volume that the recorder is set to, and the volume that the recorder is played back)* Approve student plans and allow them to conduct their experiments. Ask: **What can you conclude about the sound-absorbing properties of plastic foam?** *(Plastic foam is better at absorbing sound than air.)* **learning modality: kinesthetic**

 Integrating Technology

Ask students to sketch how the sound waves produced by the airplane earphones interact with the sound waves from the airplane's engines. **learning modality: visual**

Using the Visuals: Figure 18

Direct students to point out where the sound will get louder and softer in the diagram. *(The sound is louder where the two lines join. The sound is softer where the lines do not match up.)* **learning modality: visual**

Interference of Sound Waves

You have probably heard sound waves interfering with each other, though you may not have known what you were hearing. **Interference occurs when two or more sound waves interact.** The amplitudes of the two waves combine, causing the loudness of the sound to change. When interference is constructive, compressions of waves occur at the same place and the amplitudes combine. The resulting sound is louder than either of the two original sounds. When the interference is destructive, compressions of one wave occur at the same place as rarefactions of another wave and the amplitudes cancel each other out. The resulting wave is softer or completely concealed.

Figure 17 A concert hall must be designed to provide the highest sound quality possible. The design should eliminate echoes and destructive interference.

Acoustics The way in which sound waves interact is very important in concert halls. In a concert hall, sound waves of different frequencies reach each listener from many directions at the same time. These sound waves may come directly from the orchestra or they may first bounce off the walls or ceiling. People sitting in various seats may hear different sounds because of the particular interactions of sound waves at their locations. In a poorly designed hall, seats may be located where destructive interference occurs. The sound will seem distorted.

Acoustics describe how well sounds can be heard in a particular room or hall. When designing auditoriums, acoustical engineers must carefully consider the shape of the room and the materials used to cover walls, floors, ceilings, and seats. Because they absorb sound instead of reflecting it, some materials can eliminate the reflected waves that cause interference.

Canceling Sounds Sometimes destructive interference is welcome. **INTEGRATING TECHNOLOGY** Airplane passengers use earphones to listen to music, but the throbbing of the plane's engines can drown out much of the sound. Some airline earphones use destructive interference to cancel out the steady engine noise. The earphones produce sound waves that interfere destructively with the engine sound. The passenger's ears receive both the engine sound waves and the sound waves produced by the earphones. These waves cancel each other out, so the passenger hears neither. Only the music is left. This type of technology also allows factories to reduce noise levels to protect the hearing of workers.

Background

Facts and Figures When architects and engineers design buildings, they take into consideration how sound will be absorbed and reflected. In office buildings, for example, sound-absorbent tiles are often placed on the ceilings and walls to help dampen loud sounds. In concert halls and auditoriums, designers must maximize the quality of sound for the pleasure of the audience. These designers consider many variables, from the arrangement of the seats to the use of heavy drapes or window curtains. By analyzing these variables, acoustic engineers pinpoint where sound will bounce off and reverberate and where it will be absorbed. Even the size of the audience can affect how well a space presents sound. People absorb sound waves and can alter the acoustics of the room in which they are sitting.

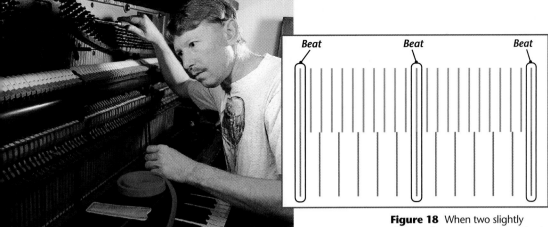

Figure 18 When two slightly different frequencies are combined, they interfere constructively at regular intervals (above right). A piano tuner listens to the sound of a note and a tuning fork together (above left). *Inferring How does the piano tuner know when a key is perfectly tuned?*

Beats If two sound waves are close in frequency, they can combine so that they interfere both constructively and destructively at regular intervals. Figure 18 shows how two frequencies can combine at certain times. The resulting sound gets louder and softer at regular intervals. The intervals depend on the difference between the two frequencies. The repeated changes in loudness are called **beats.**

Piano tuners use beats to tune pianos. A piano tuner strikes a tuning fork of a particular frequency and hits the corresponding key on a piano at the same time. If the tuner hears beats, that means that the frequency of vibration of the piano string does not exactly match that of the tuning fork. The tuner then adjusts the piano string until no beat can be heard. Then the piano key is perfectly tuned.

Section 3 Review

1. What factors determine the quality of a sound?
2. What is the difference between music and noise?
3. How can sounds cancel each other out?
4. How can the interference of two sound waves produce a louder sound?
5. What are beats?
6. **Thinking Critically Applying Concepts** Explain why a sound in an empty room will sound different from the same sound in a room with a carpet, curtains, and furniture.

Check Your Progress CHAPTER PROJECT 2
Begin building the instrument you have designed. As you build your instrument, experiment with different materials to find the most appealing sound. How do different kinds of materials affect the sounds? Explore and experiment with the sounds your instrument makes. How does adding or removing certain parts or materials affect the loudness of the sound? How can you vary the pitch of your instrument?

Program Resources

◆ **Teaching Resources** 2-3 Review and Reinforce, p. 51; 2-3 Enrich, p. 52

Answers to Self-Assessment

Caption Question

Figure 18 The tuner knows a key is perfectly tuned when he or she does not hear beats.

3 Assess

Section 3 Review Answers

1. Sound quality depends on the blending of fundamental tones and overtones.
2. Music is a set of fundamental notes and overtones that are pleasant to hear. Noise is an unpleasant mix of tones with no pleasing timbre and identifiable pitch.
3. If the compressions of one wave occur at the same place as the rarefactions of another wave, and vice versa, the waves will cancel each other out.
4. If two sound waves with the same frequency combine, they will interfere constructively, increasing the total amplitude and producing a louder sound.
5. Beats are regular pulses of alternating loud and soft sound. They result from constructive interference.
6. An empty room will reflect sound from the wall, floor, and ceiling. Drapes, carpet, and furniture will absorb the sound, so less sound is reflected.

Check Your Progress CHAPTER PROJECT 2
Encourage students to keep journals as they experiment with different materials and designs of their instruments. Students should describe each change they make and its effect on the sound produced. Ask students to organize their observations into data tables. Students can work in groups or as a class to compare their observations and come up with generalizations about the sounds produced by different designs.

Performance Assessment

Writing Have students compare and contrast the sounds produced by a clarinet and a trumpet. Then have them compare and contrast the sounds produced by squeaking chalk and a trumpet.

Musical Notes

Preparing for Inquiry

Key Concept Students will use bottles of water to produce different musical notes.
Skills Objectives Students will be able to
◆ predict and observe pitches;
◆ infer causes of changes in pitch.
Time 45 minutes
Advance Planning Obtain a sufficient number of identical glass bottles.

Guiding Inquiry

Invitation Ask students if they have ever tried to make a sound by blowing across the top of an empty bottle. *(Most will say yes.)* Ask: **How is the sound produced? How do you make a bottle produce different notes to play a tune?** In this experiment, they will discover "how it works."

Introducing the Procedure

Use tuning forks, a harmonica, or some other instrument to illustrate low, medium, and high pitches.

Troubleshooting the Experiment

Students should handle the glass bottles carefully to prevent breakage and water spillage. Wipe up any spills immediately with paper towels.

Expected Outcome

Blowing across the bottle with the shortest column of air produced the highest pitch. Tapping the bottle with the least amount of water produced the highest pitch.

Analyze and Conclude

1. When you blow across the top of a bottle, a standing wave is set up in the column of air above the water. The bottle with the most water (shortest column of air) produced the highest pitch. The bottle with the least water (longest column of air) produced the lowest pitch.
2. The lengths of the columns of air are different.
3. When the bottle of water was tapped with the pencil, both the water and the bottle vibrated. The bottle with the most

Musical Notes

Musical instruments produce sound by setting up standing waves. Those waves can be on a string or in a column of air. In this lab, you will see how you can use bottles to produce different musical notes, maybe enough to play a simple tune.

Problem

How can you produce different musical notes with bottles of water?

Skills Focus

predicting, observing, inferring

Materials

3 identical glass bottles
water
masking tape
marking pen
pencil

Procedure

1. Label the bottles A, B, and C.
2. Put water in each bottle so that bottle A is one-fourth full, bottle B is half full, and bottle C is three-fourths full.
3. Copy the data table into your lab notebook. Measure the distance from the top of each bottle to the surface of the water. Then measure the height of the water in each bottle. Record your measurements.
4. Predict the difference in pitch you will hear if you blow across the top of each bottle in turn. Give reasons for your prediction.
5. Test your prediction by blowing over the top of each bottle. Listen to the sound you produce. Describe each sound in terms of its pitch—low, medium, or high. Record the pitch of each sound.

60 ◆ O

water produced the lowest pitch. The bottle with the least water produced the highest pitch.
4. The change in pitch is caused by different heights of water in the bottles. Tapping in different places produces different types of vibration.
5. When tapping the bottles, the bottle with the least water produced the highest pitch; when blowing across the bottles, the opposite happened.
6. Blowing: The bottle with the shortest column of air produced the highest pitch.

Tapping: the bottle with the least amount of water produced the highest pitch.
7. Sounds change as the medium, or properties of the medium, change(s).

Extending the Inquiry

More to Explore Students can add food coloring to the water so that each "note" is a different color. Students with musical training can write instructions on how to play simple tunes using the colors to identify the notes.

DATA TABLE

Bottle	Length of Column of Air (cm)	Height of Water (cm)	Pitch Produced by Blowing Across Top of Bottle	Pitch Produced by Tapping Pencil on Side of Bottle
A				
B				
C				

6. When you gently tap the side of a bottle with a pencil, you produce another sound. Do you think the sound will be similar to or different from the sound produced by blowing across the top of the bottle? Explain.

7. Test your prediction by tapping on the side of each bottle with a pencil. Record the pitch of each sound.

Analyze and Conclude

1. Describe how the sound is produced in Step 5. Which bottle produced the highest pitch? Which bottle produced the lowest pitch?

2. What caused the change in pitch from bottle to bottle?

3. Describe how the sound is produced in Step 7. Which bottle produced the highest pitch? Which bottle produced the lowest pitch?

4. What caused the change in pitch from bottle to bottle? What change in pitch can you produce by tapping on a different part of the bottle?

5. Compare the sounds you produced by blowing across the bottles with those produced by tapping on the bottles. What was the difference in pitch for each bottle? Explain your observations.

6. Look at your data table. How does the length of the column of air affect the pitch? How does the height of the water affect the pitch?

7. **Think About It** Based on your observations in this lab, what statements can you make about the relationship between the sounds produced and the medium through which the sound travels?

More to Explore

To play simple tunes, you will need eight notes. Set up a row of eight bottles, each with a different amount of water. Adjust the water level in each bottle until you can play a simple scale. Practice playing a simple tune on your bottles.

Sample Data Table

Bottle	Length of column of air (cm)	Height of Water (cm)	Pitch Produced by Blowing Across Top of Bottle	Pitch Produced by Tapping Pencil on Side of Bottle
A	20	4	Low	High
B	12	12	Medium	Medium
C	4	20	High	Low

Safety

Caution students to handle the glass bottles carefully to prevent breakage and water spillage. Review the safety guidelines in Appendix A.

Program Resources

◆ **Teaching Resources** Real-World Lab blackline masters, pp. 63–65

Media and Technology

 **Lab Activity Videotape**
Sound and Light, 4

SECTION 4 How You Hear Sound

Objectives

After completing the lesson, students will be able to

◆ explain how the body interprets sound waves;

◆ identify causes of hearing loss and ways that hearing loss can be prevented.

Key Terms ear canal, eardrum, middle ear, cochlea

1 Engage/Explore

Activating Prior Knowledge

Ask students what they would do if they had difficulty hearing a friend call out across a soccer field. *(Sample: Cup a hand behind one ear.)* Explain that this and other techniques direct sound waves toward your ear. In this section, students will learn what happens to the sound waves after they reach the ear.

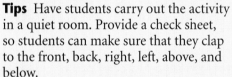

DISCOVER

Skills Focus observing
Materials *none*
Time 10 minutes
Tips Have students carry out the activity in a quiet room. Provide a check sheet, so students can make sure that they clap to the front, back, right, left, above, and below.

Expected Outcome Most students will correctly identify the horizontal position of the source, especially when it is near the left or right ear. It is more difficult to detect the vertical position of a sound, especially one directly in front of or behind the listener.

Think It Over Locations to the left or right were easy to identify. The sound arrives at each ear at slightly different times. That time difference allows you to detect where the sound is coming from.

SECTION 4 How You Hear Sound

DISCOVER

Where Is the Sound Coming From?

1. Ask your partner to sit on a chair, with eyes closed.

2. Clap your hands near your partner's left ear. Ask your partner to tell you the direction the sound came from.

3. Now clap near your partner's right ear. Again, ask your partner to tell you the direction the sound came from. Continue clapping above your partner's head, in front of the face, and below the chin in random order. How well can your partner detect the direction the sound is coming from?

4. Switch places with your partner and repeat Steps 1–3.

Think It Over

Observing As you clap, record the answers given by your partner. Which locations are easily identified? Which locations are impossible to identify? Is there a pattern? If so, can you think of a possible explanation for this pattern?

GUIDE FOR READING

◆ How do you hear sound?

◆ What causes hearing loss?

Reading Tip As you read, draw a flowchart to show how you hear sound.

62 ◆ O

The house is quiet. You are sound asleep. All of a sudden, your alarm clock goes off. Startled, you jump up out of bed. Your ears detected the sound waves produced by the alarm clock. But how exactly did your brain receive the information?

How You Hear Sound

Once the sound waves enter your ear, how does your brain receive the information? Your ear has three main sections: the outer ear, the middle ear, and the inner ear. Each has a different function. **The outer ear funnels sound waves, the middle ear transmits the waves inward, and the inner ear converts the sound waves into a form that your brain can understand.**

Outer Ear As the alarm clock rings, the sound waves reach your ears. The curved surface of the outermost part of your ear looks and acts like a funnel. It collects sound waves and directs them into a narrower region known as the **ear canal.** Your ear

---

READING STRATEGIES

Reading Tip Help students create flowcharts by beginning a flowchart on the board. Remind students to include arrows that connect an event to the event that follows it.

Path of Sound from the Ear to the Brain

Outer ear collects sound waves and directs them into ear canal.

↓

Sound waves make eardrum vibrate.

Study and Comprehension Before students read, suggest they rewrite the section headings as questions that begin with *How, What,* or *Why.* Instruct students to leave several lines of space between each question. Have partners discuss possible answers to the questions they wrote, based on what they already know about sound. After students read, have them review the section and write answers to their questions.

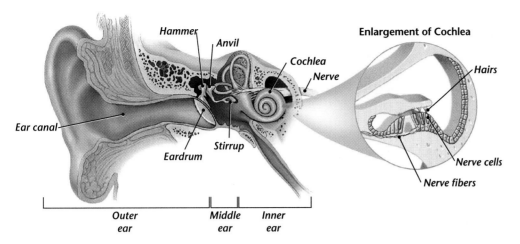

Hammer
Anvil
Cochlea
Nerve
Ear canal
Eardrum
Stirrup
Outer ear
Middle ear
Inner ear

Enlargement of Cochlea
Hairs
Nerve cells
Nerve fibers

Figure 19 The illustrations show the structure of the human ear and the inside of the cochlea. *Interpreting Diagrams How is sound transmitted through the middle ear?*

canal is a few centimeters long and ends at the eardrum. The **eardrum** is a small, tightly stretched, drumlike membrane. The sound waves make your eardrum vibrate, just as a drum vibrates when you beat it with a drumstick.

Middle Ear Behind the eardrum is an area called the middle ear. The **middle ear** contains the three smallest bones in the human body—the hammer, the anvil, and the stirrup. If you look at them in Figure 19, you'll see how they got their names. The hammer is attached to the eardrum, so when the eardrum vibrates, the hammer does too. The hammer then hits the anvil, which then shakes the stirrup.

Inner Ear The inner ear is separated from the middle ear by another membrane. Behind this membrane is a cavity filled with liquid. This cavity, the **cochlea** (KAHK lee uh), is shaped like a snail shell. Inside, it is lined with more than 10,000 nerve cells. These nerve cells have hairlike structures that float in the liquid in the cochlea. When the stirrup vibrates against the membrane, the vibrations pass into the liquid in the cochlea. As the liquid moves, the hairlike structures sway, sending messages to the brain. The brain processes these messages and tells you that you've heard sound.

☑ *Checkpoint* **What are the three main areas of the ear?**

Listen to Sounds

How does sound travel to your ears?

1. Tie two strings to the handle of a metal spoon. Each string should be about 40 cm long.

2. Hold one end of each string in each hand. Bump the bowl of the spoon against a desk or other hard solid object. Listen to the sound.

3. Now wrap the ends of the string around your fingers.

4. Put your index fingers up against your ears and bump the spoon against the object again.

Inferring How does the first sound compare with the sound you heard with your fingers up against your ears? What can you conclude about how sound travels to your ears?

Program Resources

◆ **Teaching Resources** 2-4 Lesson Plan, p. 53; 2-4 Section Summary, p. 54
◆ **Guided Study Workbook** Section 2-4

Media and Technology

 Transparencies "The Ear," Transparency 8

Answers to Self-Assessment

Caption Question

Figure 19 Vibrations from the eardrum are transferred to the hammer, through the anvil, and through the stirrup.

☑ *Checkpoint*

The outer ear, the middle ear, and the inner ear

2 Facilitate

How You Hear Sound

Using the Visuals: Figure 19

As students examine the diagram, have them create flowcharts that show the structures that sound waves pass through in the ear. Ask: **At which point do sound waves create vibrations in the ear?** *(At the ear drum)* **Where are vibrations converted into nerve impulses?** *(Inside the cochlea)* **learning modality: visual**

Including All Students

The structures of the ear have unusual names that may be difficult for students to master. To help students recall these terms, have them use a mnemonic device in which they associate each term with a particular shape or object. For example, students can associate the eardrum with a drumhead. Have students make similar connections for the bones of the middle ear. Then explain that the root meaning of the word *cochlea* is "land snail." Ask: **How does the cochlea resemble a land snail?** *(It has a coiled shape.)* **learning modality: verbal**

Skills Focus inferring
Materials *string, metal spoon*
Time 15 minutes
Tips Use heavy thread or string for best results. Caution students not to push their fingers into their ear canals.
Inferring Sound travels to your ears in waves. String carries waves better than air.
Extend Allow students to experiment with different kinds of string. **learning modality: kinesthetic**

Ongoing Assessment

Oral Presentation Have students name two structures of the ear and describe what role they have in how we hear.

Hearing Loss

3 Assess

Section 4 Review Answers

1. The outer ear focuses sound waves into the ear canal.
2. Loud sounds can damage some of the hair cells in the cochlea.
3. Sound waves in the ear canal cause the eardrum to vibrate.
4. Vibrations from the eardrum move the hammer, which moves the anvil and stirrup. The stirrup vibrates against a membrane of the inner ear. The membrane causes fluid in the cochlea to vibrate, stimulating tiny hairs that are connected to nerve cells.
5. Answers may vary. Check students' work against the chart in Figure 8.

Science at Home

Students should find that **ACTIVITY** most family members agree on pleasant and unpleasant sounds. However, there may be age differences in ratings.

Performance Assessment

Writing Have students work in small groups to design and produce pamphlets to explain how loud noises can damage hearing.

Portfolio Students can save their pamphlets in their portfolios.

Figure 20 Hearing aids can make sounds louder as the sounds enter the ear.

Hearing Loss

 INTEGRATING HEALTH The human ear can normally detect sounds as soft as breathing (about 2–10 dB). The normal range of frequencies a person can hear is 20–20,000 Hz. However, when hearing loss occurs, a person may have difficulty hearing soft sounds or high-pitched sounds. **Many people suffer hearing loss as a result of injury, infection, or aging.**

Hearing Loss Due to Injury or Infection A head injury can cause the tiny hammer, anvil, and stirrup to disconnect from one another. Then sound cannot be transmitted through the middle ear. Surgery can usually correct this type of hearing loss.

If your eardrum becomes damaged or punctured, you may experience hearing loss. (Imagine trying to play a torn drum!) For this reason, it is dangerous to put objects into your ear, even to clean it. Viral or bacterial infections can also damage the delicate inner ear, causing permanent hearing loss.

Hearing Loss Due to Aging The most common type of hearing loss occurs gradually. As a person gets older, the tiny hair cells in the cochlea become less effective at detecting the signals. Many older people have difficulty hearing higher-frequency sounds.

Extended exposure to loud sounds can damage the hair cells. If these cells are damaged by loud sounds, they can no longer transmit signals to the brain. You can prevent this type of hearing loss by wearing ear plugs or other hearing protection when you know you are going to be exposed to loud noises.

Some types of hearing loss can be helped with hearing aids. Hearing aids are amplifiers. Some are so tiny that they can fit invisibly in the ear. Others are made specifically for a person's hearing loss and amplify mainly the frequencies that the person has lost the ability to hear.

 Section 4 Review

1. How do your ears detect sound waves?
2. How can sound damage your hearing?
3. Describe how the eardrum works.
4. What happens once sound waves enter the ear?
5. **Thinking Critically Classifying** Make a chart that lists some common sounds you might hear in a day. Estimate the loudness of each sound and state whether each one could produce hearing loss. (*Hint: Refer to Figure 8 on page 47.*)

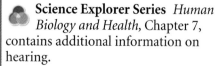
Science at Home

Invite family members to make a survey of the kinds of sounds they hear throughout one day. Have each member rate the sounds as quiet, normal, loud, or painful. Then rate each sound as pleasant, neutral, or annoying. State the source of each sound, the location, the time of day, and the approximate length of time that they are exposed to the sound. How are the ratings alike and different?

Program Resources

 Science Explorer Series *Human Biology and Health*, Chapter 7, contains additional information on hearing.
◆ **Teaching Resources** 2-4 Review and Reinforce, p. 55; 2-4 Enrich, p. 56

Media and Technology

Exploring Physical Science Videodisc
Unit 6, Side 2, "Making Silence"

Chapter 5

SCIENCE AND SOCIETY

Keeping It Quiet...

A construction worker operates a jackhammer; a woman waits in a noisy subway station; a factory worker uses loud machinery. All three are victims of noise pollution. In the United States, 80 million people say they are "continually" bothered by noise, and 40 million face danger to their health.

One burst of sound from a passing truck can be enough to raise blood pressure. People start to feel pain at about 120 decibels. Exposure to even 85 decibels (the noise level of a kitchen blender or a loudly crying baby) can eventually damage the hairlike cells of the cochlea. Noise that "doesn't hurt" can still damage your hearing. As many as 16 million Americans may have permanent hearing loss caused by noise. What can we do to keep it quiet?

The Issues

What Can Individual People Do? Some work conditions are noisier than others. Construction workers, factory employees, and people who drive large vehicles are often at risk. All workers in noisy environments can benefit from ear protectors, such as plugs or headphone-like mufflers. Ear protectors can reduce noise levels by 35 decibels.

A listener at a rock concert, a hunter firing a rifle, or someone using an electric drill can also prevent damage with ear protectors. In addition, people should, if possible, avoid extreme noise. They can buy quieter machines and respect neighbors by not using noisy machines, such as lawn mowers and snow blowers, at quiet times of day or night. Simply turning down the volume on headphones, radios, CD players, and tape players can help prevent permanent hearing loss in young people.

What Can Communities Do? Transportation—planes, trains, trucks, and cars— is the largest source of noise pollution. Fifteen million Americans live near airports or under airport flight paths. Careful planning to locate highways and airports away from homes and buildings can reduce noise. Cities and towns can also prohibit flights late at night.

Many communities have laws against noise of more than a fixed decibel level, but these laws are not always enforced. In some cities "noise police" can fine the owners of noisy equipment.

What Can Government Do? A national Office of Noise Abatement and Control was set up in the 1970s. It required labels on power tools and lawnmowers, telling how much noise they make. In 1982, this office was closed down. Some lawmakers want to bring the office back and have nationwide limits to many types of noise. But critics say that national laws have little effect in controlling noise. The federal government could also encourage—and pay for—research into making quieter vehicles and machines.

You Decide

1. **Identify the Problem**
   In your own words, describe the problem of noise pollution.

2. **Analyze the Options**
   List as many methods as you can for dealing with noise. How would each method work to reduce noise or to protect people from noise? Who would be affected by each method?

3. **Find a Solution**
   Propose one method for reducing noise in your community. Make a poster that encourages people to carry out your proposal.

Background

Integrating Science Communities try to reduce noise by limiting the noise being produced or by preventing the noise from affecting people nearby. Highway noise is a problem for almost every community, and there are many different approaches in effect. In Hillsborough, North Carolina, large trucks are no longer permitted to drive downtown. In suburban Illinois, highways that are heavily traveled by commuters are being enclosed by noise barriers—walls made of concrete or wood that protect neighborhoods from the sound of the traffic.

In Great Britain and France, new roads are being tested to reduce the amount of noise produced by traffic. These roads are surfaced with a mixture of rubber granules and materials that are more traditional. The rubber is made from recycled tires and is thought to reduce noise up to 70 percent.

SCIENCE AND SOCIETY

Keeping It Quiet...

Purpose

Identify sources of noise pollution, and propose solutions that help people find new ways to travel and work without damaging their hearing.

Panel Discussion

Time 60–70 minutes
Have students discuss noise pollution in three groups. Allow them access to books, magazine articles, or the Internet to find information on causes of and solutions for noise pollution. Encourage students to focus on how these issues affect people on an individual, community, or legislative level.

When students have had time to discuss the issues in groups, bring them back together and lead a panel discussion on solutions to the problem of noise pollution. Have each group act as a panel member, representing the viewpoint of individuals, community leaders, those who produce loud noise, or government officials. Groups should take turns presenting points in the discussion.

Extend Students could identify consumer products that they believe contribute to noise pollution, such as portable CD players or radios and lawnmowers. Encourage students to check the labels on these products for information regarding the level of noise they produce.

You Decide

Have students respond to Identify the Problem and Analyze the Options as they work in their groups before the panel discussion begins. After the panel discussion, students can complete Find a Solution individually or in their groups, using what they learned in the discussion to find solutions to the problem. Students' posters should clearly identify the problem and explain how the solution will be implemented on an individual, community, or government level.

SECTION
5 Applications of Sound

Objectives

After completing the lesson, students will be able to
- explain how sonar and bats use reflection of sound waves to locate objects;
- define ultrasound and give examples of its application.

Key Terms sonar, echolocation, sonogram

1 Engage/Explore

Activating Prior Knowledge

Ask students what happens if someone yells "Hello!" into a canyon. *(They may hear an echo.)* In this section, students learn more about what happens when sound bounces.

DISCOVER

Skills Focus inferring
Materials *meter stick, masking tape, soft ball, stopwatch*
Time 10 minutes

Tips Test the ball before you use it with students. A softer ball works better than a hard one. The ball models the reflection of sound. When sound waves hit a barrier they cannot pass through, they will bounce back and return in the form of an echo.
Expected Outcome When the ball hits the wall 3 m away, it will "reflect" and roll back to the student. When the wall is 6 m away, the ball takes longer to return to the student.
Think It Over The longer it takes the ball to return, the farther it has traveled.

66 ◆ O

DISCOVER

How Can You Use Time to Measure Distance?

1. Measure a distance 3 meters from a wall and mark the spot with a piece of masking tape.
2. Roll a soft ball in a straight line from that spot toward the wall. What happens to the ball?
3. Roll the ball again. Try to roll the ball at the same speed each time. Have a classmate use a stopwatch to record the time it takes for the ball to leave your hand, reflect off the wall, and then return to you.
4. Now move 6 meters away from the wall. Mark the spot with tape. Repeat Steps 2 and 3.
5. Compare the time for both distances.

Think It Over
Inferring What does the difference in time tell you about the distance the ball has traveled?

GUIDE FOR READING

- How is sonar used to tell distances?
- How do animals use sound?
- How is ultrasound used in medicine?

Reading Tip As you read, write a sentence or two to describe each application of sound waves.

You and your friend are in a long, dark cave. Every sound you make seems to come right back to you. For fun, both of you shout and scream and then listen as the echoes bounce around the cave.

Reflection of Sound Waves

When a sound wave hits a surface through which it cannot pass, it bounces back, or reflects. A reflected sound wave is called an echo.

Sometimes an echo is much fainter than the original sound. This is usually because some of the energy of the wave is absorbed along the way. Some materials reflect sound very well, while others absorb most of the sound that strikes them. Most of the practical applications of sound are based on the fact that sound reflects off some surfaces.

66 ◆ O

READING STRATEGIES

Reading Tip Suggest that as students write sentences describing the application of sound waves, they enhance the information by adding sketches or other visual representations. Encourage them to also write definitions for the following terms as they describe sound wave application:
- sonar
- echolocation
- sonogram

Study and Comprehension Have students preview the section by reading the headings and subheadings, and by looking at the photographs. Encourage students to suggest questions they have about sonar, echolocation, and ultrasound. Write the questions on the board. After students read the section, have them work as a class to answer the questions on the board. Encourage them to research answers not found in the section.

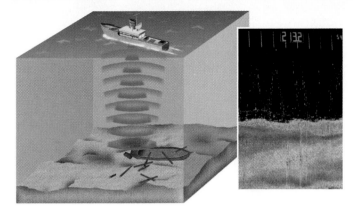

Figure 21 Sonar is used to determine distances and to locate objects under water. *Applying Concepts What two quantities must be known to calculate how far a sound wave has traveled?*

Sonar

Reflected sound waves have many uses. They can be used to determine the depth of water, to locate a sunken shipwreck or cargo, to find schools of fish, or to locate boats out on the ocean.

Sonar is a system of detecting reflected sound waves. The word *sonar* comes from the initial letters of **so**und **n**avigation **a**nd **r**anging. "Navigation" means finding your way around on the ocean (or in the air), and "ranging" means finding the distance between objects. Submarines and ships use sonar to detect other submarines and ships by sending sound waves through the water close to the surface. When the waves hit another boat near the surface of the water, they reflect back and are picked up by the sonar device.

How Sonar Works A sonar machine, or depth finder, produces a burst of high-frequency ultrasonic sound waves that travels through the water. When the waves hit an object or the ocean floor, they reflect. The reflected waves are detected by the sonar machine. **The sonar device measures the time it takes to detect the reflected sound waves.** It uses the data to calculate the distance that the sound has traveled. The intensity of the reflected waves tells the size and shape of the object that reflected the waves.

Calculating Distances The farther a sound wave travels before bouncing off a barrier, the longer it takes to come back. To calculate the depth of water, the sonar machine must calculate the distance traveled by the sound waves. It measures the time taken for the waves to come back. The sonar device then multiplies the speed of sound in water by the time taken. The total distance traveled by the sound is twice the depth of the water. Because the waves traveled to the bottom and then back, the sonar machine divides the total distance by two to find the actual depth.

☑ *Checkpoint* **What are three uses for sonar?**

Sharpen your Skills

Designing Experiments

1. Stand a square piece of cardboard on a table. Prop it up with a book.
2. Put two empty paper towel or aluminum foil tubes on the table. The tubes should be at an angle to each other and almost touching at the end near the cardboard. Leave a gap of about 6 cm between the cardboard and the ends of the tubes.
3. Put your ear near the other end of one of the tubes. Cover one ear with your hand so that the only sounds you hear are coming through the tube.
4. Place a ticking watch in the second tube and cover the open end with your hand. What do you hear?
5. Design an experiment to determine how sound reflects off different materials, such as a variety of fabrics.

Program Resources

◆ **Teaching Resources** 2-5 Lesson Plan, p. 57; 2-5 Section Summary, p. 58
◆ **Guided Study Workbook** Section 2-5

Media and Technology

 Transparencies "Sonar," Transparency 9

Answers to Self-Assessment

Caption Question

Figure 21 The time it takes for the sound wave to reflect back to the sonar machine and the speed of sound in the water

☑ *Checkpoint*

Sonar can be used to determine water depth, locate sunken ships, locate boats out on the ocean, and find schools of fish.

---

2 Facilitate

Reflection of Sound Waves

Including All Students

Materials *wall of building*
Time 15 minutes

For students having difficulty understanding how sound bounces, take them to an outside wall. Have them clap their hands sharply. Ask: **What do you hear?** (*Students hear their hands clap, then they hear the echo.*) Ask students to predict what will happen if they double their distance from the wall. Allow them to test their predictions. (*The echo takes longer to return.*) **learning modality: kinesthetic**

Sharpen your Skills

Designing Experiments

Materials *piece of cardboard, 2 cardboard tubes, metric ruler, ticking watch*
Time 15 minutes
Tips Be sure the cardboard tubes are at the same angle to the reflector. Students should be able to hear the watch ticking.
Extend Have students create data tables to record their observations. Students can list the materials they use and the degree to which the sounds are absorbed or reflected.

Sonar

Using the Visuals: Figure 21

Direct students to use one finger to trace the path of the initial and reflected sound waves. Ask: **How do the sound waves from the sunken boat differ from sound waves from the ocean floor?** (*They do not travel as far and may vary in intensity.*) **learning modality: visual**

Ongoing Assessment

Drawing Have students illustrate what happens to sound waves as they pass from a sonar machine to a school of fish.

Figure 22 Elephants communicate using low-frequency, or infrasonic, sound waves.

Sonar, continued

Building Inquiry Skills: Calculating

Ask students to calculate the depth of a sunken barrel if sonar records that it takes 8.2 seconds for sound waves to return. Students should use the speed of sound in salt water, 1,531 m/s, in their calculation. *(8.2 s ÷ 2 = 4.1 s; 4.1 s × 1,531 m/s = 6,227.1 m)* **learning modality: logical/mathematical**

Uses of Ultrasound and Infrasound

 Integrating Life Science

Guide students in understanding the meaning of *echolocation*. Explain that it is a compound word, like the word *baseball*. Have students write brief definitions for *echo* and *location*. Then ask: **How do these words combine to describe echolocation?** (*Echo means "reflected sound" and* location *means "place." Echolocation means measuring reflected sound to find an object's location or place.*) **learning modality: verbal**

Building Inquiry Skills: Making Models

Materials *box, large sheet of poster board or foam board, marbles*
Time 20 minutes

ACTIVITY

Allow students to model how sound can be used to locate things. Have student pairs take turns locating a small box hidden behind a sheet of poster board. One student holds the poster board vertically so the bottom edge is 2 cm from the table top and then places the small box at different positions behind the poster board. The second student locates the box by rolling marbles under the edge of the poster board. Ask: **How is this similar to sonar? How is it different?** (*It is similar to sonar because both use reflection to locate an item. It is different because sonar uses sound waves, rather than marbles.*) **learning modality: kinesthetic**

Uses of Ultrasound and Infrasound

The dog trainer stands quietly, watching the dog a short distance away. To get the dog's attention, the trainer blows into a small whistle. You don't hear a thing. But the dog stops, cocks an ear, and then comes running toward the trainer. What did the dog hear that you didn't? Dogs can hear ultrasonic frequencies of over 20,000 Hz, well above the upper limit for humans.

Some animals communicate using sounds with frequencies that humans cannot hear. When elephants get upset, they stomp on the ground. The stomping produces low-frequency, or infrasonic, sound waves—too low for humans to hear. The waves travel through the ground for distances of up to 50 kilometers and can be detected by other elephants.

Ultrasound in the Ocean Dolphins and whales emit pings of

Figure 23 Dolphins emit high-frequency sounds to communicate with each other, to navigate, and to find food.

INTEGRATING LIFE SCIENCE sound at frequencies that are high, but not too high for you to hear. **Echolocation** (ek oh loh KAY shun) is the use of sound waves to determine distances or to locate objects. Dolphins and whales use echolocation to find their way in the ocean, and to find their prey.

It was once thought that fish couldn't hear the high frequencies that dolphins and whales emit. But scientists have discovered that shad, herring, and some other fish can hear sounds as high as 180,000 Hz, nine times as high as the highest frequency you can hear. The fish may use this ability to avoid being eaten by dolphins and whales.

Because sound waves travel so well in water, ultrasound has many uses in the sea. Some fisherman attach ultrasonic beepers to their nets. The ultrasound annoys the dolphins, who then swim away from the nets and do not get caught. Other devices can protect divers from sharks by surrounding the divers with ultrasonic waves that keep sharks away.

68 ◆ O

Echolocation in Bats Imagine walking around in a totally dark room. You would bump into the walls and furniture quite often. Bats, however, can fly around dark areas and not bump into anything. **Bats use echolocation to navigate and to find food.**

As bats fly, they send out pulses of sound at frequencies of about 100,000 Hz. Then they listen to how long the sound takes to return. By picking up the reflections, or echoes, a bat can tell if it is about to bump into something. Though bats are not blind, they tend to rely more on their hearing than on their vision to "see" where they are going. Echolocation also tells the bat where its prey is. Bats can use echolocation to hunt. Most bats hunt insects, but some hunt small animals such as mice, rats, frogs, or birds.

Figure 24 Bats use echolocation to locate food and to avoid bumping into objects. Their large ears are used for collecting sound waves.

Ultrasound in Medicine Ultrasound allows doctors to get a **INTEGRATING HEALTH** picture, called a **sonogram,** of the inside of the human body. **Doctors use ultrasound to look inside the human body and to diagnose and treat medical conditions.**

To examine a pregnant woman, the doctor holds a small probe on the woman's abdomen. The probe generates very high-frequency sound waves (about 4 million Hz). The ultrasound device detects and measures the ultrasonic waves that bounce back. By analyzing the intensity and frequency of the reflected waves, the device builds up a picture. The sonogram can show the position of the developing baby. Sonograms can also show if more than one baby is to be born. In addition to a still picture, an ultrasound can produce a video of a developing baby in motion.

Because of their high frequency, carefully focused ultrasound waves can also painlessly destroy unwanted tissues. In many cases ultrasound treatment can eliminate the need for surgery.

Figure 25 A doctor examines a pregnant woman with an ultrasound machine. A picture of the developing baby is displayed on a screen.

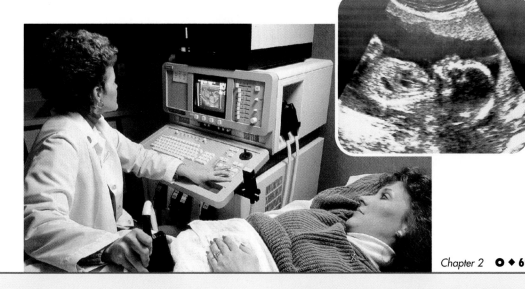

Program Resources

- **Science Explorer Series** *Animals,* Chapter 4, has more information on bats.
- **Science Explorer Series** *Human Biology and Health,* Chapter 8, contains additional information on the use of technology to diagnose and treat medical conditions.

Media and Technology

Exploring Physical Science Videodisc
Unit 6, Side 2, "Blind as a Bat"
Chapter 6

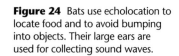

Demonstration

Materials *recording of whale song*
Time 20 minutes

Recordings of whale songs can be obtained from specialty music shops as well as local libraries. Play students a sample of a whale song. Ask students to describe what they hear. Then ask: **Is the whale song made up of infrasonic or ultrasonic sound waves? How can you tell?** (*The whale song that we hear is neither infrasonic nor ultrasonic because the sounds can be heard by humans. However, the whales may be making other sounds that we can't hear.*) **learning modality: kinesthetic**

Integrating Health

Direct students' attention to the sonogram in Figure 25. Ask them to find the face, arms, and legs of the developing baby. Then have students infer why a sonogram is a safer way to view a developing baby than an X-ray. (*The X-ray could harm the developing baby.*) **learning modality: visual**

Real-Life Learning

Materials *device that uses ultrasound, such as an auto-focus camera or an ultrasonic toothbrush*
Time 15 minutes

Allow students to examine and operate the device. Then ask them to think of other everyday items that could be improved by ultrasound. They should provide a description of the object and explain how using ultrasonic waves would improve it. **learning modality: verbal**

Ongoing Assessment

Skills Check Have students compare how ultrasonic sound waves are used in mapping the ocean floor and looking inside the human body.

3 Assess

Section 5 Review Answers

1. Sonar is a system for interpreting reflected sound waves. A sonar device sends out sound waves and measures the time it takes to detect the reflected sound waves. It then uses the time to calculate the distance that the waves have traveled.
2. Animals use ultrasound and infrasound to communicate, navigate, find prey, and avoid danger.
3. Ultrasound is used in medicine to look inside the body and to diagnose and treat some medical conditions.
4. Sonic toothbrush: sound can reach into places that bristles cannot; ultrasonic jewelry cleaner: vibrations shake dirt away without causing damage; auto-focus camera: the camera uses ultrasound to find the distance to an object.
5. 1,530 m/s × 3 s = 4,590 m; 4,590 m ÷ 2 = 2,295 m

Performance Assessment

Oral Presentation Ask students to describe several ways that ultrasonic technology has improved their quality of life.

Figure 26 Some examples of common household objects that use ultrasound include an automatic focus camera, an ultrasonic toothbrush, and an ultrasonic jewelry cleaner.

Ultrasound at Home As technology progresses, more and more everyday objects use ultrasonic waves. Imagine cleaning your teeth with sound! If you have used one of the newer electric toothbrushes, you have done just that. The toothbrush sends out high-frequency sound waves that can reach into places that the bristles of the brush cannot.

Ultrasonic jewelry cleaners can clean delicate pieces of jewelry that might be damaged by brushes or harsh detergents. The tub is filled with water and a mild detergent. When the cleaner is switched on, the sound waves move through the water. When they reach the jewelry, the vibrations shake the dirt away, without causing scratches or other damage.

Some cameras use ultrasound to focus automatically. You look through the viewfinder at the object to be photographed. As you push the button to take a picture, the camera sends out ultrasonic waves that reflect off the object and travel back to the camera. The camera measures the time taken for the waves to come back, just like a sonar machine. The camera then calculates the distance to the object and adjusts the lens accordingly.

Section 5 Review

1. What is sonar?
2. How do animals use ultrasound and infrasound?
3. How is ultrasound used in medicine?
4. What household devices use sound waves? What is the function of sound in each device?
5. **Thinking Critically** **Calculating** The speed of sound in ocean water is about 1,530 m/s. If it takes 3 seconds for a sound to travel from a ship to the bottom of the ocean and back, how deep is the water?

Check Your Progress
CHAPTER PROJECT 2

Test your musical instrument. Is it pleasing to the ear? Can you play a wide range of notes? Can you vary the loudness? Make further adjustments to your instrument. From what you have learned about pitch and frequency, what changes can you make to produce different notes? You may want to try tuning your instrument with a piano or pitch pipe. Try to play a musical scale or a simple song. Or make up your own song.

Program Resources

◆ **Teaching Resources** 2-5 Review and Reinforce, p. 59; 2-5 Enrich, p. 60

SECTION 1 The Nature of Sound

Key Ideas

◆ Sound is a disturbance that travels through a medium as a longitudinal wave.

◆ The speed of sound depends on the elasticity, density, and temperature of the medium.

Key Terms

larynx   elasticity   density

 ### SECTION 2 Properties of Sound

Key Ideas

◆ A sound wave of greater intensity sounds louder. Loudness is measured in decibels.

◆ The pitch of a sound that you hear depends on the frequency of the sound wave.

◆ As a sound source moves toward the listener, the waves reach the listener with a higher frequency. The pitch appears to increase because of the Doppler effect.

Key Terms

intensity   infrasound
loudness   pitch
decibels (dB)   Doppler effect
ultrasound

SECTION 3 Combining Sound Waves

Key Ideas

◆ The blending of the fundamental tone and the overtones makes up the characteristic sound quality, or timbre, of a particular sound.

◆ Music is a set of tones that combine in ways that are pleasing to the ear.

◆ Noise has no pleasing timbre or identifiable pitch.

◆ Interference occurs when two or more sound waves interact.

Key Terms

timbre   noise   acoustics
music   dissonance   beats

 ### SECTION 4 How You Hear Sound

INTEGRATING LIFE SCIENCE

Key Ideas

◆ The outer ear funnels sound waves, the middle ear transmits the sound inward, and the inner ear converts the sound into a form your brain can understand.

Key Terms

ear canal   eardrum   middle ear   cochlea

SECTION 5 Applications of Sound

Key Ideas

◆ A sonar device measures the time it takes to detect reflected sound waves.

◆ Animals use sound waves to communicate, to navigate, and to find food.

Key Terms

sonar   echolocation   sonogram

Organizing Information

Concept Map Copy the concept map about sound onto a separate sheet of paper. Then complete it and add a title. (For more on concept maps, see the Skills Handbook.)

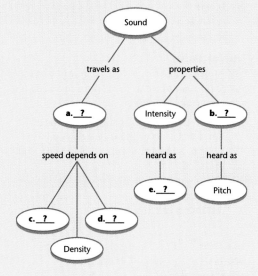

Chapter 2 **O ◆ 71**

Organizing Information

Concept Map Sample title: *Sound*; **a.** Waves **b.** Frequency **c.** Elasticity **d.** Temperature **e.** Loudness

Program Resources

◆ **Teaching Resources** Chapter 2 Project Scoring Rubric, p. 12; Chapter 2 Performance Assessment Teacher Notes, pp. 145–146; Chapter 2 Performance Assessment Student Worksheet, p. 147; Chapter 2 Test, pp. 148–151

Media and Technology

Interactive Student Tutorial CD-ROM O-2

Computer Test Bank *Sound and Light*, Chapter 2 Test

Reviewing Content
Multiple Choice
1. d 2. c 3. d 4. b 5. d

True or False
6. slower 7. intensity 8. true 9. true
10. sonar

Checking Concepts
11. Sound is a wave. The vibrating air particles next to the drumhead transmit energy to particles further away. This process continues until the sound wave reaches your ear.

12. The pitch produced by the guitar string depends on the length of the string, the thickness of the string, the tension in the string, and the material in the string. The loudness depends on how hard the string is plucked.

13. As the car approaches, you hear a higher pitch of the horn. As the car moves away, you hear a lower pitch of the horn.

14. Loud sounds can damage or kill the tiny hairs in the cochlea, making them unable to transmit signals to the brain, and therefore causing hearing loss.

15. Ultrasonic waves can penetrate the body and detect some kinds of tissues that X-rays cannot. The risks associated with ultrasound are very low, if any.

16. Answers will vary. Students' answers should describe sound as a compression wave in a solid, liquid, or gas caused by a vibrating object. Their answers should also include how sound is received by the ear.

Thinking Critically
17. Sound waves travel through the air as longitudinal waves similar to the longitudinal waves that travel along springs in spring toys. Sound waves are heard, not seen like the waves in spring toys.

18. The medium and its temperature.

19. 3.03s

20. You will hear beats at intervals that depend on the difference between the frequencies of the two notes.

21. Light travels much faster than sound.

Reviewing Content
 For more review of key concepts, see the Interactive Student Tutorial CD-ROM.

Multiple Choice
Choose the letter of the best answer.

1. Sound does *not* travel through
   a. water.
   b. steel rails.
   c. wooden doors.
   d. outer space.
2. The Doppler effect causes an apparent change in
   a. loudness.
   b. intensity.
   c. pitch.
   d. resonance.
3. Beats result from
   a. reflection.
   b. refraction.
   c. diffraction.
   d. interference.
4. The hammer, anvil, and stirrup are in the
   a. outer ear.
   b. middle ear.
   c. inner ear.
   d. cochlea.
5. Sonar is used to find
   a. time.
   b. speed.
   c. angle of reflection.
   d. distance.

True or False
If the statement is true, write true. If it is false, change the underlined word or words to make the statement true.

6. Sound travels <u>faster</u> in air than in water.
7. Loudness is how the ear perceives <u>pitch</u>.
8. <u>Timbre</u> is what you hear as the quality of sound.
9. The <u>inner</u> ear contains the cochlea.
10. The system of using sound to measure distance is called <u>acoustics</u>.

Checking Concepts
11. When a drum vibrates, the air molecules that begin vibrating next to it do not reach your ear, yet you hear the sound of the drum. Explain.

12. What are the factors that affect the sound of a vibrating guitar string?

13. As a car drives past you, the driver keeps a hand on the horn. Describe what you hear as the car approaches you then passes by.

14. How can loud noises damage your hearing?

15. Why is ultrasound useful in medicine?

16. Writing to Learn You have been hired to produce an informational brochure about sound. This brochure will be presented to soon-to-arrive visitors from outer space. They have no concept of sound, and everything they learn will come from your brochure. Write a brief description of sound for the visitors.

Thinking Critically
17. Comparing and Contrasting How do sound waves behave like the waves in spring toys? How are they different?

18. Controlling Variables If you are measuring the speed of sound, what variable(s) should you try to keep constant?

19. Calculating At 0°C, sound travels through air at a speed of 330 m/s. At this speed, how long would it take sound to travel a distance of 1000 m? *(Hint: Speed = Distance/Time)*

20. Applying Concepts If one musician plays a note on an instrument and another plays a slightly higher note on a similar instrument, what will you hear?

21. Inferring Thunder and lightning happen at the same time. Why do you think you usually see the lightning before you hear the thunder?

Applying Skills
22. Students' graphs should have the name of the animal along the *x*-axis, and frequency along the *y*-axis. There will be two bars for each animal, one for highest frequency heard and one for highest frequency produced. The two bars should be distinguished by a different color or pattern, with a key included on the graph.

23. 330 m/s ÷ 20,000 Hz = 0.0165 m

Applying Skills

The table below shows the range of frequencies produced and heard by various animals and birds. Use the data to answer Questions 22–23.

Animal	Highest Frequency Heard (Hz)	Highest Frequency Produced (Hz)
Human	20,000	1,100
Dog	50,000	1,800
Cat	65,000	1,500
Bat	120,000	120,000
Porpoise	150,000	120,000
Frog	10,000	8,000

22. Graphing Draw a bar graph to compare the highest frequencies heard by each animal and the highest frequencies produced by each animal.

23. Calculating If the speed of sound in air is 330 m/s, calculate the wavelength of the highest-frequency sound heard by humans. Use the following formula:

$$Wavelength = \frac{Speed}{Frequency}$$

Performance CHAPTER PROJECT 2 Assessment

Project Wrap Up Describe your instrument and explain how it was built. Discuss how you solved any design problems. Using your instrument, demonstrate how you can play different sounds. Show how you change the pitch or loudness of your instrument.

Reflect and Record In your journal write an evaluation of your project. How would you improve on the design of the instrument? How is your instrument like or different from the instruments your classmates built?

Test Preparation

Use these questions to prepare for standardized tests.

Study the chart. Then answer Questions 24–26.

Substance	Speed of Sound (m/s)
Rubber	60
Air at 0°C	330
Air at 25°C	346
Lead	1,210
Water at 25°C	1,498
Silver	2,680
Wood (Oak)	3,850
Glass	4,540
Aluminum	5,000
Iron	5,100
Steel	5,200

24. What information does this table provide?
a. the speed of sound in different states of the same matter
b. the speed of sound over different distances
c. the speed of sound at several different temperatures
d. the speed of sound in different substances

25. In which substance does sound travel most slowly?
a. water   b. air
c. steel   d. rubber

26. Sound travels faster through air at 25°C than it does at 0°C. This shows that sound travels
a. faster at lower temperatures.
b. more slowly at lower temperatures.
c. more slowly at higher temperatures.
d. only at temperatures above 0°C.

Performance CHAPTER PROJECT 2 Assessment

Project Wrap Up Students should demonstrate their instruments, explaining the design process and how their instruments were built and what modifications they made. Students should also play different sounds, showing how the pitch or loudness of their instruments can be changed. Encourage them to play a scale, simple tune, or a composition of their own.

Reflect and Record Encourage students to reflect on the development process. Ask students to identify places where they were stuck or spent too much time and places where they should have concentrated more of their efforts. Have students make suggestions on how they would improve their projects.

Test Preparation

24. d **25.** d **26.** b

Program Resources

◆ **Inquiry Skills Activity Book** Provides teaching and review of all inquiry skills
◆ **Standardized Test Preparation Book** Provides standardized test practice
◆ **Reading in the Content Area** Provides strategies to improve science reading skills
◆ **Teacher's ELL Handbook** Provides multiple strategies for English language learners

The Electromagnetic Spectrum

Sections	Time	Student Edition Activities		Other Activities
CHAPTER PROJECT 3 **You're on the Air** p. 075	Ongoing (2–3 weeks)	Check Your Progress, pp. 088, 0103 Project Wrap Up, p. 0109	TE	Chapter 3 Project Notes, pp. 074–75
1 **The Nature of Electromagnetic Waves** pp. 076–79 ◆ 3.1.1 Describe an electromagnetic wave and its properties. ◆ 3.1.2 Describe properties of light in relation to particles and to electromagnetic waves.	2 periods/ 1 block	**Discover** How Does a Beam of Light Travel?, p. 076 **Try This** How Do Light Beams Behave?, p. 078 **Science at Home** p. 079	TE TE TE	Building Inquiry Skills: Observing, p. 077 Building Inquiry Skills: Making Models, p. 077 Building Inquiry Skills: Relating Cause and Effect, p. 079
2 **Waves of the Electromagnetic Spectrum** pp. 080–89 ◆ 3.2.1 List and compare different types of electromagnetic waves. ◆ 3.2.2 Describe how the electromagnetic spectrum is arranged. ◆ 3.2.3 Name uses for waves of the electromagnetic spectrum.	5 periods/ $2\frac{1}{2}$ blocks	**Discover** What Is White Light?, p. 080 **Try This** What Does a Bee See?, p. 087	TE TE TE TE TE ISLM	Demonstration, p. 081 Building Inquiry Skills: Making Models, p. 082 Building Inquiry Skills: Drawing Conclusions, p. 083 Real-Life Learning, p. 084 Building Inquiry Skills: Making Models, p. 087 0-3, "In the Heat of the Light"
3 **Producing Visible Light** pp. 090–95 ◆ 3.3.1 Identify and compare different types of light bulbs.	3 periods/ $1\frac{1}{2}$ blocks	**Discover** How Do Light Bulbs Differ?, p. 090 **Sharpen Your Skills** Observing, p. 091 **Real-World Lab: You, The Consumer** Comparing Light Bulbs, pp. 094–95	TE TE TE	Inquiry Challenge, p. 091 Building Inquiry Skills: Comparing and Contrasting, p. 092 Demonstration, p. 092
4 **INTEGRATING TECHNOLOGY** **Wireless Communication** pp. 096–106 ◆ 3.4.1 Describe how signals are transmitted from broadcasting stations. ◆ 3.4.2 Explain the workings of pagers and cellular phones. ◆ 3.4.3 State how satellites relay information and find the position of objects.	$5\frac{1}{2}$ periods/ 2–3 blocks	**Discover** How Can Radio Waves Change?, p. 096 **Try This** Produce Electromagnetic Interference, p. 098 **Real-World Lab: How It Works** Build a Crystal Radio, pp. 0104–106	TE TE	Including All Students, p. 097 Building Inquiry Skills: Making Models, p. 099
Study Guide/Assessment pp. 0107–109	1 period/ $\frac{1}{2}$ block		ISAB	Provides teaching and review of all inquiry skills

For Standard or Block Schedule The Resource Pro® CD-ROM gives you maximum flexibility for planning your instruction for any type of schedule. Resource Pro® contains Planning Express®, an advanced scheduling program, as well as the entire contents of the Teaching Resources and the Computer Test Bank.

Key: **SE** Student Edition
PLM Probeware Lab Manual
ISAB Inquiry Skills Activity Book

CHAPTER PLANNING GUIDE

Program Resources	Assessment Strategies	Media and Technology
TR Chapter 3 Project Teacher Notes, pp. 066–67 **TR** Chapter 3 Project Overview and Worksheets, pp. 068–71	**TE** Check Your Progress, pp. 088, 0103 **TE** Performance Assessment: Chapter 3 Project Wrap Up, p. 0109 **TR** Chapter 3 Project Scoring Rubric, p. 072	Science Explorer Internet Site Audio CDs and Audiotapes, English-Spanish Section Summaries
TR 3-1 Lesson Plan, p. 073 **TR** 3-1 Section Summary, p. 074 **TR** 3-1 Review and Reinforce, p. 075 **TR** 3-1 Enrich, p. 076	**SE** Section 1 Review, p. 079 **TE** Ongoing Assessment, p. 077 **TE** Performance Assessment, p. 079	Interactive Student Tutorial CD-ROM, 0-3
TR 3-2 Lesson Plan, p. 077 **TR** 3-2 Section Summary, p. 078 **TR** 3-2 Review and Reinforce, p. 079 **TR** 3-2 Enrich, p. 080 **SES** Book D, *Human Biology and Health,* Chapter 6 **SES** Book B, *Animals,* Chapter 2 **SES** Book J, *Astronomy,* Chapter 3	**SE** Section 2 Review, p. 088 **TE** Ongoing Assessment, pp. 081, 083, 085, 087 **TE** Performance Assessment, p. 088	Exploring Physical Science Videodisc, Unit 6 Side 2, "The Electromagnetic Spectrum" Transparencies 10, "The Electromagnetic Spectrum"; 11, "Exploring the Electromagnetic Spectrum"
TR 3-3 Lesson Plan, p. 081 **TR** 3-3 Section Summary, p. 082 **TR** 3-3 Review and Reinforce, p. 083 **TR** 3-3 Enrich, p. 084 **TR** Real-World Lab blackline masters, pp. 089–90 **SES** Book B, *Animals,* Chapter 3	**SE** Section 3 Review, p. 093 **SE** Analyze and Conclude, p. 095 **TE** Ongoing Assessment, p. 091 **TE** Performance Assessment, p. 093	Lab Activity Videotape, *Sound and Light,* 5 Transparency 12, "Incandescent Light Bulb"
TR 3-4 Lesson Plan, p. 085 **TR** 3-4 Section Summary, p. 086 **TR** 3-4 Review and Reinforce, p. 087 **TR** 3-4 Enrich, p. 088 **TR** Real-World Lab blackline masters, pp. 091–93	**SE** Section 4 Review, p. 0103 **SE** Analyze and Conclude, p. 0106 **TE** Ongoing Assessment, pp. 097, 099, 0101 **TE** Performance Assessment, p. 0103	Lab Activity Videotape, *Sound and Light,* 6 Transparencies 13, "Amplitude Modulation and Frequency Modulation"; 14, "AM/FM Radio Waves"
GSW Provides worksheets to promote student comprehension of content **RCA** Provides strategies to improve science reading skills **ELL** Provides multiple strategies for English language learners	**SE** Study Guide/Assessment, pp. 0107–109 **TR** Performance Assessment, pp. 0152–154 **TR** Chapter 3 Test, pp. 0155–158 **CTB** *Sound and Light,* Chapter 3 Test **STP** Provides standardized test practice	Computer Test Bank, *Sound and Light,* Chapter 3 Test Interactive Student Tutorial CD-ROM, 0-3

TE Teacher's Edition
RCA Reading in the Content Area
GSW Guided Study Workbook

TR Teaching Resources
ISLM Integrated Science Laboratory Manual
ELL Teacher's ELL Handbook

CTB Computer Test Bank
STP Standardized Test Preparation Book
SES Science Explorer Series Text

Meeting the National Science Education Standards and AAAS Benchmarks

National Science Education Standards	Benchmarks for Science Literacy	Unifying Themes

Science as Inquiry (Content Standard A)

◆ **Use appropriate tools and techniques to gather, analyze, and interpret data** Students conduct surveys of wireless communication use and present their interpretations of data. *(Chapter Project)*

Physical Science (Content Standard B)

◆ **Transfer of energy** Light bulbs convert electrical energy into heat and light. *(Real-World Lab, Comparing Light Bulbs)* Electromagnetic radiation carries energy as transverse waves at a variety of frequencies. *(Section 2)*

Science and Technology (Content Standard E)

◆ **Evaluate completed technological designs** Students compare the quality of light produced by different bulbs. *(Real-World Lab, Comparing Light Bulbs)* Students construct crystal radios and compare them to modern radios. *(Real-World Lab, Build a Crystal Radio)*

◆ **Understandings about science and technology** Wireless communication technologies and light-production systems have different advantages and disadvantages. *(Sections 3, 4; Real-World Labs; Chapter Project)*

Science in Personal and Social Perspectives (Content Standard F)

◆ **Risks and benefits** Students evaluate the potential risks and benefits of irradiated food. *(Science and Society)*

1A The Scientific World View As scientists have learned more about electromagnetic waves, they have created increasingly sophisticated communication systems. *(Section 4)*

3C Issues in Technology The development of artificial lighting and wireless communication has shaped the world's ability to communicate. *(Sections 3, 4)* Technological devices, such as different light bulbs, pagers, cellular telephone systems, and radio broadcast stations, have different drawbacks and strengths. *(Sections 2, 4; Real-World Labs; Chapter Project)* Students analyze the risks and benefits of irradiated food. *(Science and Society)*

4E Energy Transformations Electromagnetic waves can be distinguished by their frequencies. *(Section 1)* Sound waves are converted into electric signals that are carried by radio waves during radio or television broadcasts. AM waves carry signals as changes in amplitude, while FM waves carry signals as changes in frequency. *(Section 2)*

8D Communication Wireless devices, including radios, televisions, pagers, cellular telephone systems, radar devices, and satellite connections, transmit electronic signals that are used for communication. *(Sections 2, 4; Real-World Lab, Build a Crystal Radio)*

◆ **Energy** Electromagnetic waves occupy a variety of frequencies; those with higher frequencies have greater energy. *(Section 2)*

◆ **Systems and Interactions** Electromagnetic waves, which include light, sometimes behave like waves and sometimes like particles. *(Section 1)* There are many different kinds of light bulbs. *(Section 3; Real-World Lab, Comparing Light Bulbs)* Radio waves of different frequencies provide a wide array of communication devices. *(Section 4; Real-World Lab, Build a Crystal Radio; Chapter Project)* Students examine how irradiating food affects its nutritional value. *(Science and Society)*

Take It to the Net

 Interactive text at www.phschool.com

Science Explorer comes alive with iText.

- **Complete student text** is accessible from any computer with a browser.

- **Animations, simulations, and videos** enhance student understanding and retention of concepts.

- **Self-tests and online study tools** assess student understanding.

- **Teacher management tools** help you make the most of this valuable resource.

STAY CURRENT with **SCIENCE NEWS** ®

Find out the latest research and information about the electromagnetic spectrum at: **www.phschool.com**

Go to **www.phschool.com** and click on the Science icon. Then click on Science Explorer under PH@school.

ACTIVITY	Time (minutes)	Materials Quantities for one work group	Skills
Section 1			
Discover, p. 76	10	**Consumable** 4 large index cards, string **Nonconsumable** hole punch, ruler, binder clips or modeling clay, flashlight	Inferring
Try This, p. 78	10	**Consumable** water **Nonconsumable** 2 plastic cups, pan or sink, slide, slide projector, flashlight	Drawing Conclusions
Science at Home, p. 79	home	**Nonconsumable** sunglasses	Observing, Inferring
Section 2			
Discover, p. 80	15	**Consumable** cardboard box, white paper **Nonconsumable** prism, colored pencils	Forming Operational Definitions
Try This, p. 87	30	**Consumable** UV-sensitive film **Nonconsumable** camera	Observing
Section 3			
Discover, p. 90	10	**Nonconsumable** clear (uncoated) incandescent light bulb, fluorescent light bulb	Posing Questions
Sharpen Your Skills, p. 91	15	**Nonconsumable** spectroscope, incandescent bulb, colored pencils, fluorescent bulb	Observing
Science at Home, p. 93	home	No special materials are required.	Observing, Communicating
Real-World Lab, pp. 94–95	45	**Consumable** medium-sized cardboard box, wax paper, plain paper **Nonconsumable** a variety of incandescent light bulbs that can fit in the same lamp or socket, light socket or lamp (without shade), meter stick, scissors	Designing Experiments, Controlling Variables, Measuring, Drawing Conclusions
Section 4			
Discover, p. 96	10	**Consumable** tracing paper **Nonconsumable** flat piece of stretchable latex, about 20 cm square	Making Models
Try This, p. 98	10	**Nonconsumable** non-cabled television set, electric mixer or hair dryer	Drawing Conclusions
Real-World Lab, pp. 104–106	60	**Consumable** 1 cardboard tube (paper towel roll), aluminum foil, 2 pieces of cardboard (sizes can range from 12.5 cm × 20 cm to 30 cm × 48 cm), masking tape **Nonconsumable** 3 pieces of enameled or insulated wire, one about 30 m long and two about 30 cm long each; wirestrippers or sandpaper; 2 alligator clips; scissors; 1 crystal diode (from an electronics supply store); earphone (from an electronics supply store); two pieces of copper-insulated antenna wire, one about 30 m long and one about 0.5 m long	Measuring, Interpreting Diagrams, Observing, Problem Solving, Drawing Conclusions

A list of all materials required for the Student Edition activities can be found beginning on page T15. You can obtain information about ordering materials by calling 1-800-848-9500 or by accessing the Science Explorer Internet site at: **www.phschool.com**

Communication technology has changed dramatically since the days of the first wireless telegraph message. As it continues to change, the world changes with it. Students can study the technology that is used today and learn about the advances that will change communication between people in the future.

Purpose In this project, students create and distribute survey sheets to find out how people use communication devices. Students collect data, then compile and analyze the data to find out how different people rely on different forms of communication. Finally, students create graphs and present their conclusions to classmates.

Skills Focus After completing the Chapter 3 Project, students will be able to
◆ design survey sheets to collect relevant information;
◆ analyze, graph, and draw conclusions based on their data;
◆ communicate their findings about communication technology to their classmates.

Project Time Line This project will take approximately two weeks to complete. Allow students two or three days to brainstorm and design their surveys. At the end of the first week, they should have composed their surveys and distributed them to classmates, friends, neighbors, and relatives. At the middle of the second week, they collect the surveys and analyze the data. At the end of the second week, students interpret the data and observations they have made, then present their findings to the class. Before beginning the project, see Chapter 3 Project Teacher Notes on pages 66–67 in Teaching Resources for more details on carrying out the project. Also distribute to students the Chapter 3 Project Overview, Worksheets, and Scoring Rubric on pages 68–71 in Teaching Resources.

Possible Materials Suggested materials for this project are listed below. Encourage students to suggest and use other materials for their presentations.

These satellite dishes are used in long-distance communication.

WEB ACTIVITY www.phschool.com

SECTION **1** The Nature of Electro-magnetic Waves

Discover **How Does a Beam of Light Travel?**
Try This **How Do Light Beams Behave?**

SECTION **2** Waves of the Electro-magnetic Spectrum

Discover **What Is White Light?**
Try This **What Does a Bee See?**

SECTION **3** Producing Visible Light

Discover **How Do Light Bulbs Differ?**
Sharpen Your Skills **Observing**
Real-World Lab **Comparing Light Bulbs**

74 ◆ O

◆ copy paper
◆ poster board
◆ clipboard
◆ graphing paper
◆ acetate sheets
◆ colored markers
◆ computer spreadsheet programs

Launching the Project Ask students how they communicate with people who do not live in the same city. Ask students to give examples of long-distance communication. Then ask: **Is it possible for you to talk with almost any**

person, anytime, in any place? (*Many students will say that they can communicate almost instantly with anyone who has a phone or a computer.*)

Allow time for students to read the description of the project in their text and the Chapter Project Overview on pages 68–69 in Teaching Resources. Answer any initial questions students may have. Review with students the Chapter 3 Project Worksheets.

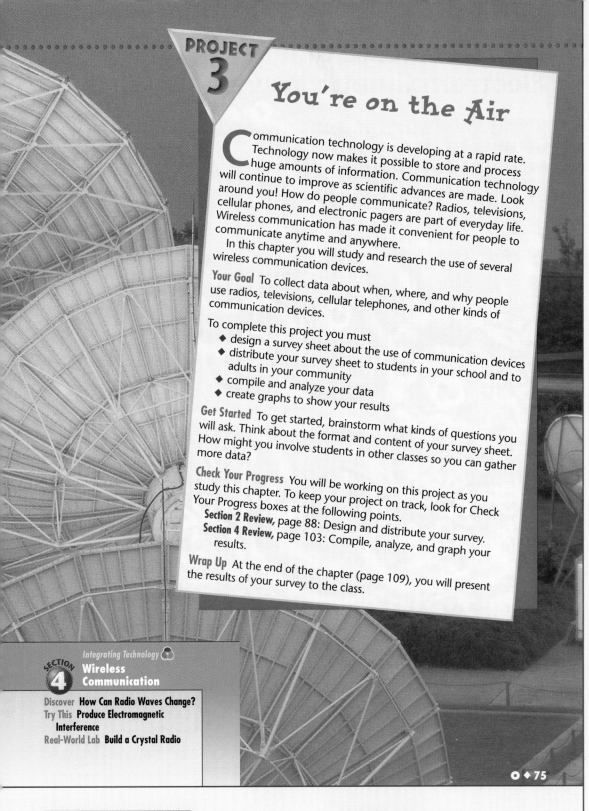

You're on the Air

Communication technology is developing at a rapid rate. Technology now makes it possible to store and process huge amounts of information. Communication technology will continue to improve as scientific advances are made. Look around you! How do people communicate? Radios, televisions, cellular phones, and electronic pagers are part of everyday life. Wireless communication has made it convenient for people to communicate anytime and anywhere.

In this chapter you will study and research the use of several wireless communication devices.

Your Goal To collect data about when, where, and why people use radios, televisions, cellular telephones, and other kinds of communication devices.

To complete this project you must
◆ design a survey sheet about the use of communication devices
◆ distribute your survey sheet to students in your school and to adults in your community
◆ compile and analyze your data
◆ create graphs to show your results

Get Started To get started, brainstorm what kinds of questions you will ask. Think about the format and content of your survey sheet. How might you involve students in other classes so you can gather more data?

Check Your Progress You will be working on this project as you study this chapter. To keep your project on track, look for Check Your Progress boxes at the following points.
Section 2 Review, page 88: Design and distribute your survey.
Section 4 Review, page 103: Compile, analyze, and graph your results.

Wrap Up At the end of the chapter (page 109), you will present the results of your survey to the class.

SECTION 4

Integrating Technology 🌐
Wireless Communication

Discover How Can Radio Waves Change?
Try This Produce Electromagnetic Interference
Real-World Lab Build a Crystal Radio

O ◆ 75

Program Resources

◆ **Teaching Resources** Chapter 3 Project Teacher Notes, pp. 66–67; Chapter 3 Project Overview and Worksheets, pp. 68–71; Chapter 3 Project Scoring Rubric, p. 72

www.phschool.com

You will find an Internet activity, chapter self-tests for students, and links to other chapter topics at this site.

Media and Technology

 Audio CDs and **Audiotapes** English-Spanish Section Summaries

---

Discuss types of communication devices with the class. Let students brainstorm how they think these devices work and how popular or useful they are. Then ask each student to choose one aspect of communication they would like to learn more about. Help students identify their interest by asking them questions about communicating in an emergency, communicating over long distances, or talking to people with similar interests. Group students according to their interests and have them discuss questions they think will be appropriate for their surveys.

Students can complete the project in small groups as a cooperative learning task. To ensure that every student will have ample opportunity to participate, each group should consist of no more than five students.

Performance Assessment

The Chapter 3 Project Scoring Rubric on page 72 of Teaching Resources will help you evaluate how well students complete the Chapter 3 Project. Students will be assessed on
◆ whether the survey questions are well designed and elicit useful information;
◆ how well they organize their data collection and sort the responses;
◆ their analyses of the data;
◆ the thoroughness and organization of their presentations.
By sharing the Chapter 3 Scoring Rubric with students at the beginning of the project, you will make it clear to them what they are expected to do.

SECTION 1 The Nature of Electro-magnetic Waves

Objectives

After completing the lesson, students will be able to
◆ describe an electromagnetic wave and its properties;
◆ describe properties of light in relation to particles and to electromagnetic waves.

Key Terms electromagnetic wave, electromagnetic radiation, polarized light, photoelectric effect, photon

1 Engage/Explore

Activating Prior Knowledge

Ask students to describe what they know about how television and radio signals are broadcast. Encourage students to discuss the distance between the source of the signal and the receiver. Ask students how far away from home they can travel before they are no longer able to receive their hometown radio stations.

DISCOVER

Skills Focus inferring
Materials 4 large index cards, hole punch, ruler, binder clips or modeling clay, string, flashlight
Time 10 minutes
Tips Use a small pocket flashlight or penlight for best results.
Expected Outcome When the cards are aligned, the light from the flashlight is visible on the wall. When one card is moved out of alignment, the light is not visible.
Think It Over Moving the card blocked the path of the light. Students should infer that light travels in a straight line and cannot pass through an index card.

SECTION 1 The Nature of Electromagnetic Waves

DISCOVER ACTIVITY

How Does a Beam of Light Travel?

1. Punch a small hole (about 0.5 cm in diameter) in each of four large index cards.

2. Stand each card upright so that the long side of the index card is on the tabletop. Use binder clips or modeling clay to hold the cards upright.

3. Space the cards about 10 cm apart. To make sure the holes in the cards are in a straight line, run a piece of string through the four holes and pull it tight.

4. Place the flashlight in front of the card nearest you. Shut off all the lights, so that the only light you see comes from the flashlight. What do you see on the wall?

5. Move one of the cards sideways about 3 cm and repeat Step 4. Now what do you see on the wall?

Think It Over
Inferring Explain what happened in Step 5. What does this activity tell you about the path of light?

GUIDE FOR READING

◆ What is an electromagnetic wave?
◆ What is light?

Reading Tip As you read, keep a list of the words that are used to describe the nature of electromagnetic waves.

Close your eyes for a moment and imagine you are in a shower of rain. Are you getting wet? Do you feel anything? Believe it or not, you are being "showered" all the time. Not by rain but by waves, most of which you cannot feel or hear. As you read this, you are surrounded by radio waves, infrared waves, visible light, ultraviolet waves, and maybe even tiny amounts of X-rays and gamma rays. If you have ever tuned a radio, spoken on a cordless or cellular phone, felt warmth on your skin, turned on a light, or had an X-ray taken, you have experienced electromagnetic waves.

Figure 1 Even though you cannot feel electromagnetic waves, you are being showered by them.

READING STRATEGIES

Reading Tip Students may want to work with partners to list words used to describe the nature of electromagnetic waves. Encourage students to sketch visual images that help them understand the information about electromagnetic waves. Invite volunteers to draw the images on the board and explain the concepts that the drawings relate to.

Study and Comprehension As students read and list words, have them write questions they have about the words on their lists. As they read, have them answer the questions using the text. When students have finished reading the section, they can work with partners to answer any remaining questions.

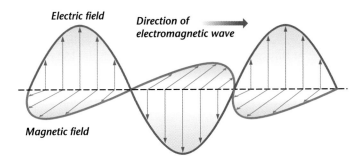

Figure 2 An electromagnetic wave occurs when electric and magnetic fields vibrate at right angles to each other.

Electromagnetic Waves

You have seen waves travel through water and move along ropes and springs. You have also heard sound waves travel through air, metal, and water. All these waves have two things in common—they transfer energy from one place to another, and they require a medium through which to travel.

But a group of waves called electromagnetic waves can transfer energy without a medium. **Electromagnetic waves** are transverse waves that have some electrical properties and some magnetic properties. **An electromagnetic wave consists of changing electric and magnetic fields.**

Electric and Magnetic Fields Electromagnetic waves travel as vibrations in electric and magnetic fields. An electric field is a region in which charged particles can be pushed or pulled. Wherever there is an electric charge, there is an electric field associated with it. A moving electric charge is part of an electric current.

An electric current is surrounded by a magnetic field. A magnetic field is a region in which magnetic forces are present. If you place a paper clip near a magnet, the paper clip moves toward the magnet because of the magnetic field surrounding the magnet.

When the electric field changes, so does the magnetic field. The changing magnetic field causes the electric field to change. When one field vibrates, so does the other. In this way, the two fields constantly cause each other to change. The result is an electromagnetic wave, as shown in Figure 2.

Electromagnetic Radiation The energy that is transferred by electromagnetic waves is called **electromagnetic radiation.** Because electromagnetic radiation does not need a medium, it can travel through the vacuum of outer space. If it could not, light from the sun and stars could not travel through space to Earth. NASA officials could not make contact with space shuttles in orbit.

Program Resources

◆ **Teaching Resources** 3-1 Lesson Plan, p. 73; 3-1 Section Summary, p. 74
◆ **Guided Study Workbook** Section 3-1

2 Facilitate

Electromagnetic Waves

Building Inquiry Skills: Observing

Materials *inflated balloon, small pieces of tissue paper, piece of wool, paper, iron filings, bar magnet*
Time 15 minutes

This activity allows students to compare the effects of electric and magnetic fields. Students should rub the balloon on their hair or on a piece of wool, then hold the balloon over the pile of tissue pieces. Ask students to describe what happened. *(The pieces of paper moved toward the balloon.)* Tell students that an electric field affected the pieces of paper. Then have students sprinkle the iron filings onto a piece of paper, then bring the magnet near the filings. Ask students to describe what happened. *(The iron filings lined up and then moved toward the magnet.)* Tell students that a magnetic field affected the filings. **learning modality: visual**

Building Inquiry Skills: Making Models

Materials *stiff paper or cardboard, scissors, tape*
Time 10 minutes

As students examine Figure 2, make sure they understand that the waves are perpendicular. Encourage students to use the paper or cardboard to make a three-dimensional model of an electromagnetic wave. **limited English proficiency**

Ongoing Assessment

Writing Ask students to write short paragraphs to describe how an electromagnetic wave is generated. *(Electric currents are created by moving electric charges. Each charge is surrounded by an electric field. The current is surrounded by a magnetic field. Any change in either field affects the other. Electromagnetic waves are the result of these changing fields.)*

Electromagnetic Waves, continued

Building Inquiry Skills: Applying Concepts

Tell students that the speed of electromagnetic waves such as light is such a reliable constant that it is used to define the length of one meter. Explain that one meter is equal to the distance that light travels in about $\frac{1}{300,000,000}$ of a second. Ask: **Why is this a good way to define the length of a meter?** *(Samples: Because light always travels at the same speed in a vacuum, the length of a meter will always be the same; scientists with the right equipment can measure a standard meter no matter where they are.)*
learning modality: logical/ mathematical

Waves or Particles?

Skills Focus drawing conclusions
Materials *2 plastic cups, water, pan or sink, slide, slide projector, flashlight*
Time 10 minutes
Tips Students should work in pairs to complete this activity. They may need to observe the streams of water more than once to get the best results.
Expected Outcome The streams of water collide and splash into the sink. The beams of light pass through each other, with no effect on the picture.
Drawing Conclusions This activity supports the wave model of light because the beams of light pass through each other; and the water streams, which consist of particles, do not.
learning modality: visual

How Do Light Beams Behave?

1. Fill two plastic cups with water. Slowly pour the water from the two cups into a sink. Aim the stream of water from one cup across the path of the water from the other cup.
2. How do the two streams interfere with each other?
3. Now darken a room and project a slide from a slide projector onto the wall. Shine a flashlight beam across the projector beam.
4. How do the two beams of light interfere with each other? What effect does the interference have on the projected picture?

Drawing Conclusions How is the interference between light beams different from that between water streams? Does this activity support a wave model or a particle model of light? Explain.

Speed of Electromagnetic Waves All electromagnetic waves travel at the same speed—about 300,000,000 meters per second in a vacuum. You can also think of this as 300,000 kilometers per second. At this speed, light from the sun travels the 150 million kilometers to Earth in about 8 minutes. Nothing can travel faster! When electromagnetic waves travel through a medium such as the atmosphere or glass, they travel more slowly. But even at slower speeds, electromagnetic waves travel about a million times faster than sound can travel in air.

Checkpoint *What is the speed of electromagnetic waves in a vacuum?*

Waves or Particles?

In general, the wave model can explain many of the properties of electromagnetic radiation. However, some properties of electromagnetic radiation do not fit the wave model. **Light has many of the properties of waves. But light can also act as though it is a stream of particles.**

When light passes through a polarizing filter, it has the properties of a wave. An ordinary beam of light has waves that vibrate in all directions. A polarizing filter acts as though it has tiny slits that are either horizontal or vertical. When light enters a polarizing filter, only some waves can pass through. The light that passes through is called **polarized light.**

To help you understand polarization, think of waves of light as being like transverse waves on a rope. They vibrate up and down, left and right, or at any other angle. If you shake a rope through a fence with vertical slats, as shown in Figure 3, only waves that vibrate up and down will pass through. The other waves are blocked. A polarizing filter acts like the slats in a fence. It allows only waves that vibrate in one direction to pass through.

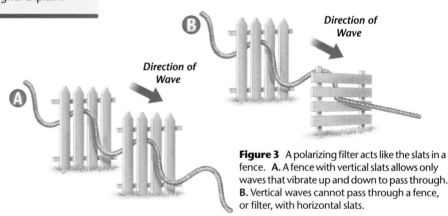

Figure 3 A polarizing filter acts like the slats in a fence. **A.** A fence with vertical slats allows only waves that vibrate up and down to pass through. **B.** Vertical waves cannot pass through a fence, or filter, with horizontal slats.

Background

History of Science Albert Einstein's 1905 theory that light energy consists of photons, or tiny packets of energy, was not initially taken seriously. Einstein deduced his theory by comparing energy changes in an ideal gas and energy changes of electromagnetic radiation. He used his theory to explain the photoelectric effect, and concluded by predicting that the electrons emitted by the photoelectric effect would have more energy if the light frequency increased. Some physicists at the time thought Einstein's ideas were poor science. For example, Max Planck urged the admissions committee of the Prussian Academy for Sciences not to hold Einstein's wild hypothesis against him! By 1912, other scientists began to verify some of Einstein's predictions. In 1922, Arthur Holly Compton presented physical evidence that light energy behaves like particles of matter.

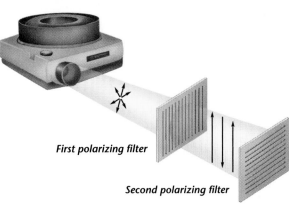

First polarizing filter

Second polarizing filter

Figure 4 The first polarizing filter allows only waves that vibrate up and down to pass through. When a second polarizing filter is placed in front of the first, and at right angles to it, no light passes through. *Applying Concepts Does the way that light passes through a polarizing filter support the wave model or the particle model of light?*

If you place one polarizing filter on top of another and rotate one of them, you will see how the amount of light coming through changes. If the two polarizing filters are placed so that one is rotated 90° from the other, no light can come through. All the light is blocked.

Here is an example of how light can act like a stream of particles. When a beam of light shines on some substances, it causes tiny particles called electrons to move. This movement causes an electric current to flow. Sometimes light can even knock electrons out of the substance. This is called the **photoelectric effect.** The photoelectric effect can only be explained by thinking of light as a stream of tiny packets, or particles, of energy. Each packet is called a **photon.** Albert Einstein's explanation of the photoelectric effect in 1905 was important for our understanding of photons as particles of light.

It may be difficult for you to picture light as being particles and waves at the same time. Many scientists find it difficult, too. But both models are necessary to explain all the properties of electromagnetic radiation.

 Section 1 Review

1. What do electromagnetic waves consist of?
2. Describe one behavior that shows that light is a set of particles.
3. Describe one behavior that shows that light is a wave.
4. **Thinking Critically Comparing and Contrasting** How are light and sound alike? How are they different?

Science at Home

On the next sunny day, have family members go outside wearing their sunglasses. Compare the sunglasses. Which sunglasses have polarizing lenses? How can you tell? Through the sunglasses, look at surfaces that create glare, such as water or glass. Compare the effects of different pairs of sunglasses. Which kind of sunglasses are best designed to reduce glare on a sunny day? **CAUTION:** Do not look directly at the sun.

Program Resources

◆ **Teaching Resources** 3-1 Review and Reinforce, p. 75; 3-1 Enrich, p. 76

Answers to Self-Assessment

Caption Question

Figure 4 It supports the wave model. Only waves that vibrate in one direction can pass through the filter.

☑ *Checkpoint*

About 300,000,000 meters per second, or 300,000 kilometers per second

---

Materials *2 polarizing light filters, flashlight* **Time** 10 minutes

Have students shine the flashlight through one of the filters or hold the filter up to the window. Ask students to infer why the light dims. *(Some light is absorbed by the filter.)* Allow students to experiment with the second filter, then challenge them to arrange both filters so that no light passes through. Ask: **Why are two filters required to block all the light?** *(Because light consists of waves in all directions.)* **learning modality: kinesthetic**

3 Assess

Section 1 Review Answers

1. They consist of changing electrical and magnetic fields.
2. The photoelectric effect. When light shines on some materials, electrons move, causing electric current to flow. Sometimes electrons are knocked out of the material.
3. Polarization. When light enters a polarizing filter, only some waves can pass through.
4. Both are waves; light—electromagnetic, transverse, can travel through a vacuum; sound—mechanical, longitudinal, requires a medium

Science at Home

Materials *sunglasses*

Students should note that polarizing lenses greatly reduce the glare of the sun. When two polarizing lenses are combined at a 90° angle, no light should come through.

Performance Assessment

Writing Have students describe electromagnetic waves and explain how they travel.

Objectives

After completing the lesson, students will be able to
♦ list and compare different types of electromagnetic waves;
♦ describe how the electromagnetic spectrum is arranged;
♦ name uses for waves of the electromagnetic spectrum.

Key Terms electromagnetic spectrum, radio wave, microwave, radar, magnetic resonance imaging, infrared ray, thermogram, visible light, ultraviolet ray, X-ray, gamma ray

1 Engage/Explore

Activating Prior Knowledge

Ask students what they might see if they had X-ray vision, such as the kind of vision that fictional superheroes sometimes have. *(Most students will say that they would have the ability to see through objects.)* Then ask: **How do you think real X-rays are similar to the X-ray vision described in fiction?** *(Real X-rays can pass through things that regular light cannot.)*

········ **DISCOVER** ········

Skills Focus forming operational definitions
Materials *cardboard box, white paper, prism, colored pencils*
Time 15 minutes
Tips Caution students not to look directly at the sun. Students may need some help positioning the prism so they can see the color band.
Expected Outcome The prism will form a rainbow inside the box.
Think It Over The band of colors shows the range or spectrum of colors that make up white light.

SECTION
2 Waves of the Electromagnetic Spectrum

DISCOVER ···················· ACTIVITY····

What Is White Light?

1. Line the inside of a cardboard box with white paper. Hold a small triangular prism up to direct sunlight. **CAUTION:** *Do not look directly at the sun.*

2. Rotate the prism until the light coming out of the prism appears on the inside of the box. What colors do you see? What is the order of the colors? Describe how the colors progress from one to the next.

3. Using colored pencils, draw a picture of what you see inside the box.

Think It Over
Forming Operational Definitions The term *spectrum* describes a range. How do you think this term is related to what you just observed?

GUIDE FOR READING

♦ How do electromagnetic waves differ from each other?

♦ What are the waves of the electromagnetic spectrum?

Reading Tip Before you read, use the headings to make an outline about the different electromagnetic waves. As you read, make notes about each type of wave.

Can you imagine trying to keep food warm with a flashlight? How about trying to tune in a radio station on your television? Light and radio waves are both electromagnetic. But each has properties that make it useful for some purposes and useless for others. What makes radio waves different from light or ultraviolet rays?

Characteristics of Electromagnetic Waves

All electromagnetic waves travel at the same speed, but they have different wavelengths and different frequencies. Radiation in the wavelengths that your eyes can see is called visible light. Only a small portion of electromagnetic radiation is visible light. The rest of the wavelengths are invisible. Your radio detects wavelengths that are much longer and have a lower frequency than visible light.

Recall how speed, wavelength, and frequency are related:

$$Speed = Wavelength \times Frequency$$

Since the speed of all electromagnetic waves is the same, as the wavelength decreases, the frequency increases. Waves with the longest wavelengths have the lowest frequencies. Waves with the shortest wavelengths have the highest frequencies. The amount of energy carried by an electromagnetic wave increases with frequency. The higher the frequency of a wave, the higher its energy.

READING STRATEGIES

Reading Tip Have students write brief summaries of the information under each major heading. Remind students to include main ideas and key details and to use their own words in the summaries. Invite volunteers to use their notes to give oral summaries of information under the headings. Students can use their summaries as study guides for the section.

Study and Comprehension Provide each student with six note cards. As students read, instruct them to write the name of a type of electromagnetic wave on one side of a card and a brief definition on the other side of the card. When students have finished reading, have partners use the cards to quiz each other on types of electromagnetic waves.

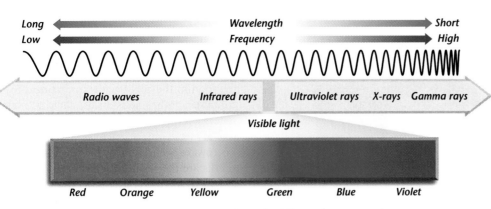

Figure 5 The electromagnetic spectrum shows the different electromagnetic waves in order of increasing frequency and decreasing wavelength.
Interpreting Diagrams Which electromagnetic waves have the highest frequencies?

The **electromagnetic spectrum** is the name for the range of electromagnetic waves when they are placed in order of increasing frequency. Figure 5 shows the electromagnetic spectrum. **The electromagnetic spectrum is made up of radio waves, infrared rays, visible light, ultraviolet rays, X-rays, and gamma rays.**

☑ *Checkpoint* How are the frequency and wavelength of electromagnetic waves related?

Radio Waves

Radio waves are the electromagnetic waves with the longest wavelengths and lowest frequencies. Like all electromagnetic waves, radio waves can travel through a vacuum. Most of the radio waves we receive, though, have traveled through air. Antennas pick up radio waves from the air and send them through wires to your radio. The radio converts the electromagnetic waves into the sound that comes out of the radio speakers.

Each radio station in an area broadcasts at a different frequency. To change the station on your radio, you adjust the tuning dial or press a button. This allows the tuner to pick up waves of a different frequency. The numbers on your radio tell you the frequency of the station you are listening to.

Microwaves The radio waves with the shortest wavelengths and the highest frequencies are **microwaves.** One of their most common uses is in microwave ovens. When you switch on a microwave oven, it gives off electromagnetic waves that bounce around inside the oven, penetrating the food. Water molecules in the food absorb the energy from the microwaves, causing the food to get hot.

Social Studies CONNECTION

In 1920, only about 20,000 people using homemade radio sets were receiving radio signals. As an experiment, Frank Conrad of the Westinghouse Company began to broadcast recorded music and sports results. Because public response was so enthusiastic, the company began broadcasting programs on a regular basis. By 1922, there were more than 500 radio stations in the United States.

In Your Journal

Imagine you are the advertising director for an early radio station. Write a letter to a business of your choice telling the owners why they should buy advertising time from your radio station.

Answers to Self-Assessment

Caption Question

Figure 5 Gamma rays

☑ *Checkpoint*

The speed of a wave is equal to its frequency times its wavelength. Because the speed of electromagnetic waves is constant in a particular medium, the frequency increases as the wavelength decreases, and vice versa.

---

2 Facilitate

Characteristics of Electromagnetic Waves

Demonstration

Materials *microwave oven without rotating tray, microwave-safe baking dish, marshmallows, metric ruler*

ACTIVITY

Time 25 minutes

Completely cover the bottom of the dish with a layer of marshmallows. Cook on low power, checking the marshmallows periodically until four or five spots have begun to melt. Remove the dish and measure the distances between adjacent melted spots. *(The distances will be the same. Sample: about 12 cm)* Tell students that the distance equals the wavelength of the electromagnetic wave because the spots represent the high-energy points of the wave. Find the label on the microwave giving the frequency of the waves. *(Typical value: 2,450 MHz)* Challenge students to find the speed of the waves. *(Sample: approximately 300,000,000 m/s)* **learning modality: logical/mathematical**

Radio Waves

Social Studies CONNECTION

Suggest students find out when their favorite station began broadcasting and what kinds of programs were played when the station first went on the air.

In Your Journal Students' letters should explain how the "new" technology of radio will allow the company's message to reach thousands of people. **learning modality: verbal**

Ongoing Assessment

Skills Check Have students identify one property all electromagnetic waves have in common, and two properties that distinguish types of waves.

Radio Waves, continued

Addressing Naive Conceptions

Students may think that microwaves give off heat. Explain that microwaves such as those used in a microwave oven do not give off heat but that they give off energy that causes the water molecules inside food to vibrate. The friction between the vibrating particles causes them to heat up. Ask students to compare this method of heating up food with the way gas or electric ovens heat up food. *(Students should explain that gas and electric ovens heat the air around the food and the pans containing the food. This eventually causes the molecules in the food to vibrate, then to heat up.)* **learning modality: verbal**

Building Inquiry Skills: Making Models

Materials *wrapping paper tube, marble, plastic or cardboard disc that fits snugly in the tube*

Time 10 minutes

Pair students. Have one partner look away while the other places the plastic disc inside the cardboard tube. Challenge the first partner to roll a marble into the tube and indicate where the disc is located by pointing to the location on the outside of the tube. Allow both partners to have a turn hiding the disk. Then ask: **How was the marble like a radio wave in a radar device?** *(The marble bounced off the disc and indicated where the disc was located, just as radio waves bounce off objects and indicate where they are located.)* **learning modality: kinesthetic**

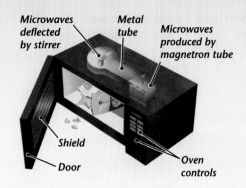

Microwaves deflected by stirrer — Metal tube — Microwaves produced by magnetron tube — Shield — Door — Oven controls

Figure 6 Microwaves produced in a microwave oven are absorbed by water molecules in foods. The energy raises the temperature of the food faster than the heat from an ordinary oven, so the food takes less time to cook.
Applying Concepts Why are metal containers not suitable for use in a microwave oven?

Microwaves can pass right through some substances, such as glass and plastic. For this reason, microwaves do not heat glass and plastic containers. If the container gets hot, it is because the food in the container transfers heat to the container. Other substances, such as metals, reflect microwaves. If you have ever accidentally put a metal object, such as a spoon, into a microwave oven, you may have seen sparks. The sparks are the result of a buildup of electrical energy in the metal caused by the microwaves. Metal containers and utensils should never be used in microwave ovens.

Microwaves are not easily blocked by structures such as trees, buildings, and mountains. For this reason, microwaves are used to transmit cellular telephone calls. You will read more about cellular phones in Section 4.

Radar Short-wavelength microwaves are used in radar. **Radar,** which stands for **ra**dio **d**etection **a**nd **r**anging, can be used to locate objects. A radar device sends out short pulses of radio waves. These waves are reflected by objects that they strike. A receiver detects the reflected waves and measures the time it takes for them to come back. From the time and the known speed of the waves, the receiver calculates the distance to the object. Radar is used to monitor airplanes landing and taking off at airports, as Figure 7 shows. Radar is also used to locate ships at sea and to track weather systems.

In Chapter 2, you learned how the frequency of a sound wave seems to change when the source of the sound moves toward you or away from you. The Doppler effect occurs with electromagnetic waves too, and has some very useful applications. Police use radio waves and the Doppler effect to find the speeds of vehicles.

Figure 7 Radar is used to monitor airplanes taking off and landing at airports.

Background

Integrating Science The sinking of the *Titanic* in 1912 led to the creation of the International Ice Patrol in the North Atlantic. The patrol uses radar equipment on aircraft to locate and track the movement of icebergs that may harm ships. When icebergs are most active, the patrol reports to ships twice a day. The patrol tracks approximately 1,000 icebergs each year.

Only about one seventh of an iceberg is above the water. In foggy weather, the patrol cannot see the icebergs from the plane, but radar waves can travel through the fog and allow the patrol to make images of the water's surface. Radar detection is most effective with skyscraper-sized icebergs on calm seas; choppy waters may disrupt radar images, and piano-sized icebergs sometimes go undetected.

Figure 8 Radio waves and the Doppler effect are used to find the speeds of moving vehicles (left) and of moving balls at sporting events such as tennis matches (right).

A radar gun sends blips of radio waves toward a moving car. The waves are then reflected. Because the car is moving, the frequency at which the reflected blips arrive back at the radar gun is different from the frequency at which the blips were sent out. The radar device uses the difference in frequency to calculate the speed of the car. If the car is going faster than the speed limit, the police often give a speeding ticket.

Radar is also used at some sports events to measure the speed of a moving ball. The radio waves bounce off a moving ball. The speed at which the ball is hit or thrown can then be displayed on a board like the one in Figure 8.

Magnetic Resonance Imaging (MRI) Radio waves are also used in medicine to produce pictures of tissues in the human body. This process is called **magnetic resonance imaging,** or MRI. In MRI, a person is placed in a machine that gives out short bursts of radio waves. The radio waves, combined with strong magnetic fields, cause atoms within the body to line up in the same direction. The atoms return to their original directions at different rates. By analyzing the responses, the MRI machine can create pictures of internal organs, including the brain. The pictures show clear images of muscles and other soft tissues that do not show up on X-rays. MRI is particularly useful in detecting brain and spine disorders.

☑ *Checkpoint* *What are three uses of radio waves?*

Infrared Rays

If you switch on an electric stove, you can feel infrared rays before the element turns red. As the element gets warmer, it gives out energy as heat. This energy is infrared radiation, or infrared rays.

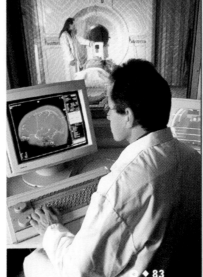
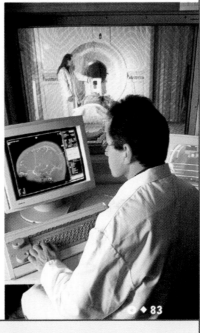

Figure 9 Magnetic resonance imaging (MRI) uses radio waves to create pictures of human tissue. It is used to examine the brain, spinal cord, and other organs.

Answers to Self-Assessment

Caption Question

Figure 6 Metal containers reflect microwaves, and electrical energy builds up in the metal, causing sparks.

☑ *Checkpoint*

Sample: To heat food, monitor speeds or locations of objects, take pictures of soft body tissues

Infrared Rays, continued

Real-Life Learning

Materials *drawing paper, colored markers, thermometer, metric ruler*

Time 30 minutes

As a class activity or as an individual at-home project, have students find the temperature at different locations in a room. For example, students should check the temperature near doors, windows, the ceiling, the floor, and near heat sources. Students should take pictures at different heights at the same part of the room, and at the same height in different parts of the room. Then have them complete a thermogram of the room. Students should draw maps showing both a bird's-eye view and a side view of the room. They should first draw the map, and then shade areas of different temperatures with different colors. Ask: **How is your thermogram similar to one made by an infrared camera?** *(Both indicate areas of different temperatures.)* Have students use their drawings to find places in rooms where outside air is leaking in. Ask: **Where would you predict most leaks would occur?** *(Around windows and doors where there are openings to the outside)* Have students explain whether their drawings support their predictions. **learning modality: visual**

Infrared rays have shorter wavelengths and higher frequencies than radio waves. *Infra-* is a prefix that means "below." So *infrared* means "below red." The next waves in the spectrum are red light.

Infrared rays range in wavelength from a little shorter than radio waves to just longer than visible light. Because you can feel the longest infrared rays as warmth, these rays are often called heat rays. Heat lamps have bulbs that give off more infrared rays and less visible light waves than regular bulbs. Some people have heat lamps in their bathrooms. You may also have seen heat lamps keeping food warm at cafeteria counters.

Most objects give off some infrared rays. Warmer objects give off infrared waves with more energy and higher frequencies than cooler objects. An infrared camera takes pictures using infrared

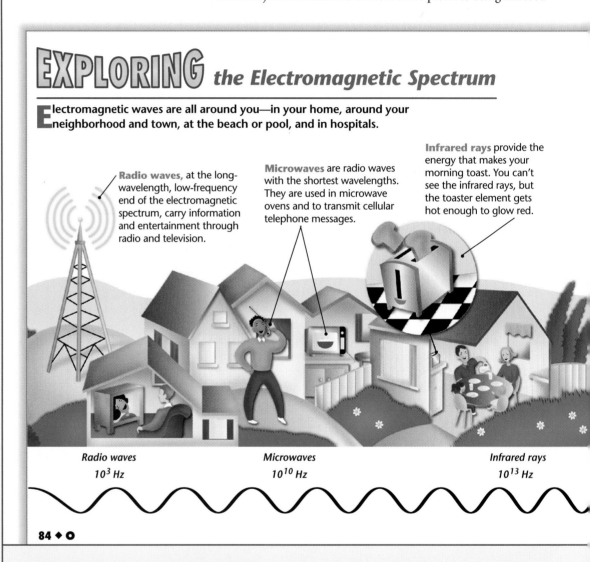

EXPLORING *the Electromagnetic Spectrum*

Electromagnetic waves are all around you—in your home, around your neighborhood and town, at the beach or pool, and in hospitals.

Radio waves, at the long-wavelength, low-frequency end of the electromagnetic spectrum, carry information and entertainment through radio and television.

Microwaves are radio waves with the shortest wavelengths. They are used in microwave ovens and to transmit cellular telephone messages.

Infrared rays provide the energy that makes your morning toast. You can't see the infrared rays, but the toaster element gets hot enough to glow red.

Radio waves	Microwaves	Infrared rays
10^3 Hz	10^{10} Hz	10^{13} Hz

Background

History of Science German-born British astronomer William Herschel (1738–1822) began his career as a musical entertainer. Unsatisfied with this career, he began studying music theory and teaching music. His interest in harmonics led him to read about other branches of physics, including optical systems. He soon mastered the art of constructing telescopes, grinding his own lenses and building larger and larger mirrors with which to observe the sky. In 1781, Herschel discovered the first new planet since ancient times—Uranus. This discovery made him famous, and Herschel gave up his career in music to pursue greater feats in astronomy. In 1800, Herschel measured the temperature of sunlight rays that had passed through a prism. In the course of this exploration, he discovered infrared rays.

rays instead of light. These pictures are called thermograms. A **thermogram** shows regions of different temperatures in different colors. Figure 10 shows a thermogram of a person. Thermograms identify the warm and cool parts of an object by analyzing infrared rays. Thermograms are especially useful for checking structures, such as houses, for energy leaks.

Even though your eyes cannot see the wavelengths of infrared rays, you can use an infrared camera or binoculars to detect people or animals in the dark. Satellites in space use infrared cameras to study the growth of plants and to observe the motions of clouds to help determine weather patterns.

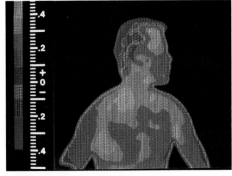

Figure 10 Infrared rays can be used to produce a thermogram. On a thermogram, regions of different temperatures appear in different colors.

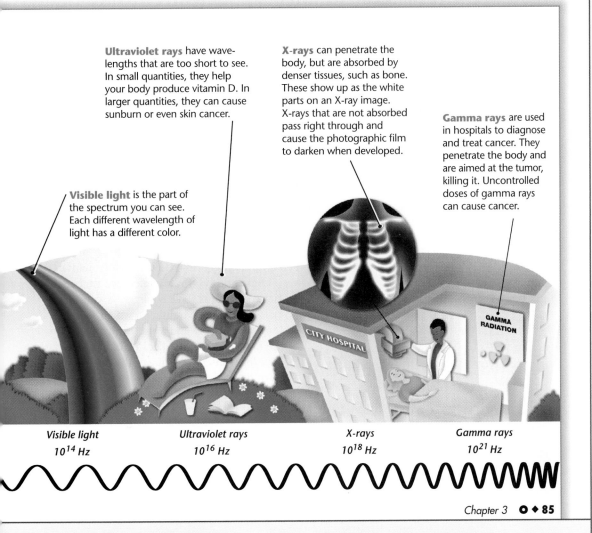

Ultraviolet rays have wavelengths that are too short to see. In small quantities, they help your body produce vitamin D. In larger quantities, they can cause sunburn or even skin cancer.

X-rays can penetrate the body, but are absorbed by denser tissues, such as bone. These show up as the white parts on an X-ray image. X-rays that are not absorbed pass right through and cause the photographic film to darken when developed.

Gamma rays are used in hospitals to diagnose and treat cancer. They penetrate the body and are aimed at the tumor, killing it. Uncontrolled doses of gamma rays can cause cancer.

Visible light is the part of the spectrum you can see. Each different wavelength of light has a different color.

Visible light	Ultraviolet rays	X-rays	Gamma rays
10^{14} Hz	10^{16} Hz	10^{18} Hz	10^{21} Hz

Media and Technology

 Transparencies "Exploring the Electromagnetic Spectrum," Transparency 11

 Exploring Physical Science Videodisc Unit 6, Side 2, "The Electromagnetic Spectrum" Chapter 7

Program Resources

◆ **Integrated Science Laboratory Manual** O-3 "In the Heat of the Light"

EXPLORING
the Electromagnetic Spectrum

As students examine the Exploring, challenge them to identify electromagnetic waves that are useful for health, communication, and cooking. (*Health—X-rays, gamma rays, ultraviolet waves; communication—radio waves (including microwaves); cooking—infrared rays and microwaves*) Then have students identify waves that are potentially harmful to living things. (*Ultraviolet waves, infrared rays, gamma rays, X-rays*) Have students compare the diagram of the wave at the bottom of the visual to each type of wave and make generalizations about the wavelength of a wave and its ability to penetrate other materials. (*Short-wavelength waves such as X-rays and gamma rays can penetrate many materials.*)

Extend Have students describe how they could detect each different type of wave in the electromagnetic spectrum. (*Samples: Infrared rays can be felt or detected as warmth; radio waves cause interference on televisions, radios, and cell phones.*) **learning modality: logical/mathematical**

Ongoing Assessment

Oral Presentation Have students compare and contrast infrared waves and radio waves. (*Infrared waves have shorter wavelengths and can be detected as warmth. Radio waves have long wavelengths and can be used to carry information long distances on Earth. Both travel at the same speed in a vacuum and are produced by interactions between changing electric and magnetic fields.*)

Visible Light

Building Inquiry Skills: Inferring

Have students describe the conditions under which rainbows are formed. *(When the sun shines through raindrops)* Inform students that a rainbow always appears in the part of the sky opposite the sun's position. Ask students to infer what colors the rainbow would be if the sun produced electromagnetic waves only at the shorter end of the visible light spectrum. *(Green, blue, and violet with no red, orange, or yellow colors)* **learning modality: visual**

Ultraviolet Rays

Real-Life Learning

Students may be familiar with "black lights." Explain that these lights usually produce ultraviolet light. Ask students to describe what objects look like under these lights. *(Sample: Some objects seem to glow.)* Explain that the high-energy UV waves are absorbed by molecules in some materials. These molecules release their excess energy by producing visible light. **learning modality: verbal**

Integrating Life Science

Help students understand how flowers benefit from an insect's ability to see ultraviolet light. Ask: **What happens to the flower when a bee lands on it?** *(The insect picks up pollen from the flower; this helps the plant to reproduce.)* **learning modality: verbal**

TRY THIS

Skills Focus observing
Materials *camera, UV-sensitive film*
Time 30 minutes
Tips You may want to do this as a demonstration.
Expected Outcome Prints should show that many flowers have patterns that can only be detected with UV-sensitive film. Bees can see these patterns, which help them to find nectar.
Extend Students can also experiment with infrared-sensitive film. **learning modality: visual**

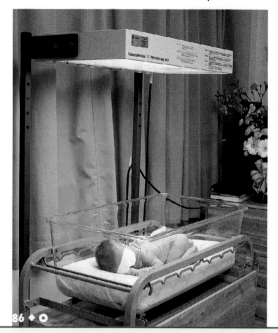

Figure 11 Visible light is made up of different wavelengths. Each wavelength has its own color. When light bounces off a bubble, interference produces some of the colors of the visible spectrum.

Visible Light

The electromagnetic waves that you can see are light. They make up only a small part of the electromagnetic spectrum. **Visible light** has shorter wavelengths and higher frequencies than infrared waves. The longest wavelengths of visible light are red. As the wavelengths decrease and the frequencies increase, you can see other colors of light. The shortest wavelengths are purple, or violet.

Have you ever seen a rainbow in the sky, colors on a bubble, or light passing through a prism? Recall what happens when waves enter a new medium, such as water or glass. The waves bend, or refract. Different wavelengths of light refract by different amounts, so the waves separate into the various colors. The colors in the visible spectrum are red, orange, yellow, green, blue, and violet, in order of increasing frequencies. Most visible light is made up of a mixture of these colors.

☑ *Checkpoint* *What are the colors of the visible spectrum?*

Ultraviolet Rays

Electromagnetic waves with wavelengths just shorter than those of visible light are called **ultraviolet rays,** or UV. *Ultra-* is a Latin prefix that means "beyond." So *ultraviolet* means "beyond violet." UV waves have higher frequencies than visible light, so they carry more energy. Because the energy of ultraviolet rays is great enough to damage or kill living cells, ultraviolet lamps are often used to kill bacteria on hospital equipment and in food processing plants.

Small doses of ultraviolet rays are beneficial to humans. Ultraviolet rays cause skin cells to produce vitamin D, which is needed for healthy bones and teeth. Ultraviolet lamps are used to treat jaundice, a condition of the liver that causes yellowing of the skin, in newborn babies.

Figure 12 Ultraviolet light is used to treat jaundice in newborn babies. The baby's eyes are protected because too much ultraviolet light could damage them.

The ultraviolet rays present in sunlight can burn your skin. Too much exposure can cause skin cancer and damage your eyes. If you apply sunblock lotion and wear sunglasses, you can limit the damage to your body caused by UV rays.

INTEGRATING LIFE SCIENCE Although ultraviolet light is invisible to humans, many insects can see it. For example, bees have good color vision, but they do not see the same range of wavelengths that humans do. Bees see less of the lower frequency red waves and more of the higher frequency ultraviolet waves. Flowers that appear to be one color to a human appear very different to a honeybee. To the bee, the part of a flower that contains nectar looks different from the rest of the flower. The bee can head straight for the nectar!

X-Rays

X-rays are electromagnetic waves with very short wavelengths. Their frequencies are just a little higher than ultraviolet rays. Because of their high frequencies, X-rays carry more energy than ultraviolet rays and can penetrate most matter. Dense matter, such as bone or lead, absorbs X-rays and does not allow them to pass through. For this reason, X-rays are used to make images of bones inside the body. X-rays pass right through skin and soft tissues and cause the photographic film in the X-ray machine to darken when it is developed. The bones, which absorb X-rays, appear as the lighter areas on the film, as shown in Figure 13.

Too much exposure to X-rays can cause cancer. If you've ever had a dental X-ray, you'll remember how the dentist gave you a lead apron to wear during the procedure. The lead absorbs X-rays and prevents them from entering the body.

X-rays are sometimes used in industry and engineering. For example, to find out if a steel or concrete structure has tiny cracks, engineers can take an X-ray image of the structure. X-rays will pass through tiny cracks that are invisible to the human eye. Dark areas on the X-ray film show the cracks. This technology is often used to check the quality of joints in oil and gas pipelines.

What Does a Bee See?

Load a roll of UV-sensitive **ACTIVITY** film into a camera. Take photos of a variety of flowers. Include white flowers and flowers that you see bees near. Have the film developed and look at the prints.

Observing What can bees see that you cannot? How is this useful to the bees?

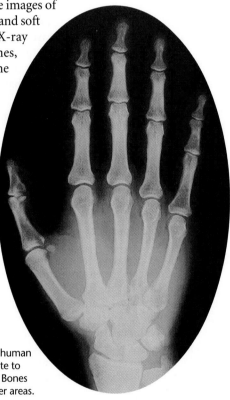

Figure 13 X-rays pass through softer human tissues and cause the photographic plate to darken behind them when developed. Bones absorb X-rays so they show up as lighter areas.

X-Rays

Using the Visuals: Figure 13

Have students point out the areas where X-rays were absorbed. *(The bones)* Then ask them to name the kinds of tissue the X-rays passed through. *(Skin, muscle, blood)* Finally, have students describe what a broken thumb bone would look like on the X-ray. *(The crack would show up as a dark line where the bone pieces were separated.)* **learning modality: visual**

Building Inquiry Skills: Making Models

Materials *telephone directory, cardboard, tissue paper, cotton ball, pencil with dull point, push pin*
Time 20 minutes

Have students stack the following items: first the phone book, then the cardboard, then the tissue paper on top. Students can use a cotton ball to represent visible light, a dull pencil to represent ultraviolet light, and a push pin to represent X-rays. Have students press each of these into the stack. Then ask: **How did each item model the penetrating abilities of different waves?** *(Visible light is least penetrating; the cotton ball did not penetrate the stack. Ultraviolet rays are somewhat penetrating; the dull pencil pressed through only the tissue paper. X-rays are more penetrating; the push pin went through the paper and cardboard into the phone book.)* **learning modality: kinesthetic**

Answers to Self-Assessment

☑ *Checkpoint*
Red, orange, yellow, green, blue, violet

Ongoing Assessment

Oral Presentation Ask students to describe characteristics of and identify uses for ultraviolet waves and X-rays. *(Sample: Both have frequencies higher than those of visible light. Ultraviolet lights are used to treat jaundice in babies, X-rays are used to examine teeth and bones and to look for cracks in steel and concrete structures.)*

Gamma Rays

Integrating Space Science

Ask students: **If nuclear weapons on Earth produce gamma rays, what kind of reactions do you think might occur when dying stars collide in space?** *(Nuclear reactions)* **learning modality: logical/mathematical**

3 Assess

Section 2 Review Answers

1. Alike—can travel in a vacuum, travel at the same speed; different—in frequency, wavelength, energy level, and uses
2. Radio waves—transmit information; infrared waves—radiate heat; visible light—allows humans and other animals to see; ultraviolet—causes skin cells to produce vitamin D; X-rays—used to detect bone fractures; gamma rays—kill cancer cells
3. In radar, radio waves are directed at a moving object and reflected. By comparing the frequency of the reflected waves to the original waves, the speed of the moving object can be calculated.
4. X-rays are useful in examining the bones of the body and for testing structures. Overexposure to X-rays can damage body tissues.
5. As wavelength decreases, frequency and energy increase.

Check Your Progress CHAPTER PROJECT 3

Encourage students to try out sample questions on each other to make sure their questions elicit relevant information. Make sure students develop surveys that can be answered in a short time. Students should distribute their surveys to a diverse group of students and community members.

Performance Assessment

Oral Presentation Ask groups of students to create poster displays that show one type of electromagnetic wave and its sources and uses.

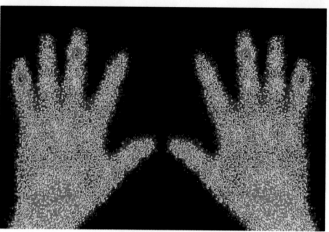

Figure 14 Doctors can inject radioactive liquids into the body and use gamma-ray detectors to trace them. The detectors build images that doctors can use to examine the inside of the body.

Gamma Rays

Gamma rays have the shortest wavelengths and highest frequencies of the electromagnetic spectrum. Because they have the greatest amount of energy, they are the most penetrating of all the electromagnetic waves.

Some radioactive substances and certain nuclear reactions produce gamma rays. Because of their great penetrating ability, gamma rays can cause serious illness. However, when used in controlled conditions, gamma rays have some medical uses. For example, gamma rays can be used to kill cancer cells in radiation therapy. Gamma rays can also be used to examine the body's internal structures. A patient can be injected with a fluid that emits gamma-rays. Then a gamma-ray detector can form an image of the inside of the body.

INTEGRATING SPACE SCIENCE Some objects far out in space give off bursts of gamma rays. The gamma rays travel for billions of years before they reach Earth. Earth's atmosphere blocks these gamma rays, so gamma-ray telescopes that detect them must orbit above Earth's atmosphere. Astronomers think that collisions of dying stars in distant galaxies could produce these gamma rays. Some gamma-ray telescopes also detect the stronger gamma rays given off in the atmosphere as a result of nuclear weapons tests on Earth.

Section 2 Review

1. How are all electromagnetic waves alike? How are they different?
2. List in order of increasing frequency the kinds of waves that make up the electromagnetic spectrum. Name one use for each.
3. Explain how radio waves are used to find the speed of a moving object.
4. How are X-rays useful? How are they dangerous?
5. **Thinking Critically** **Applying Concepts** As the wavelength of electromagnetic waves decreases, what happens to the frequency? To the energy?

Check Your Progress CHAPTER PROJECT 3

Write the questions for your survey. Some categories you might want to include are types of communication devices, how often they are used, when and where they are used, and the purposes for which they are used. Do people use these devices for personal reasons or for business? (*Hint:* To make your survey easy to complete, ask questions that require short answers.) Give the survey sheet to your classmates and other students in the school for their families and neighbors to complete.

Program Resources

◆ **Teaching Resources** 3-2 Review and Reinforce, p. 79; 3-2 Enrich, p. 80
Science Explorer Series *Astronomy,* Chapter 3, has more information about the electromagnetic spectrum.

SCIENCE AND SOCIETY

Food Irradiation

Food sometimes travels a long way to reach your plate. Potatoes from Maine and strawberries from Florida or Mexico must stay fresh until you eat them. But every so often, food makes people ill. Millions of Americans get sick every year from contaminated or spoiled food.

One way to prevent such illness is to treat food by irradiation. In the most common method, gamma rays are sent through fresh or frozen food. The radiation slows decay and kills organisms that could make people sick. It makes food safer to eat and also helps the food stay fresh longer. Five minutes of irradiation will allow strawberries to stay fresh for an extra nine or ten days.

Some people worry about the possible dangers of eating irradiated food. More than 40 countries, including the United States, permit food irradiation. Others forbid it. Is food irradiation safe?

TREATED BY IRRADIATION

The Issues

Does Irradiation Destroy Nutrients in Food? Radiation kills living cells. But it can also make chemical changes in the food itself. It may destroy useful nutrients, such as vitamins A, B-1, E, and K. Up to ten percent of these vitamins can be lost when food is irradiated. Of course, other methods of protecting and preserving food—such as refrigeration or canning fruits and vegetables—also lead to small losses in nutrition. Even cooking food makes it lose some vitamins.

Does Irradiation Change the Food Itself? Irradiating food doesn't make the food radioactive. But irradiation may change the molecular structure of some foods, creating chemicals such as benzene and formaldehyde. In small doses, these substances have little effect. But large amounts can be harmful to people. Supporters say that these same substances are found naturally in food. Some critics say irradiation should not be used until

there is further research. Researchers want to determine whether people who eat irradiated food for a long time are more likely to develop cancer or other diseases. Other experts say that the short-term research already done shows that irradiation is safe. Some alternatives to irradiation, such as spraying with pesticides, are clearly more harmful.

Will Irradiating Food Make People Less Careful About Handling Food? In the United States, all irradiated food must be labeled. But if people are not careful about washing their hands before preparing food, irradiated food can still become contaminated. Also, the amounts of radiation allowed won't kill all harmful organisms. It's still necessary to cook food properly before eating it, especially meat and eggs. Some food experts worry that irradiation will make people feel falsely safe and become careless about preparing food.

You Decide

1. Identify the Problem

In your own words, explain the problem of food irradiation.

2. Analyze the Options

List reasons for and against: (a) requiring all food to be irradiated; (b) permitting, but not requiring, food irradiation; and (c) banning food irradiation.

3. Find a Solution

You see two containers of a food at the supermarket. One is irradiated; one is not. The price is the same. Which would you buy? Explain why.

Background

Facts and Figures Food irradiation is endorsed by such associations as the American Dietetic Association and the American Medical Association. According to the ADA, nutrient losses from irradiation are often less than losses from other preservation methods. They consider that substances produced by irradiation are identical to those from cooking, pasteurization, and freezing.

You Decide

Have students write their responses to the first two questions as they prepare for the debate. They can discuss issues raised in the debate as they answer the final question.

Make sure students understand that there are no "correct" opinions or solutions. Also recognize that students whose family members produce or sell irradiated food may have strong feelings about the subject.

SCIENCE AND SOCIETY

Food Irradiation

Purpose

To provide students with an understanding of the issues surrounding food irradiation.

Debate

Time one class period for research and preparation, 30 minutes to conduct the debate

◆ Begin by asking students if they have ever knowingly eaten food that was irradiated. Explain that federal law currently requires that all such food be labeled as irradiated.

◆ Tell students that they can find information in support of their position in the library, on the Internet, or by contacting local authorities.

◆ Separate the class into small groups: half will support the proposition that food irradiation is a good method of food preservation, the other half will oppose it. Have groups research the issue and prepare their arguments, then meet with other groups on the same side of the issue to compare notes.

◆ Both sides should support their viewpoints critically and constructively. Encourage students supporting irradiation to explain illnesses associated with food contaminants such as *Trichinella* and *Salmonella*. Encourage students on the other side to consider the loss of nutrients from irradiation. Remind students that arguments should be clear and succinct without using harsh language.

Extend

Suggest students gather information from informal surveys of friends, neighbors, and relatives, then use the information to determine community viewpoints and to find out what kind of information people might need to make an informed decision.

Objective

After completing the lesson, students will be able to
◆ identify and compare different types of light bulbs.

Key Terms illuminated, luminous, spectroscope, incandescent light, fluorescent light, neon light, sodium vapor light, tungsten-halogen light, bioluminescence

1 Engage/Explore

Activating Prior Knowledge

Ask students: **If a light bulb has just burned out, would you reach up and unscrew it right away? Why or why not?** *(No. It would be too hot to touch.)* Tell students they will learn why some light bulbs get hot in this section.

DISCOVER

Skills Focus posing questions
Materials *1 clear (uncoated) incandescent light bulb, 1 fluorescent light bulb, goggles*
Time 10 minutes
Tips Students must be careful to avoid breaking the delicate glass bulbs. If a bulb breaks, make sure students call you immediately. Wear gloves and follow appropriate procedures for cleaning up broken glass.
Think It Over Students' questions will vary. Samples: What substance gives off the light? How hot does each bulb become? Which bulb is more efficient?

DISCOVER

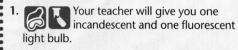

How Do Light Bulbs Differ?

1. Your teacher will give you one incandescent and one fluorescent light bulb.
2. Examine each bulb closely. What is the shape and size of each? Describe the differences between the bulbs. Draw each type of bulb and record your observations.
3. How do you think each bulb produces light?

Think It Over
Posing Questions Make a list of five questions you could ask to help you understand how each bulb works.

GUIDE FOR READING

◆ What are the different types of light bulbs?
◆ What colors of light are produced by an incandescent bulb?

Reading Tip As you read, compare and contrast the different ways in which light can be produced.

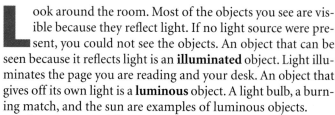

Figure 15 An incandescent light bulb glows when electricity passes through the tungsten filament. *Inferring Why do incandescent bulbs get so hot?*

Glass — Tungsten filament

Look around the room. Most of the objects you see are visible because they reflect light. If no light source were present, you could not see the objects. An object that can be seen because it reflects light is an **illuminated** object. Light illuminates the page you are reading and your desk. An object that gives off its own light is a **luminous** object. A light bulb, a burning match, and the sun are examples of luminous objects.

There are many different types of lighting. **Common types of lighting include incandescent, fluorescent, neon, sodium vapor, and tungsten-halogen light bulbs.** Some light bulbs produce a continuous spectrum of wavelengths. Others produce only a few wavelengths of light. You can use an instrument called a **spectroscope** to view the different colors of light produced by each type of bulb.

Incandescent Lights

Have you heard the phrase "red hot"? When some objects get hot enough, they glow, giving off a faint red light. If they get even hotter, the glow turns into white light. The objects are said to be "white hot." **Incandescent lights** (in kun DES unt) glow when a filament inside them gets hot.

Look closely at a clear, unlit incandescent bulb. You'll notice that inside is a thin wire coil called a filament. It is made of a metal called tungsten. When an electric current passes through this filament, it heats up. When the filament gets hot enough, it gives off red light, which has low frequencies. As it gets hotter, the filament begins to give off light waves with higher

---

READING STRATEGIES

Reading Tip Suggest students create compare/contrast tables. Partial sample:

Type of bulb	Incandescent	Fluorescent
How light is produced	Electric current passes through filament.	Electric current causes gas to emit UV waves that cause powder to emit light.
Advantages	widely available	inexpensive

Study and Comprehension Before students read the section, have them create charts using the column headings *What I Know, What I Want to Know,* and *What I Learned.* Have students write what they know about light sources in the first column, and questions about the subject in the second column. After students read the section they can write what they learned in the third column.

frequencies. Once the filament gets hot enough to give off enough violet light, all the frequencies of light combine to produce white light. **Incandescent lights give off all the colors of visible light: red, orange, yellow, green, blue, and violet.**

The American inventor Thomas Edison is credited with developing a long-lasting incandescent light bulb in 1879. Edison knew that if he passed an electric current through a wire, it would get hot and glow. By experimenting with different types of filaments, Edison developed a light bulb that would glow for a long time.

Incandescent bulbs are not very efficient in giving off light. Less than ten percent of the energy is actually given out as light. Most of the energy produced by an incandescent bulb is given off as infrared rays. Incandescent bulbs can get quite hot when they have been left on for a while.

Fluorescent Lights

Have you ever noticed the long, narrow light bulbs in stores and offices? They are **fluorescent lights** (floo RES uhnt). Maybe you have some in your school. Each glass tube contains a gas and is coated on the inside with a powder.

When an electric current passes through a fluorescent bulb, it causes the gas to emit ultraviolet waves. When the ultraviolet waves hit the powder coating inside the tube, the coating emits visible light. This process is called fluorescing.

Unlike incandescent lights, fluorescent lights give off most of their energy as light. They usually last longer than incandescent bulbs and use less electricity, which makes them less expensive to run.

☑ *Checkpoint* *Why are fluorescent bulbs more economical than incandescent bulbs?*

Figure 16 Fluorescent lights are commonly used in offices, stores, and schools. They are efficient and inexpensive.

Sharpen your Skills

Observing ACTIVITY

Use a spectroscope to observe light from different sources. **CAUTION:** *Do not look at the sun with the spectroscope.*

1. Look through the spectroscope at an incandescent light. Using colored pencils, draw and label the band of colors as they appear in the spectroscope.

2. Now, look at a fluorescent light through the spectroscope. Again, draw and label what you see.

How are the two bands of color the same? How are they different? Can you explain the differences?

---

2 Facilitate

Incandescent Lights

Inquiry Challenge

Materials *3 flashlights or slide projectors; red, blue, and green light filters; white poster board*
Time 10 minutes

Challenge small groups of students to use different colors of light to create white incandescent light. Tape the poster board to the wall for students to aim their lights at. When the three colored light beams overlap, white light forms. White light is made up of different colors of light. Challenge students to find out what happens when they use different combinations of colored light. For example, students can combine two red light beams and one green light beam.
learning modality: visual

Fluorescent Lights

Sharpen your Skills

Observing

Materials *spectroscope, incandescent bulb, colored pencils, fluorescent bulb*
Time 15 minutes
Tips Demonstrate for students how to use the spectroscope.
Answers The spectrum observed is different for different light sources, because different light sources give off different wavelengths of light.
Extend Students can use a spectroscope to examine neon lights, mercury vapor lights, sodium vapor lights, or halogen lights.

Program Resources

◆ **Teaching Resources** 3-3 Lesson Plan, p. 81; 3-3 Section Summary, p. 82
◆ **Guided Study Workbook** Section 3-3

Answers to Self-Assessment

Caption Question

Figure 15 Because they give off most of their energy as heat.

☑ *Checkpoint*

They give most of their energy as light so they use less electricity. They also last longer.

Ongoing Assessment

Oral Presentation Have students explain how electric currents produce light in incandescent and fluorescent bulbs.

Fluorescent Lights, continued

Building Inquiry Skills: Comparing and Contrasting

Materials *incandescent light bulb, fluorescent light bulb*

Time 10 minutes

Turn on both bulbs for 2 minutes. Have students slowly bring their hands close to each bulb. CAUTION: *Incandescent lights get very hot very quickly. Do not allow students to touch the bulbs.* Ask: **Which bulb gave off less heat? Explain.** (*The fluorescent bulb; hands could be brought closer to it before feeling heat.*) Ask: **What property of fluorescent lights does this show?** (*They give off most of their energy as light, not heat.*) **learning modality: kinesthetic**

Neon Lights

Using the Visuals: Figure 17

Ask students to identify the gases used to produce each color of light shown. (*Red—neon; green-blue—argon or mercury vapor; yellow—helium; violet—krypton*) **learning modality: visual**

Sodium Vapor Lights

Building Inquiry Skills: Relating Cause and Effect

Have students trace the energy changes that occur when a sodium vapor light glows. (*When electricity is applied to the neon and argon gas in the light, they glow. This heats up the solid sodium in the light, which changes into a vapor that gives off light energy.*) **learning modality: logical/mathematical**

Tungsten-Halogen Lights

Demonstration

Materials *halogen lamp, spectroscope*

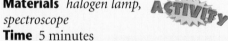

Time 5 minutes

Turn the lamp on. Ask: **Does this look like light from an incandescent bulb or a fluorescent bulb?** (*incandescent*) Students can check their observations with the spectroscope. **learning modality: visual**

Figure 17 Neon lights are used in advertising signs and decoration. *Applying Concepts Why are neon lights so colorful?*

Neon Lights

Some gases can be made to produce light by passing an electric current through them. For example, a **neon light** consists of a sealed glass tube filled with neon. When an electric current passes through the neon, particles of the gas absorb energy. However, the gas particles cannot hold the energy for very long. The energy is released in the form of light. This process is called electric discharge through gases.

Pure neon gives out red light. Often, what is called a neon light has a different gas, or a mixture of gases, in the tube. Different gases produce different colors of light. For example, both argon gas and mercury vapor produce greenish blue light. Helium gives a golden yellow light. Krypton gives a pale violet light. Sometimes the gases are put into colored glass tubes to produce other colors. Neon lights are commonly used for bright, flashy signs.

Sodium Vapor Lights

Sodium vapor lights contain a small amount of solid sodium as well as some neon and argon gas. When the neon and argon gas are heated, they begin to glow. This glow heats up the sodium, causing it to change from a solid into a gas. The particles of sodium vapor give off energy in the form of yellow light.

Sodium vapor lights are commonly used for street lighting. They require very little electricity to give off a great deal of light, so they are quite economical.

Figure 18 Sodium vapor light bulbs give off a yellow light. They are commonly used to illuminate streets and parking lots.

Background

Facts and Figures In early movie making, films were shot on roofless stages to allow natural light to illuminate the scene. After 1903, mercury-vapor light bulbs were used. Incandescent lights were available, but early film was insensitive to the lower frequencies of visible light, and the images produced were not appealing. Movie-makers then tried carbon-arc lights, but they crackled. When films became "talkies" and sound was recorded with images, carbon-arc lights were cast aside. In 1934, the problem with incandescent light was partially solved by the invention of Fresnel-lens spotlights that could be mounted to focus strong beams in specific locations. However, incandescent light altered the colors of color film. In the 1960s, tungsten-halogen lamps were introduced. These give strong lighting which does not interfere with sound or color.

Tungsten-Halogen Lights

Tungsten-halogen lights work partly like incandescent bulbs. They have tungsten filaments and contain a gas. The gas is one of a group of gases called the halogens. When electricity passes through the filament, the filament gets hot and glows. The halogen makes the filament give off a bright white light.

Tungsten-halogen lights have become very popular because they provide bright light from small bulbs, but use relatively little electricity. They are used in overhead projectors and also in floor lamps. Because halogen bulbs become very hot, they must be kept away from flammable materials, such as paper and curtains.

Figure 19 Tungsten-halogen light bulbs contain a tungsten filament and a halogen gas. Even small bulbs can produce very bright light.

Bioluminescence

 INTEGRATING LIFE SCIENCE Have you ever seen a firefly? On a warm summer evening, they flash their lights in patterns to attract mates. Fireflies are examples of organisms that produce their own light in a process called bioluminescence. **Bioluminescence** (by oh loo muh NES uns) occurs as a result of a chemical reaction among proteins and oxygen in an organism. The reaction produces energy that is given off in the form of light. Unlike a light bulb, which gives off most of its energy as infrared rays, the reaction that produces bioluminescence gives off almost all of its energy as light.

There are also bioluminescent organisms in the oceans. Some types of jellyfish give off light when they are disturbed. Deep in the ocean, where sunlight cannot reach, bioluminescence is the only source of light. Some deep-sea fish use bioluminescence to search for food or to attract mates.

Figure 20 This jellyfish produces its own light by bioluminescence.

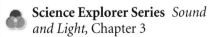
Section 3 Review

1. What are five common types of lighting?
2. How does an incandescent light bulb work?
3. Compare luminous objects with illuminated objects. Give two examples of each.
4. Why are fluorescent lights commonly used in businesses and schools?
5. **Thinking Critically Making Judgments** Make a list of the different rooms in your home. Which type of light do you think is best for each room? Give reasons for each choice.

Science at Home

Invite family members to visit a hardware store that sells light bulbs. Ask the salesperson to describe the different kinds of bulbs available. Read the information about each bulb on the side panel of each package. Ask the salesperson to explain any terms you don't understand. Look for the cost and expected life of the bulbs, too. How does this information help you and your family purchase the most economical bulbs?

Answers to Self-Assessment

Caption Question

Figure 17 Because they are made with gases that release energy in different colors of light.

Bioluminescence

Integrating Life Science

Ask students to infer when they think fireflies are most active and explain their inferences. (*At night; that is when their light signal is most visible.*) **learning modality: verbal**

3 Assess

Section 3 Review Answers

1. Incandescent, fluorescent, neon, sodium vapor, tungsten-halogen
2. An electric current passes through a filament, causing it to heat up. As it becomes hot, it begins to glow and emits all the colors of white light.
3. Luminous objects, such as the sun or a candle, give off light. Illuminated objects, such as this book or the moon, reflect light.
4. Fluorescent lights are efficient. They give off most of their energy as light and little energy as heat.
5. Samples: Kitchen—fluorescent, for bright, inexpensive light; bedroom—incandescent, for soft, warm light

Science at Home

Encourage students to describe how light bulbs work to their family. Students should explain what criteria they used to choose the most economical bulb.

Performance Assessment

Organizing Information Have students include the key terms in concept maps to describe methods of producing visible light.

Portfolio Students can save their concept maps in their portfolios.

O ◆ 93

Comparing Light Bulbs

Preparing for Inquiry

Key Concept People use different light bulbs to provide lighting for different purposes. Students will compare the light produced by different bulbs.

Skills Objectives Students will be able to

♦ design experiments to compare the illumination provided by different light bulbs;

♦ control variables and conduct several trials to collect data on how the manipulated variable affects the responding variable;

♦ measure the illumination produced by each light bulb;

♦ draw conclusions and compare results to predictions made before the experiment.

Time 45 minutes

Advance Planning Purchase a variety of incandescent light bulbs that fit in the same socket. Obtain wax paper. Provide a cardboard box and light socket for each student team.

Alternative Materials To decrease the time needed to do the lab, substitute a light meter for the light box. If students are interested in testing halogen bulbs, you may want to set up a halogen lamp and demonstrate the procedure. Do not allow students to handle halogen bulbs.

Guiding Inquiry

Invitation

♦ Show students several light bulbs and their packages, such as a "soft white" bulb, a standard bulb, a "long-life" bulb, and a compact fluorescent bulb. Ask them what kinds of bulbs they use in their homes.

♦ Review what the wattage rating means. Emphasize that an incandescent light bulb emits more heat than light. For example, an incandescent 60-watt bulb produces only about 6 watts of light energy.

♦ Explain that the life expectancy rating is a statistical number.

Real-World Lab

You, the Consumer

Comparing Light Bulbs

In this lab, you will design an experiment to compare the illumination provided by different light bulbs.

Problem

Which light bulb provides the best illumination?

Skills Focus

designing experiments, controlling variables, measuring, drawing conclusions

Materials

a variety of incandescent light bulbs that can fit in the same lamp or socket
medium-sized cardboard box
light socket or lamp (without shade)
meter stick   wax paper
scissors   plain paper

Procedure

1. Following the instructions below, construct your own light box. The box allows you to test the illumination that is provided by each light bulb.

2. Make a data table like the one shown at the right to record your data.

3. With a partner, examine the different bulbs. What is the power (watts), light output (lumens), and life (hours) for each bulb? Predict which light bulb will be the brightest. Explain your choice.

4. How will you test your prediction?
   ♦ What kinds of incandescent light bulbs will you use?
   ♦ What variables will you keep constant? What variables will you change?

5. Review your plan. Will your procedure help you find an answer to the problem?

How to Build and Use a Light Box

A. Use a medium-sized cardboard box, such as the kind of box copy paper comes in. If the box has flaps, cut them off.

B. Carefully cut a viewing hole (about 2 cm × 4 cm) in the bottom of the box. This will be on top when the box is used. This is hole A.

C. Punch another hole (about 1 cm × 1 cm) on one side of the box. This is hole B. It will allow light from the bulb to enter the box.

D. To decrease the amount of light that can enter, cover hole B with two layers of wax paper.

E. Put one of your light bulbs in the lamp and place it to the side of the box, about 1 m from hole B.

F. Have your partner write a secret letter on a piece of plain paper. Put the paper on the table. Place the light box over the paper with the viewing hole facing up.

G. Now look through hole A.

H. Turn the lamp on and move the light toward the box until you can read the secret letter. Measure the distance between the light bulb and hole B.

Program Resources

♦ **Teaching Resources** Real-World Lab blackline masters, pp. 89–90

Media and Technology

 Lab Activity Videotape
Sound and Light, 5

Safety

Students should wear their safety goggles throughout the activity. Caution them to use care when handling the glass light bulbs. Make sure students change light bulbs only when their lamps are switched off and unplugged. Allow time for bulbs to cool. Remind students to point sharp scissors away from themselves and others. Review the safety guidelines in Appendix A.

DATA TABLE

Bulb #	Brand Name	Power (watts)	Light Output (lumens)	Life (hrs)	Cost ($)	Distance from Bulb to Light Box (cm)

6. Ask your teacher to check your procedure.

7. Before you repeat the steps for a second light bulb, look back at your procedure. How could you improve the accuracy of your results?

8. Test the illumination of the rest of your light bulbs.

Analyze and Conclude

1. How does the distance between the bulb and hole B affect how easily you can read the secret letter?

2. Based on your observations, what can you infer about the illumination provided by each bulb? Which bulb gave the most illumination?

3. How did your results compare with your prediction? What did you learn that you did not know when you made your prediction?

4. What factors affect the illumination given by a light bulb?

5. **Apply** Based on your results, do you think that the most expensive bulb is the best?

More to Explore

Modify your light box and repeat the activity. What different materials would you use? Would you make the light box smaller or larger than the original? How do different light boxes compare in testing illumination by light bulbs?

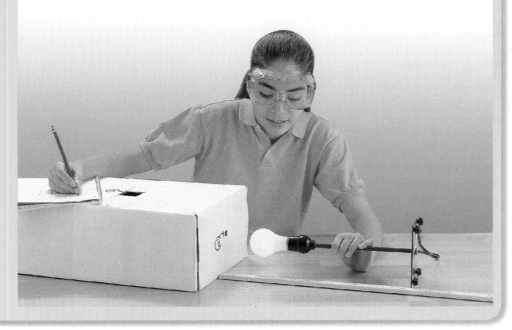

Sample Data Table

Bulb #	Brand Name	Power (watts)	Light Output (lumens)	Life (hrs)	Cost ($)	Distance from bulb to Light Box (cm)
1	A, soft-white	75	1,170	750	1.89	43
2	B, long-life	75	1,125	1,125	2.59	42
3	C, discount	75	1,170	1,000	.99	39
4	D, soft-white	60	860	1,000	1.68	30
5	E, fluorescent	15	860	10,000	4.05	53

Introducing the Procedure

Discuss the procedure and the bulbs that students choose. You may wish to have some groups compare different types of 75-W bulbs, while others compare different wattages of the same type of bulb. Students could also compare two 60-W bulbs to a 100-W bulb.

Troubleshooting the Experiment

◆ The light measurements will give valid results only if the students control the light entering the hole.

◆ The same student should do the viewing for each bulb. Remind students to wait for their pupils to stop dilating before making observations. Make sure students do not look directly at the light.

◆ Students should measure from the center of the bulb to the side of the box for each trial.

Expected Outcome

◆ Results will vary depending on the bulbs chosen. Example: a "long-life" bulb emits a little less light than a normal-life bulb.

◆ Because the intensity of light is inversely proportional to the square of the distance, the amount of light emitted is related to, but not directly proportional to, the distance at which the letter can be read.

Analyze and Conclude

1. The closer the bulb is to hole B, the easier it is to read the secret letter.

2. Answers will vary. The bulb with the greatest distance measurement produces the greatest illumination.

3. Answers will vary depending on students' predictions. In general, bulbs with higher wattages produce greater illumination.

4. The wattage, the life expectancy, the quality, whether it is incandescent or fluorescent.

5. Answers may vary. Based on the sample data table, students might say that the most expensive bulb (the fluorescent bulb) is the best because it lasts about 10 times as long as the other bulbs and uses less energy.

Extending the Inquiry

More to Explore Provide a variety of additional boxes and different materials to cover hole B for students to use in modifying their boxes. Check students' plans for safety.

 SECTION 4 Wireless Communication

Objectives

After completing the lesson, students will be able to

◆ describe how signals are transmitted from broadcasting stations;

◆ explain the workings of pagers and cellular phones;

◆ state how satellites relay information and find the position of objects.

Key Terms amplitude modulation, frequency modulation

1 Engage/Explore

Activating Prior Knowledge

Ask students to describe making a phone call to someone in another country. Have them describe the path their voices take from the caller's mouth to the listener's ear. (*Students may describe the voice being translated into a digital signal and being sent through cables or transmitted from a tower to a satellite.*)

DISCOVER

Skills Focus making models

Materials *tracing paper; flat piece of stretchable latex, about 20 cm square*

Time 10 minutes

Tips Review the terms *amplitude, wavelength,* and *frequency.*

Expected Outcome The wave on the stretched latex in Step 2 is longer and more spread apart. The wave on the stretched latex in Step 3 is narrower and taller.

Think It Over The vertical stretch (Step 3) changes the amplitude. The horizontal stretch (Step 2) changes the frequency.

SECTION 4 Wireless Communication

DISCOVER · ACTIVITY

How Can Radio Waves Change?

1. Trace the wave diagram onto a piece of tracing paper. Then transfer the wave diagram onto a flat piece of latex from a balloon or latex glove.

2. Stretch the latex horizontally. How is the stretched wave different from the wave on the tracing paper?

3. Now stretch the latex vertically. How is this wave different from the wave on the tracing paper? How is it different from the wave in Step 2?

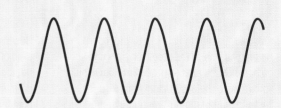

Think It Over
Making Models Which stretch changes the amplitude of the wave? Which stretch changes the frequency of the wave?

GUIDE FOR READING

◆ How are radio waves used to transmit information?

◆ How do cellular phones and pagers use electromagnetic waves?

◆ How are satellites used to relay information?

Reading Tip Before you read, preview the diagrams and captions in the section. List any terms you are not familiar with. As you read, write the definition of each term on your list.

R ecent advances in technology have turned our world into a global village. Today it is possible to communicate with people on the other side of the world in just seconds. You can watch a television broadcast of a soccer game from Europe or a news report from the Middle East. Once scientists discovered that messages could be carried on electromagnetic waves, they realized that communication signals could travel at the speed of light.

Radio and Television

How does your favorite radio station or television program travel to you? Both radio and television programs are carried, or transmitted, by radio waves. Radio transmissions are produced when charged particles move back and forth in transmission antennas. These transmissions are broadcast, or sent out in all directions. Radio waves carry information from the antenna of a broadcasting station to the receiving antenna of your radio or television. Don't confuse the sound that comes from your radio with radio waves. Your radio converts the radio transmission into sound waves.

There are many different radio and television stations, all sending out signals. So how can each individual program or song come through clearly? As you move your radio tuner up and down the dial, you can hear different radio stations. Look at the radio dial in Figure 21. Each number on the dial represents a

---

READING STRATEGIES

Reading Tip Have students work with partners to preview the diagrams and captions in the section. Encourage partners to discuss questions they have about wireless communication. Have one student in each pair list unfamiliar terms and write questions about the subject. After students read the section, instruct them to work together to write definitions of the unfamiliar terms and answer the questions.

Study and Comprehension Have students write summaries of the information under each section heading. Write each section heading on a note card. Place the note cards face down on a table. Then invite a volunteer to select one card and use his or her summary notes to give a brief oral report on the heading written on the card. Repeat with the remaining cards.

Figure 21 The radio dial shows the FM and AM frequency bands. Each radio station is assigned a different carrier frequency.

different frequency measured in either kilohertz (kHz) or megahertz (MHz).

Recall that a hertz is one cycle per second. If something vibrates 1,000 times a second, it has a frequency of 1,000 Hz, or 1 kilohertz (kHz). (The prefix *kilo-* means "one thousand.") If something vibrates 1,000,000 times a second, it has a frequency of 1,000,000 Hz, or 1 megahertz (MHz). (The prefix *mega-* means "one million" and is represented by a capital M.)

In the United States, the Federal Communications Commission, or FCC, assigns different frequencies of radio waves for different uses. Radio stations are allowed to use one part of the spectrum, and television stations use other parts. Taxi and police radios are also each assigned a set of frequencies. In this way, the entire spectrum of radio waves is divided into bands that are used for different purposes.

Each radio or television station is assigned a basic broadcast frequency, known as a carrier frequency. Each station is identified by the frequency at which it broadcasts. Radio stations broadcast in one of two main frequency bands—AM and FM.

AM Radio AM stands for **amplitude modulation.** On AM broadcasts, the frequency of the wave remains constant. The information that will become sound, such as speech and music, is coded in changes, or modulations, in the amplitude of the wave. **At the broadcasting station, music and speech are converted from sound into electronic signals. The electronic signals for AM broadcasts are then converted into a pattern of changes in the amplitude of a radio wave.**

Figure 22 Sound signals are carried by varying either the amplitude (AM) or the frequency (FM) of radio waves.
Interpreting Diagrams What remains constant in the AM wave? In the FM wave?

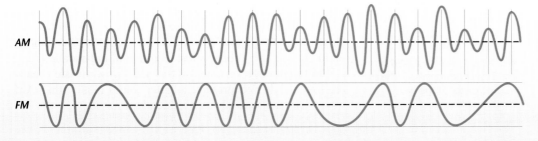

AM

FM

Radio and Television

Including All Students

Materials *stopwatch, pencil and paper*
Time 15 minutes

To help students who are having difficulty understanding the unit of measurement for frequency, pair students. Have one student draw transverse waves while the partner times him or her for 5 seconds with the stopwatch. Challenge the student to draw five waves in 5 seconds. Then have the students divide the number of waves drawn by 5 to find the frequency. Ask: **What was the frequency of the wave you drew?** *(1 wave/sec or 1 Hz)* Then have students repeat to find out how many waves they can draw in a second. Ask: **What was the highest frequency of waves that you drew?** *(A typical value will be 2 or 3 Hz.)* Each student should take turns timing the other. Finally, ask students how many waves they would have to draw to reflect frequencies of 1 kHz and 1 MHz. *(1,000 waves per second; 1 million waves per second)*
learning modality: logical/ mathematical

Using the Visuals: Figure 22

Have students use a thumb and forefinger or a ruler to compare the amplitude and frequency of the AM waves farthest to the left and the amplitude and frequency of the waves in the center and to the far right. Ask: **What happened to each value?** *(The amplitude of the wave changed. The frequency stayed the same.)* Have them repeat the process for the FM waves. *(The amplitude stayed the same and the frequency changed.)*
learning modality: logical/ mathematical

Ongoing Assessment

Writing Have students describe how different radio stations use radio waves to transmit information. *(Each radio station transmits at a specific frequency.)*

Program Resources

◆ **Teaching Resources** 3-4 Lesson Plan, p. 85; 3-4 Section Summary, p. 86
◆ **Guided Study Workbook** Section 3-4

Media and Technology

 Transparencies "Amplitude Modulation and Frequency Modulation," Transparency 13

Answers to Self-Assessment

Caption Question

Figure 22 AM—frequency; FM—amplitude

Radio and Television,
continued

Building Inquiry Skills: Inferring

Occasionally, residents of San Antonio, Texas receive radio broadcasts from cities in Mexico. Ask students to infer whether these are FM or AM stations. *(These are probably AM stations, because AM radio waves can travel farther than FM radio waves.)* **learning modality: verbal**

Skills Focus drawing conclusions

Materials *non-cabled television set, electric mixer or hair dryer*

Time 10 minutes

Tips Caution students to use care when handling the electric appliance. Students should observe that the television image is distorted when the appliance is turned on. Changing the speed on the appliance interrupts the television image.

Drawing Conclusions Mixers and hair dryers send out radio waves that interfere with the radio waves the television set receives.

Extend Have students find out at which frequency the television station broadcasts. Then have them draw conclusions about the frequency emitted by the electric appliance. **learning modality: kinesthetic**

Building Inquiry Skills: Making Generalizations

Explain that television stations in different cities sometimes broadcast at the same frequencies. Ask students: **How can these stations use the same frequencies without interference?** *(High-frequency VHF and UHF waves cannot travel the distance between faraway cities, so channels at the same frequency do not interfere with each other.)* **learning modality: verbal**

Figure 23 AM radio waves are reflected by the ionosphere. FM radio waves pass through the ionosphere. *Applying Concepts Which type of broadcast has a longer range on Earth?*

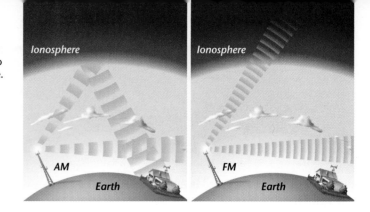

Produce Electromagnetic Interference

Find out which appliances produce radio waves.

1. Turn on a non-cabled television set. Keep the volume low. Observe the image on the screen.
2. Plug an electric mixer or a hair dryer into a nearby outlet and switch it on. What happens to the image on the television?
3. Change the speed of the mixer or hair dryer. What happens to the image on the television?

Drawing Conclusions What can you conclude about the electric mixer or the hair dryer? Explain.

Your radio picks up the wave and converts the coded information back into an electronic signal. This signal travels to your radio's speaker and comes out as sound waves.

The AM frequencies used for radio broadcasts range from 535 kHz to 1,605 kHz. These radio waves vibrate at frequencies from 535 thousand to 1,605 thousand times per second.

AM waves have relatively long wavelengths and are easily reflected by Earth's ionosphere. The ionosphere is an electrically charged layer high in the atmosphere. Figure 23 shows how this reflection allows the AM waves to bounce back to Earth's surface. This is why AM radio stations can broadcast over long distances, especially at night when the absorption of radio waves by the ionosphere is reduced. However, the reception of AM waves is sometimes not very clear. For this reason, AM radio stations usually broadcast more talk shows than music.

FM Radio FM stands for **frequency modulation.** On FM broadcasts, the amplitude of the wave remains constant. **FM signals travel as changes, or modulations, in the frequency of the wave.**

If you look at an FM dial on a radio, you will see that the stations broadcast at frequencies from 88 MHz to 108 MHz. FM radio waves vibrate from 88 million to 108 million times each second. The frequencies of FM stations are much higher than the frequencies of AM radio stations, which vibrate only thousands of times per second.

Because FM waves have higher frequencies and more energy than AM waves, they penetrate the atmosphere instead of being reflected back to Earth. For this reason, FM waves do not travel as far as AM waves. If you've ever gone on a long car trip with the radio on, you have probably lost reception of radio stations and had to tune in new ones as you traveled. FM waves are usually received clearly and produce a better sound quality than AM waves. They are generally used to broadcast music.

Background

Facts and Figures Using radio waves to transmit pictures is much more complex than transmitting sound. To begin with, each image on the television screen is broken down into about 100,000 picture elements or *pixels*. This information must travel at several million electrical impulses per second, so television stations broadcast at radio frequencies over 54 MHz. Also, as the images on the screen change, the rate of pixel transmission varies. This means that the television broadcast must be able to handle a wide range of frequencies all the time. The radio wave spectrum can support fewer television stations than radio stations because a television station requires a much broader range of frequencies. If television station frequencies were too close together on the radio spectrum, the stations would interfere with each other.

Television Television broadcasts are similar to radio broadcasts, except that the electromagnetic waves carry picture signals as well as sound. There are two main bands of television wave frequencies: Very High Frequency (VHF) and Ultra High Frequency (UHF). VHF television channels range from frequencies of 54 MHz to 216 MHz, and correspond to Channels 2 through 13 on your television set. This band of frequencies includes some FM radio frequencies, so television stations are restricted from using the frequencies that are reserved for radio stations. UHF channels range from frequencies of 470 MHz to 806 MHz, and correspond to Channels 14 through 69.

Weather can affect the reception of television signals. For better reception, cable companies now pick up the signals, improve them, and send them through cables into homes. Cable television reception is usually clearer than reception with an antenna. About half of American homes that have television now have cable reception.

☑ *Checkpoint* **What do the terms VHF and UHF mean?**

Cellular Telephones

Cellular phones have become very common. **Cellular telephones transmit and receive signals using high-frequency radio waves, or microwaves.** The cellular system works over regions divided up into many small cells. Each cell has its own transmitter and receiver. Cells that are next to each other are assigned different frequencies, but cells that are not next to each other can be assigned the same frequency. Cellular telephone signals are strong enough to reach only a few nearby cells. They cannot travel great distances. This allows many phones in different areas to use the same frequency at the same time, without interfering with each other.

As cellular phone users travel from one cell to another, the signals are transferred from one cell to another with very little interruption. If you travel outside one cellular phone company's area, another company becomes responsible for transmitting the signals.

Most cellular phones are more expensive to use than wired phones. But they are becoming more and more affordable. Cellular phones allow users to make and receive calls almost anywhere without having to use someone else's phone or look for a pay phone.

Figure 24 Cellular telephones transmit and receive radio waves that travel short distances.

O ◆ 99

Answers to Self-Assessment

Caption Question

Figure 23 AM

☑ *Checkpoint*

VHF—Very High Frequency; UHF—Ultra High Frequency

Cordless Telephones

Building Inquiry Skills: Applying Concepts

Tell students that the radio waves used to transmit signals between a cordless phone handset and base travel at a specific frequency and can usually only travel about 100 m. Ask students to infer why cordless phones usually only pick up the signal from their own base. (*Because signals from other bases are at different frequencies.*) **learning modality: verbal**

Pagers

Real-Life Learning

Have students check advertisements or contact local providers of wireless services, then compare the costs of the services. They can create tables to compare the types of wireless service offered and the average cost of each service per month. After students complete their analyses, ask: **Do you think most wireless services are worth the cost? Explain.** (*Students' answers will vary. Many may be surprised at the high monthly cost of wireless services.*) **learning modality: logical/ mathematical**

Building Inquiry Skills: Communicating

Have a class discussion about pagers and the technology that is used to send messages to pagers. Ask: **Can a pager tell you more information than just the phone number of the person who called you? Give examples.** (*Yes; pagers can deliver text or voice messages.*) Remind students that pagers receive messages carried by electromagnetic waves. Challenge students to think of ways that pagers could receive messages other than by using the telephone. (*Sample responses include using radios or other devices to send messages. Students may also mention that some pagers can receive electronic mail and other messages sent by computers.*) **learning modality: verbal**

Cordless Telephones

Cellular telephones should not be confused with cordless telephones. The bases of cordless telephones are connected to the telephone system just like ordinary phones. The only difference is that there is no cord between the handset and the base. The information is transmitted from the handset to the base by radio waves, so you can walk away from the base as you talk on the phone.

Pagers

Pagers are small electronic devices that people can carry in their pockets or attach to their clothes. To page someone, you must

SCIENCE & History

Wireless Communication

Since the late 1800s, many developments in communication have turned our world into a global village.

1895
First Wireless Transmission

Italian engineer and inventor Guglielmo Marconi successfully used radio waves to send a coded wireless signal a distance of more than 2 km.

1923
Ship-to-Ship Communication

For the first time, people on one ship could talk to people on another. The signals were sent as electromagnetic waves, received by an antenna, and converted into sound.

1900 — **1920**

1888
Electromagnetic Waves

German scientist Heinrich Hertz proved James Clerk Maxwell's prediction that radio waves exist. Hertz demonstrated that the waves could be reflected, refracted, diffracted, and polarized just like light waves.

1901
First Transatlantic Signals

On December 12, the first transatlantic radio signal was sent from Poldhu Cove, Cornwall, England, to Signal Hill, Newfoundland. The coded electromagnetic waves traveled more than 3,000 km through the air.

Cornwall, England

Signal Hill, Newfoundland

100 ◆ O

Background

Facts and Figures The first working network of cellular telephones was implemented in 1979 in Japan, but work on this technology began several decades earlier in the United States. The first mobile telephones were introduced in 1946. To place a call, the caller would scan the dial for an unused channel and call the operator, who would then dial the number. The phones worked like a CB radio or two-way radio set; the caller had to hold down a button on the phone to talk, so only one person could talk at a time. In 1964, a new mobile telephone service was introduced. These phones dialed automatically and allowed callers to talk without pushing a button. However, there were only a limited numbers of channels available.

The first cellular phone system in the United States was installed in 1983.

dial the telephone number of the pager. This can be done from a telephone or another pager. Depending on the pager, you can then enter your telephone number or leave a voice message. Some pagers even allow the user to receive text messages.

When you leave a message for a pager, the information is first sent to a receiving station. There it is coded and sent as electromagnetic waves to the correct pager. The pager then beeps or vibrates, letting the owner know that there is a message. Some pagers are two-way pagers. This means that the pager can return electromagnetic signals to the receiving station, which sends them to the person who sent the original message.

In Your Journal

At your local or school library, find out more about Guglielmo Marconi. Imagine you were hired as his assistant. Write a letter to a friend that describes your new job.

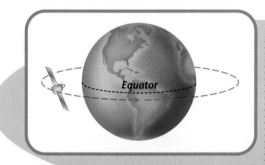

1963

Geosynchronous Orbit

Communications satellites are launched into orbits at altitudes of about 35,000 km. At this altitude, a satellite orbits Earth at the same rate as Earth rotates. A satellite orbiting above the equator remains above the same location as Earth turns.

Equator

| 1940 | 1960 | 1980 |

1957

Sputnik I

On October 4, the Soviet Union became the first country to successfully launch an artificial satellite into orbit. This development led to a new era in communications. Since then, more than 5,000 artificial satellites have been placed in orbit.

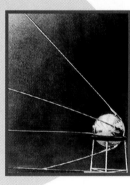

1979

Cellular Phone Network

The world's first cellular phone network was set up in Japan. It allowed people to make and receive telephone calls without wired phones.

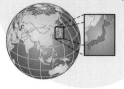

Chapter 3　**O ◆ 101**

As students read each segment of the time line, challenge them to write one or two newspaper headlines that describe the events. Headlines should summarize the key aspects of the technology. (*Samples: Electromagnetic waves—Radio Waves: You Can't See Them, But They're Out There; first wireless transmission— Marconi Sends Message: Look Ma, No Wires!; transatlantic signal—A New Kind of Wave Crosses the Ocean; ship-to-ship communication—Calls from the Deck, Not the Dock; Sputnik 1—Heads Up! There's Something New Orbiting Earth; geosynchronous orbit—As the Earth Turns, So Does the Geosynchronous Satellite; cellular phone network— Telephones To Go*)

Extend Challenge students to find actual headlines and news stories for current technological developments.

In Your Journal Encourage students to imagine what their responsibilities might be as Marconi's assistant. Students' letters should explain how a wireless message is sent. **learning modality: verbal**

 Students can save their letters in their portfolios.

Ongoing Assessment

Writing Have students prepare brochures explaining how a paging system works.

 Students can save their brochures in their portfolios.

O ◆ 101

Communications Satellites

Using the Visuals: Figure 25

Ask students: **Why can't the radio waves travel directly between the tower and the house?** *(The waves cannot curve around Earth's surface.)* Then have students use a straightedge to trace the path of the waves from the tower to the satellite and then to the house. Ask: **Is the house the only place the satellite can send the signals?** *(No, the satellite can send the signals in any direction, so there are many places on Earth that could receive the signals.)* **learning modality: visual**

Building Inquiry Skills: Inferring

Ask students to infer why a GPS receiver would be extremely useful for ships and airplanes that travel over oceans. *(Over oceans, captains and pilots cannot navigate using visible landmarks.)* Have students brainstorm a list of other situations in which a GPS receiver would be helpful. **learning modality: verbal**

Communications Satellites

Since the development of satellite technology, long-distance communications have become faster and cheaper. Communications satellites work like the receivers and transmitters of a cellular phone system. Satellites orbiting Earth receive radio, television, and telephone signals, and transmit them around the world. **The radio waves are sent from Earth up to the satellite, which then relays the waves to other receivers on Earth.** Most satellites strengthen the signals before sending them back to Earth. Communications satellites can relay several signals at the same time.

Because a satellite can "see" only part of Earth at any given time, it is necessary to have more than one satellite in orbit for any given purpose. In this way, signals can be sent all around the world at any time.

Satellite Telephone Systems In recent years, the use of telephones has increased so much that telephone companies have had to develop new ways of transmitting electromagnetic waves. Several companies have developed satellite telephone systems. The radio waves from one phone are sent up through the atmosphere, received by one of the communications satellites, and transmitted back to Earth to the receiving phone. This system makes calling available anywhere in the world, but it is more expensive than using the more common cellular telephone system.

Figure 25 Communications satellites are remote-controlled spacecraft that orbit Earth. Because electromagnetic waves travel in straight lines, they cannot curve around Earth. Satellites receive signals from Earth and transmit them to parts of the world they could not otherwise reach.

Background

Integrating Science Meteorologists rely on satellite transmissions to analyze Earth's weather. Certain weather satellites orbit from one pole to the other, rather than around Earth's equator. These satellites take photographs of Earth and then transmit the images as television signals. Receivers in many nations allow meteorologists to have a constant surveillance of weather systems. This requires the cooperation of meteorologists in many different countries.

The first meteorological satellite was put into orbit in 1960. Since then, the United States has launched several geosynchronous satellites that orbit at the same rate as Earth rotates on its axis. When images from these satellites are used together, they can provide continual global weather coverage. Weather satellites have also been launched by Japan and Russia.

Television Satellites Television networks use communications satellites to send their signals to local stations across the country. The television signals are changed into radio waves using frequency modulation.

Some people have their own antennas to receive signals directly from satellites. Because the antennas are dish-shaped, they are known as satellite dishes. Older satellite dishes were very large. As the signals broadcast from satellites have become more powerful, the dishes required to receive them have become a lot smaller. Also, modern satellites are much more powerful.

The Global Positioning System The Global Positioning System (GPS) was originally designed for use by the United States military. Now, many thousands of civilians use the system for navigation. The Global Positioning System uses a group of two dozen communications satellites that work together. The GPS satellites broadcast radio signals to Earth. These signals carry information that can tell you your exact location on Earth's surface, or even in the air. Anybody on Earth with a GPS receiver can receive these signals.

Today, GPS receivers are becoming increasingly common in airplanes, boats, and even in cars. In some cars you can type your destination into a computer and have the GPS system map out your route. A computerized voice might even tell you when to turn right or left.

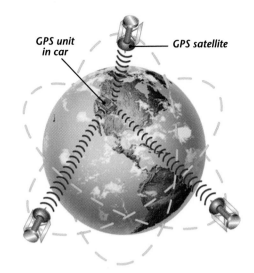

GPS unit in car — GPS satellite

Figure 26 The Global Positioning System (GPS) uses a group of 24 satellites, each traveling in its own orbit. Receivers in cars, boats, and airplanes use signals from at least three satellites at a time to determine their exact location on Earth.

Section 4 Review

1. Describe how the sounds from a radio station, such as speech or music, are converted into radio waves.
2. What is the difference between AM and FM radio broadcasts?
3. How does the cellular phone system work?
4. How does a satellite relay radio and television signals?
5. **Thinking Critically** **Predicting** What do you think might happen if the Federal Communications Commission did not control the use of different frequencies of radio waves?

Check Your Progress CHAPTER PROJECT 3

Collect your surveys and tally your results. As you analyze your data, look for patterns. You can use bar graphs or circle graphs to display your findings. Include information about cost, time, and any other questions you asked in your survey. Write one or two paragraphs explaining your conclusions.

Program Resources

◆ **Teaching Resources** 3-4 Review and Reinforce, p. 87; 3-4 Enrich, p. 88

3 Assess

Section 4 Review Answers

1. At a broadcasting station, sounds are converted into electric signals and transmitted as electromagnetic waves.
2. AM radio stations broadcast by changing the amplitude of the waves. FM stations change the frequency of the waves. AM waves can travel longer distances than FM waves, but the sound quality is not as high.
3. Cellular transmitters send signals to nearby receivers. In a long-distance call, the signals are relayed from cell to cell until they reach the cell nearest the destination.
4. A satellite receives signals from Earth, amplifies them, and retransmits them to parts of Earth that they could not reach traveling in a straight line.
5. If the frequencies of radio waves were not controlled, different broadcasters might try to use the same frequencies and there would be a lot of interference.

Check Your Progress CHAPTER PROJECT 3

To help students compile data, allow them to use computer spreadsheet programs if available. If necessary, review graphing skills. Students may want to complete a bar graph for each question asked on the survey.

Performance Assessment

Oral Presentation Have small groups of students make displays to show how radio waves are involved when people send and return pages, or when they make phone calls using cellular phones.

Build a Crystal Radio

Preparing for Inquiry

Key Concept Students will build crystal radios to receive radio signals and convert the signals into sound.

Skills Objectives Students will be able to
- measure the components of their radios according to the specifications given in the lab procedure;
- interpret diagrams and use them as models;
- observe how the crystal radios operate and how they are affected by changing different variables;
- solve problems by changing one variable at a time to determine how their radios work best;
- draw conclusions about the structure and function of a crystal radio and its components.

Time 60 minutes

Advance Planning Purchase the earphone, crystal diode, wire, and alligator clips from an electronics supply store. Collect enough cardboard and cardboard tubes for each group, or have students bring them from home. To save time and for safety reasons, you may want to strip the ends of the wires yourself. Test the diodes and earphones with an ammeter or multimeter to make sure they work.

Alternative Materials Mount the circuit on a board and use screws instead of clips to make connections.

Guiding Inquiry

Invitation Ask students how a radio works. *(Most students will mention radio waves but will not know how they are converted into sound.)* Discuss how waves travel through different media. Then tell students that radio waves are received by the radio's antenna, converted into an electronic signal, then the electronic signal is converted into sound by the speaker. Remind students how sound waves travel through the air, into the ear, and finally as signals to the brain.

Real-World Lab

How It Works

Build a Crystal Radio

The first radio, called a crystal set, was invented in the early 1900s. At first, people built their own crystal sets to receive broadcast transmissions from local radio stations. In this lab, you will build your own crystal radio and learn how it works.

Problem

How can you build a device that can collect and convert radio signals?

Skills Focus

measuring, observing, making models, drawing conclusions

Materials

cardboard tube (paper towel roll)
3 pieces of enameled or insulated wire, 1 about 30 m long, and 2 about 30 cm long
wirestrippers or sandpaper
2 alligator clips
scissors
aluminum foil
2 pieces of cardboard (sizes can range from 12.5 cm × 20 cm to 30 cm × 48 cm)
masking tape
crystal diode
earphone
2 pieces of insulated copper antenna wire, 1 about 30 m long, and 1 about 0.5 m long

Procedure ✂

Part 1 Wind the Radio Coil

(Hint: All ends of the insulated wires need to be stripped to bare metal. If the wire is enameled, you need to sandpaper the ends.)

1. Carefully punch two holes approximately 2.5 cm apart in each end of a cardboard tube. The holes should be just large enough to thread the insulated wire through.
2. Feed one end of the 30-m piece of insulated wire through one set of holes. Leave a 50-cm lead at that end. Attach alligator clip #1 to this lead. See Figure 1.
3. Wind the wire tightly around the cardboard tube. Make sure the coils are close together but do not overlap one another.
4. Wrap the wire until you come to the end of the tube. Feed the end of the wire through the other set of holes, leaving a 50-cm lead as before. Attach alligator clip #2 to this lead. See Figure 2.

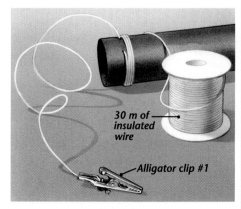
30 m of insulated wire

Alligator clip #1

Figure 1 Winding the Coil

Introducing the Procedure

Go over the construction procedure. Refer to the apparatus diagrams and explain the purpose of each component. You may want to set up a demonstration radio ahead of time for students to refer to as they work.

Troubleshooting the Experiment

- The crystal radio needs no source of electrical energy. Students should not connect their radios to electrical outlets or electrical appliances.

- Caution students to handle their diodes carefully as they can break easily. Students should test the diode and earphone to make sure they work before connecting them.
- Inform students that the diode arrow must point towards the earphone for the radio to work.
- For Part 4, students can use themselves as the ground by holding the loose end of the shorter antenna wire instead of connecting it to the water pipe or faucet. The longer antenna wire should be extended and lie flat.

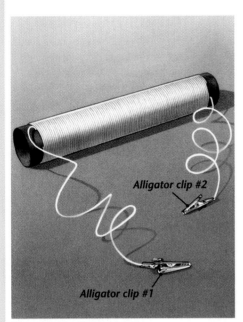

Figure 2 The Finished Coil

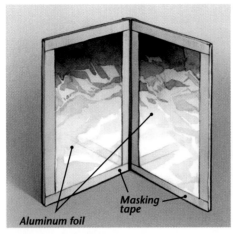

Figure 3 The Tuning Plates

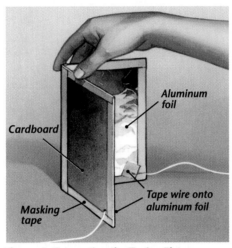

Figure 4 Connecting the Tuning Plates

Part 2 Make the Tuning Plates

5. Without wrinkling the aluminum foil, cover one side of each piece of cardboard with the foil. Trim off any excess foil and tape the foil in place.

6. Hold the pieces of cardboard together with the foil facing inward. Tape along one edge to make a hinge. It is important for the foil pieces to be close together but not touching. See Figure 3.

7. Make a small hole through the cardboard and foil near a corner of one side. Feed one of the short pieces of insulated wire through the hole and tape it onto the foil as shown. Tape the other short piece of insulated wire to the corner of the other side. See Figure 4.

8. Connect one end of the wire from the foil to alligator clip #1. Connect the other wire from the foil to alligator clip #2.

Part 3 Prepare the Earphone

9. Handle the diode carefully. Connect one wire from the diode to alligator clip #1. The arrow on the diode should point to the earphone. Tape the other end of the diode wire to one of the earphone wires.

10. Connect the other wire from the earphone to alligator clip #2. See Figure 5.

Expected Outcome

Students should be able to pick up the signals of some radio stations with the crystal radios they construct.

Analyze and Conclude

1. Answers will vary. Students' logs should describe the position of the tuning plates and the antenna for each station they receive. They should also compare the strength of the signal.

2. Adjusting the tuning plates allows the radio to receive signals from different stations. Different stations transmit signals at different frequencies.

3. Students should use examples from their observations to support their opinions. Students may realize that some materials, such as metal, make better antennas. In addition, students will probably say that the radio works better when the antenna is connected to a water pipe or is held by a person.

4. Students should compare this radio with modern radios. They will probably state that the modern radio uses electrical current from a wall outlet or from batteries. Students should support their opinions about which radio is more efficient.

Extending the Inquiry

Design an Experiment Check students' designs for safety and thoroughness. Students should develop procedures that will allow them to control variables. Students will find that signal reception is better at night when the absorption of radio waves by the ionosphere is reduced.

Safety

Caution students not to connect their radios to electrical outlets or electrical appliances. Students should wear goggles and use care when stripping wire; wire strippers are sharp. Review the safety guidelines in Appendix A.

Program Resources

◆ **Teaching Resources** Real-World Lab blackline masters, pp. 91–93

Media and Technology

 Lab Activity Videotape
Sound and Light, 6

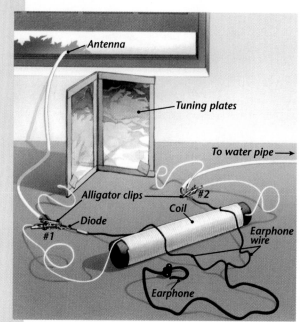

Antenna

Tuning plates

To water pipe →

Alligator clips — #2

Coil

Diode

#1

Earphone wire

Earphone

Figure 5 The Completed Radio

Part 4 Hook Up the Antenna

11. String the long piece of antenna wire along the floor to an outside window. Connect the other end of the wire to alligator clip #1.
12. Connect one end of the shorter piece of antenna wire to a cold-water pipe or faucet. Connect the other end to alligator clip #2. See Figure 5.
13. Put on the earphone and try to locate a station by squeezing the tuning plates slowly until you hear a signal. Some stations will come in when the plates are close together. Other stations will come in when the plates are opened far apart.

Analyze and Conclude

1. How many stations can you pick up? Where are the stations located geographically? Which station has the strongest signal? Keep a log of the different stations you receive.
2. How does adjusting the tuning plates affect the radio signals?
3. A crystal radio is not a powerful receiver. You can improve reception by having a good antenna. How can you improve your antenna?
4. **Apply** What are the similarities and differences between a modern radio and a crystal radio? How is one more efficient?

Design an Experiment

Use your crystal radio or any radio to test signal reception at various times of the day. Do you receive more stations at night or in the morning? Why do you think certain times of the day are better for receiving radio waves?

SECTION 1 The Nature of Electromagnetic Waves

Key Ideas

◆ An electromagnetic wave transfers energy by means of changing electric and magnetic fields.
◆ Sometimes light acts as though it is a set of waves. Sometimes light acts as though it is a stream of particles.

Key Terms

electromagnetic wave   photoelectric effect
electromagnetic radiation   photon
polarized light

 SECTION 2 Waves of the Electromagnetic Spectrum

Key Ideas

◆ All electromagnetic waves travel at the same speed, but they have different wavelengths and different frequencies.
◆ The electromagnetic spectrum is made up of radio waves, infrared rays, visible light, ultraviolet rays, X-rays, and gamma rays.
◆ Radio waves and the Doppler effect can be used to tell the speeds of moving objects.

Key Terms

electromagnetic spectrum   thermogram
radio wave   visible light
microwave   ultraviolet ray
radar   X-ray
magnetic resonance imaging   gamma ray
infrared ray

SECTION 3 Producing Visible Light

Key Ideas

◆ Light bulbs can be incandescent, fluorescent, neon, sodium vapor, or tungsten-halogen.

Key Terms

illuminated   neon light
luminous   sodium vapor light
spectroscope   tungsten-halogen light
incandescent light   bioluminescence
fluorescent light

 SECTION 4 Wireless Communication

INTEGRATING TECHNOLOGY

Key Ideas

◆ At broadcasting stations, music and speech are converted from sound into an electrical signal and then into a pattern of changes in a radio wave.
◆ AM broadcasts transmit information by modifying the amplitude of the signal. FM broadcasts change the frequency of the signal.
◆ Cellular telephones transmit and receive signals using high-frequency radio waves.
◆ When you leave a message for a pager, the information is first sent to a receiving station. There it is coded and directed to the correct pager.
◆ Radio, television, and telephone signals are sent from Earth up to communications satellites, which then relay the signals to receivers around the world.

Key Terms

amplitude modulation (AM)
frequency modulation (FM)

Organizing Information

Concept Map Copy the concept map about electromagnetic waves onto a sheet of paper. Then complete it and add a title. (For more on concept maps, see the Skills Handbook.)

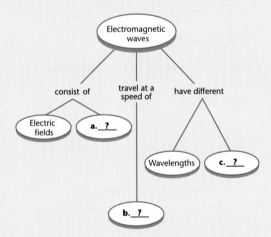

Organizing Information

Concept Map Sample title: *Properties of Electromagnetic Waves;* **a.** Magnetic fields **b.** Light, or 300,000 km/s in a vacuum **c.** Frequencies

Program Resources

◆ **Teaching Resources** Chapter 3 Project Scoring Rubric, p. 72; Chapter 3 Performance Assessment Teacher Notes, pp. 152–153; Chapter 3 Performance Assessment Student Worksheet, p. 154; Chapter 3 Test, pp. 155–158

Media and Technology

Interactive Student Tutorial CD-ROM O-3

Computer Test Bank
Sound and Light, Chapter 3 Test

Reviewing Content
Multiple Choice
1. b 2. a 3. b 4. c 5. d

True or False
6. true 7. Infrared 8. visible light
9. frequency 10. true

Checking Concepts
11. Because sunlight comes to Earth through space.
12. Students' answers should reflect an understanding that a polarizing filter blocks waves that move in all directions but one, and that this would not happen if light were composed of particles.
13. When radio waves are directed at a moving object, the reflected waves have a different frequency than the original waves. By finding the difference in frequency, the speed of the moving object can be calculated.
14. Cellular telephones send signals to towers; cordless phones only send signals to a base unit.
15. Amplitude modulation varies the amplitude of a carrier wave, while frequency modulation varies its frequency. The signal is FM because the flashlight always has the same brightness but is turned on and off for different periods of time.
16. Students' articles should describe at least two advantages of fluorescent lights.

Thinking Critically
17. A thermogram of a house shows where heat is escaping. This could be used to decide where to add insulation to save energy.
18. The high frequency waves have more energy. This allows them to penetrate more substances, come into more contact with matter, and cause more harm.
19. Samples: Luminous—burning match, light bulb, sun, computer display, stars; illuminated —chair, person, pencil, computer keyboard, desk
20. You would use incandescent bulbs because they are the only type that produce mainly heat.

Reviewing Content

 For more review of key concepts, see the Interactive Student Tutorial CD-ROM.

Multiple Choice
Choose the letter of the best answer.

1. All electromagnetic waves have the same
   a. frequency.
   b. speed.
   c. wavelength.
   d. energy.
2. The electromagnetic waves with the longest wavelengths are
   a. radio waves.
   b. infrared rays.
   c. X-rays.
   d. gamma rays.
3. Which of the following does *not* belong in the electromagnetic spectrum?
   a. X-ray
   b. sound
   c. infrared ray
   d. radio wave
4. Light bulbs that glow when a filament inside them gets hot are called
   a. bioluminescent lights.
   b. fluorescent lights.
   c. incandescent lights.
   d. neon lights.
5. Television signals are transmitted by
   a. gamma rays.   b. infrared rays.
   c. X-rays.   d. radio waves.

True or False
If the statement is true, write true. If it is false, change the underlined word or words to make the statement true.

6. The photoelectric effect is evidence that light can act as a <u>particle</u>.
7. <u>Ultraviolet</u> rays can be felt as heat.
8. Fluorescent lights give off most of their energy as <u>infrared rays</u>.
9. A radio station is identified by the <u>amplitude</u> at which it broadcasts.
10. Radio and television transmitters can be placed on <u>satellites</u> and sent into orbit.

Checking Concepts
11. How do you know that electromagnetic waves can travel through a vacuum?
12. How does polarization show that light can act as a wave?
13. How is the Doppler effect used to find the speeds of moving objects?
14. Explain the difference between cellular telephones and cordless telephones.
15. A person lost in the woods at night may signal for help by turning a flashlight on and off according to a code known as Morse code. This is actually a modulated signal. Is it AM or FM? Explain your answer.
16. **Writing to Learn** Develop an advertising campaign to sell fluorescent lights. Your ad should describe two advantages of fluorescent lights over incandescent lights. Be sure to include a catchy slogan.

Thinking Critically
17. **Applying Concepts** What important information can be gathered from a thermogram of a house? How could this information be used to help save energy?
18. **Relating Cause and Effect** The waves of the electromagnetic spectrum that have the greatest frequency are also the most penetrating and can cause the most harm. Explain.
19. **Classifying** List five examples of luminous objects and five examples of illuminated objects.
20. **Problem Solving** Suppose you are building an incubator for young chicks and need a source of heat. What type of light bulbs would you use? Explain.
21. **Comparing and Contrasting** Make a table to compare the different types of wireless communication. Include headings such as: type of information transmitted; distance over which signal can be transmitted; one-way or two-way communication.

---

21. Tables will vary but should include the type of information transmitted, the distance range of the signals, and whether the communication is one way or two way.

Applying Skills
22. Longest—KLIZ, 580 kHz; shortest—KMOM, 103.7 MHz
23. KLIZ and WDAD are AM stations, KMOM and WJFO are FM stations.
24. KLIZ, because it is AM

Applying Skills

The table below gives information about four radio stations. Use the table to answer Questions 22–24.

Call letters	Frequency
KLIZ	580 kHz
KMOM	103.7 MHz
WDAD	1030 kHz
WJFO	89.7 MHz

22. Interpreting Data Which radio station broadcasts at the longest wavelength? The shortest wavelength?

23. Classifying Which radio stations are AM? Which are FM?

24. Predicting You are going on a car trip across the United States. Which station would you expect to receive for the greater distance: KLIZ or KMOM?

Project Wrap Up Now you are ready to present your findings to your classmates. You could mount your graphs on posterboard. Alternatively, you could put your graphs on transparencies and use an overhead projector to show the results of your survey. You could also use a computer to create a slide show.

Reflect and Record What in your results was most surprising? How could you have done a better job of collecting your data? Has this project given you a better understanding of the usage of the various devices? Think about the world 25 years from now. Predict the types of devices that will be used in the future.

Test Preparation

Use these questions to prepare for standardized tests.

Use the diagram to answer Questions 25–29.

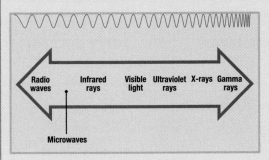

Radio waves · Infrared rays · Visible light · Ultraviolet rays · X-rays · Gamma rays

Microwaves

25. Low-frequency waves have
 a. short wavelengths and high energy.
 b. long wavelengths and low energy.
 c. short wavelengths and low energy.
 d. long wavelengths and high energy.

26. Which waves have the lowest frequency?
 a. radio waves **b.** infrared rays
 c. visible light **d.** gamma rays

27. Which waves have the shortest wavelength?
 a. radio waves **b.** infrared rays
 c. visible light **d.** gamma rays

28. Microwaves are a type of
 a. radio waves. **b.** visible light.
 c. X-rays. **d.** ultraviolet rays.

29. Waves with higher frequencies have higher energies. Which rays have the highest energy?
 a. ultraviolet rays **b.** visible light
 c. gamma rays **d.** microwaves

Project Wrap Up Students may present their findings by using overhead transparencies, creating slide shows or multi-media presentations on the computer, or by placing their graphs on poster board to present to their class-mates. Graphs should be accompanied by written analyses. For example, students' written analyses could include answers to the following questions: Which type of device was used the most? The least? What made one type more popular than another? Was there a significant difference in types of devices used by different age groups? Their presentations should also include a description of how the data was collected, sorted, and analyzed.

Reflect and Record Encourage students to identify new devices or features that would be helpful to certain groups of people. Have students compare the methods they used to methods used for market research to develop new products. Students should use this information to predict what devices will be used in the future.

Test Preparation

25. b **26.** a **27.** d **28.** a **29.** c

Program Resources

- ◆ **Inquiry Skills Activity Book** Provides teaching and review of all inquiry skills
- ◆ **Standardized Test Preparation Book** Provides standardized test practice
- ◆ **Reading in the Content Area** Provides strategies to improve science reading skills
- ◆ **Teacher's ELL Handbook** Provides multiple strategies for English language learners

Sections	Time	Student Edition Activities	Other Activities	
CHAPTER PROJECT 4 **What a Sight!** p. 0111	Ongoing (3 weeks)	Check Your Progress, pp. 0116, 0127, 0142 Project Wrap Up, p. 0145	TE	Chapter 4 Project Notes, pp. 0110–111
1 Reflection and Mirrors pp. 0112–116 ◆ 4.1.1 Describe what happens when light strikes opaque, transparent, and translucent objects. ◆ 4.1.2 Identify the ways in which images can be reflected.	$2\frac{1}{2}$ periods/ 1–2 blocks	**Discover** How Does Your Reflection Wink?, p. 0112 **Sharpen Your Skills** Classifying, p. 0114	TE TE TE ISLM	Building Inquiry Skills: Classifying, p. 0113 Inquiry Challenge, p. 0114 Demonstration, p. 0115 0-4, "Plane-Mirror Images"
2 Refraction and Lenses pp. 0117–122 ◆ 4.2.1 Explain refraction. ◆ 4.2.2 Describe how a lens forms an image and distinguish between concave and convex lenses.	3 periods/ $1\frac{1}{2}$ blocks	**Discover** How Can You Make an Image Appear on a Sheet of Paper?, p. 0117 **Try This** Disappearing Glass, p. 0118 **Science at Home** p. 0121 **Skills Lab: Controlling Variables** Looking at Images, p. 0122	TE TE TE	Including All Students, p. 0118 Building Inquiry Skills: Observing, p. 0119 Including All Students, p. 0120
3 Color pp. 0123–128 ◆ 4.3.1 Identify the factors that determine the color of an object. ◆ 4.3.2 Explain and compare how colors are combined in light and in pigments.	3 periods/ $1\frac{1}{2}$ blocks	**Discover** How Do Colors Mix?, p. 0123 **Sharpen Your Skills** Developing Hypotheses, p. 0125 **Real-World Lab: How It Works** Changing Colors, p. 0128	TE TE TE	Building Inquiry Skills: Making Models, p. 0124 Inquiry Challenge, p. 0126 Demonstration, p. 0127
4 *INTEGRATING LIFE SCIENCE* **Seeing Light** pp. 0129–132 ◆ 4.4.1 Describe how light waves are sensed and interpreted as images by humans. ◆ 4.4.2 Identify types of vision problems and kinds of lenses that can be used to correct the problems.	2 periods/ 1 block	**Discover** Can You See Everything With One Eye?, p. 0129 **Try This** True Colors, p. 0131 **Science at Home** p. 0132	TE TE TE	Building Inquiry Skills: Observing, p. 0130 Building Inquiry Skills: Observing, p. 0131 Demonstration, p. 0132
5 Using Light pp. 0133–142 ◆ 4.5.1 Explain how telescopes, cameras, and microscopes use light. ◆ 4.5.2 Describe the differences between laser light and ordinary light and list uses of lasers. ◆ 4.5.3 Identify and cite uses for optical fibers.	5 periods/ $2\frac{1}{2}$ blocks	**Discover** How Does a Pinhole Viewer Work?, p. 0133 **Try This** What a View! p. 0134	TE TE TE TE TE	Building Inquiry Skills: Observing, pp. 0135, 0140, 0141 Including All Students, p. 0136 Demonstration, p. 0137 Music Connection, p. 0139 Demonstration, p. 0140
Study Guide/Assessment pp. 0143–145	1 period/ $\frac{1}{2}$ block		ISAB	Provides teaching and review of all inquiry skills

 For Standard or Block Schedule The Resource Pro® CD-ROM gives you maximum flexibility for planning your instruction for any type of schedule. Resource Pro® contains Planning Express®, an advanced scheduling program, as well as the entire contents of the Teaching Resources and the Computer Test Bank.

Key: **SE** Student Edition
PLM Probeware Lab Manual
ISAB Inquiry Skills Activity Book

CHAPTER PLANNING GUIDE

Program Resources	Assessment Strategies	Media and Technology
TR Chapter 4 Project Teacher Notes, pp. 094–95 **TR** Chapter 4 Project Overview and Worksheets, pp. 096–99	**TE** Check Your Progress, pp. 0116, 0127, 0142 **TE** Perf. Assessment: Project Wrap Up, p. 0145 **TR** Chapter 4 Project Scoring Rubric, p. 0100	Science Explorer Internet Site Audio CDs and Audiotapes, English-Spanish Section Summaries
TR 4-1 Lesson Plan, p. 0101 **TR** 4-1 Section Summary, p. 0102 **TR** 4-1 Review and Reinforce, p. 0103 **TR** 4-1 Enrich, p. 0104	**SE** Section 1 Review, p. 0116 **TE** Ongoing Assessment, pp. 0113, 0115 **TE** Performance Assessment, p. 0116	Exploring Physical Science Videodisc, Unit 6 Side 1, "The Dark Tomb" Transparency 15, "Concave and Convex Mirrors"
TR 4-2 Lesson Plan, p. 0105 **TR** 4-2 Section Summary, p. 0106 **TR** 4-2 Review and Reinforce, p. 0107 **TR** 4-2 Enrich, p. 0108 **TR** Skills Lab blackline masters, pp. 0121–123 **SES** Book I, *Weather and Climate,* Chapter 2	**SE** Section 2 Review, p. 0121 **SE** Analyze and Conclude, p. 0122 **TE** Ongoing Assessment, p. 0119 **TE** Performance Assessment, p. 0121	Lab Activity Videotape, *Sound and Light,* 7 Transparencies 16, "Concave Lens"; 17, "Convex Lens"
TR 4-3 Lesson Plan, p. 0109 **TR** 4-3 Section Summary, p. 0110 **TR** 4-3 Review and Reinforce, p. 0111 **TR** 4-3 Enrich, p. 0112 **TR** Real-World Lab blackline masters, pp. 0124–125	**SE** Section 3 Review, p. 0127 **SE** Analyze and Conclude, p. 0128 **TE** Ongoing Assessment, p. 0125 **TE** Performance Assessment, p. 0127	Lab Activity Videotape, *Sound and Light,* 8 Exploring Physical Science Videodisc, Unit 6 Side 1, "Why Is the Sky Blue?" Transparency 18, "The Primary Colors of Light and Pigment"
TR 4-4 Lesson Plan, p. 0113 **TR** 4-4 Section Summary, p. 0114 **TR** 4-4 Review and Reinforce, p. 0115 **TR** 4-4 Enrich, p. 0116 **SES** Book D, *Human Biology and Health,* Chapter 7	**SE** Section 4 Review, p. 0132 **TE** Ongoing Assessment, p. 0131 **TE** Performance Assessment, p. 0132	Transparency 19, "The Eye"
TR 4-5 Lesson Plan, p. 0117 **TR** 4-5 Section Summary, p. 0118 **TR** 4-5 Review and Reinforce, p. 0119 **TR** 4-5 Enrich, p. 0120 **SES** Book D, *Human Biology and Health,* Chapter 7	**SE** Section 5 Review, p. 0142 **TE** Ongoing Assessment, pp. 0135, 0137, 0139, 0141 **TE** Performance Assessment, p. 0142	Exploring Physical Science Videodisc, Unit 6 Side 2, "The Nova Laser" Transparency 20, "Camera"
GSW Provides worksheets to promote student comprehension of content **RCA** Provides strategies to improve science reading skills **ELL** Provides multiple strategies for English language learners	**SE** Study Guide/Assessment, pp. 0143–145 **TR** Performance Assessment, pp. 0159–161 **TR** Chapter 4 Test, pp. 0162–165 **TR** Book Test, pp. 0166–169 **CTB** *Sound and Light,* Chapter 4 Test **STP** Provides standardized test practice	Computer Test Bank, *Sound and Light,* Chapter 4 Test Interactive Student Tutorial CD-ROM, O-4

TE Teacher's Edition
RCA Reading in the Content Area
GSW Guided Study Workbook

TR Teaching Resources
ISLM Integrated Science Laboratory Manual
ELL Teacher's ELL Handbook

CTB Computer Test Bank
STP Standardized Test Preparation Book
SES Science Explorer Series Text

Meeting the National Science Education Standards and AAAS Benchmarks

National Science Education Standards	Benchmarks for Science Literacy	Unifying Themes

Science as Inquiry (Content Standard A)

◆ **Design and conduct a scientific investigation** Students investigate how distance between an object and a convex lens affects the image of the object. *(Skills Lab)*

Physical Science (Content Standard B)

◆ **Transfer of energy** Light can be transmitted, scattered, or absorbed by objects. *(Section 1; Chapter Project)* Objects appear colored when they reflect certain wavelengths of light. *(Section 3; Real-World Lab)* The retina sends signals to the brain that allow us to interpret the images that we see. *(Section 4)*

Life Science (Content Standard C)

◆ **Structure and function in living systems** In the human eye, the cornea refracts light, the iris opens to allow light into the eye, the lens refracts light, and the retina contains light-sensitive cells that send signals to the brain. *(Section 4)*

Science and Technology (Content Standard E)

◆ **Design a solution or a product.** Students design and build an optical device. *(Chapter Project)*

Science in Personal and Social Perspectives (Content Standard F)

◆ **Science and technology in society** Cameras, lasers, and optical fibers are technological devices that use light. *(Section 5)*

1A The Scientific World View Optical systems have undergone tremendous changes as scientists have discovered more about the properties of light. *(Section 5)*

3A Technology and Science Uses for light include viewing objects in space, seeing microscopic objects, laser technologies, and communication via optical fibers. *(Section 5)* Students apply their understanding of how light works to build an optical device. *(Chapter Project)*

4F Motion Light waves can be transmitted, reflected, or refracted by objects. *(Sections 1, 2; Chapter Project)* Visible light is made up of different frequencies of colored light. *(Section 3; Real-World Lab)* The human eye forms images from electromagnetic waves in the visible light spectrum. *(Section 4)*

5C Cells The human eye is a specialized organ for sight; it focuses images and sends signals to the brain about what those images are. *(Section 4)*

8D Communication Wireless devices, including radios, televisions, pagers, cellular telephone systems, radar devices, and satellite connections transmit electronic signals that are used for communication. *(Sections 2, 4; Skills Lab)*

◆ **Patterns of Change** When light strikes a surface, it can be transmitted, absorbed, or reflected. If it is transmitted, the path of the light wave may be bent. *(Sections 1, 2, 3; Skills Lab)*

◆ **Scale and Structure** Light passes through the cornea, iris, and lens before it is focused onto the retina of the human eye. *(Section 4)* By controlling the wavelengths of light in a tube, a laser beam can be produced. *(Section 5)*

◆ **Unity and Diversity** All colors of the visible spectrum are combined to form white light. Colored objects absorb some colors and reflect or transmit others. When light is transmitted, the path of different colors of light are bent by different amounts, so the light is separated into its colors. *(Sections 2, 3; Real-World Lab)*

◆ **Systems and Interactions** When light strikes a plane mirror, it is reflected and forms a virtual image. When it strikes a concave mirror, it can form a virtual or real image. *(Section 1)* When light changes mediums, it refracts. Convex lenses form real images. *(Section 2; Skills Lab)* Objects appear to be the color of light that they reflect. The primary colors of light combine to form white light; the primary colors of pigment combine to form black. *(Section 3; Real-World Lab)* Light can be used to form images of distant or tiny objects and to take photographs. *(Section 4; Chapter Project)*

ACTIVITY	Time (minutes)	Materials *Quantities for one work group*	Skills
Section 1			
Discover, p. 112	10	**Consumable** tape **Nonconsumable** 2 plane mirrors	Observing
Sharpen Your Skills, p. 114	10	**Nonconsumable** shiny metal spoon	Classifying
Section 2			
Discover, p. 117	10	**Nonconsumable** hand lens, white paper	Observing
Try This, p. 118	15	**Consumable** water, vegetable oil **Nonconsumable** small drinking glass, large drinking glass	Inferring
Science at Home, p. 121	home	**Consumable** water **Nonconsumable** pencil, drinking glass	Observing
Skills Lab, p. 122	45	**Consumable** tape, cardboard stand, blank sheet of paper **Nonconsumable** convex lens, light bulb and socket, clay, battery and wires, meter stick	Controlling Variables
Section 3			
Discover, p. 123	15	**Consumable** white cardboard **Nonconsumable** crayons or markers, 1 m string, compass	Observing
Sharpen Your Skills, p. 125	15	**Consumable** white cardboard **Nonconsumable** colored pencils or markers, string, compass	Developing Hypotheses
Real-World Lab, p. 128	45	**Consumable** shoe box, removable tape **Nonconsumable** flashlight; scissors; red object; yellow object; blue object; red, green, and blue cellophane	Observing, Predicting, Inferring
Section 4			
Discover, p. 129	5	**Consumable** white paper **Nonconsumable** pencil	Posing Questions
Try This, p. 131	10	**Nonconsumable** white paper	Observing
Science at Home, p. 132	home	**Consumable** sheet of blank paper	Observing
Section 5			
Discover, p. 133	15	**Consumable** paper cup, rubber band, wax paper **Nonconsumable** pin	Classifying
Try This, p. 134	10	**Nonconsumable** 2 hand lenses of different strengths	Classifying

A list of all materials required for the Student Edition activities can be found beginning on page T15. You can obtain information about ordering materials by calling 1-800-848-9500 or by accessing the Science Explorer Internet site at: **www.phschool.com**

What a Sight!

Mirrors and lenses can be used in different combinations to produce a variety of optical effects.

Purpose In this project, students construct an optical instrument using concepts they learn in the chapter.

Skills Focus After completing the Chapter 4 Project, students will be able to

◆ pose questions about how the reflection and refraction of light affect the image they see;

◆ experiment with refraction and reflection as they control variables such as the distances between lenses;

◆ communicate their descriptions of the design and use of their optical instruments to their classmates.

Project Time Line This project will take approximately four weeks to complete. During the first week, students should experiment with reflection by studying how such materials as mirrors, windows, liquid-filled containers, and computer screens affect light. The second week will involve experimentation with refraction using different lenses. By the third week, students should be comfortable with both reflection and refraction and should be able to design, construct, and modify their optical instruments. Class presentations should be scheduled for the fourth week. Before beginning the project, see Chapter 4 Project Teacher Notes on pages 94–95 in Teaching Resources for more details on carrying out the project. Also distribute to students the Chapter 4 Project Overview, Worksheets, and Scoring Rubric on pages 96–100 in Teaching Resources.

Possible Materials Provide a wide variety of materials from which students can choose. Miscellaneous items they will need include tape, clay, filters (colored cellophane works well), cardboard tubes, flashlights, shoe boxes, protractors, rulers, and meter sticks. Some optical components will be required and can be purchased from a scientific supply house.

◆ convex and concave lenses
◆ plane mirrors
◆ concave mirrors

CHAPTER 4 Light

This kaleidoscope image is formed by two mirrors at right angles. Light reflected from colored objects between the mirrors is reflected again to form a repeated pattern.

WEB ACTIVITY www.phschool.com

SECTION 1 Reflection and Mirrors

Discover **How Does Your Reflection Wink?**
Sharpen Your Skills **Classifying**

SECTION 2 Refraction and Lenses

Discover **How Can You Make an Image Appear on a Sheet of Paper?**
Try This **Disappearing Glass**
Skills Lab **Looking at Images**

SECTION 3 Color

Discover **How Do Colors Mix?**
Sharpen Your Skills **Developing Hypotheses**
Real-World Lab **Changing Colors**

◆ convex mirrors
◆ optical bench or meter stick; optical bench kit

Launching the Project To introduce the project and to stimulate student interest, set up an example telescope using two lenses, a cardboard tube, and tape. Each lens should be securely taped to one end of the cardboard tube. The distance between the two lenses must equal the sum of the focal length of both lenses or the telescope may not work properly. Alternatively, you may cut the cardboard in half crosswise and slide one half inside the other so

the distance between the two lenses can be adjusted.

Allow time for students to read the description of the project in their text and the Chapter Project Overview. Then encourage discussions on the various types of optical devices that could be constructed and the materials that could be used. Answer any initial questions students may have and allow students to review the Chapter 4 Project Worksheets.

Allow time in class for students to experiment with the reflection and refraction

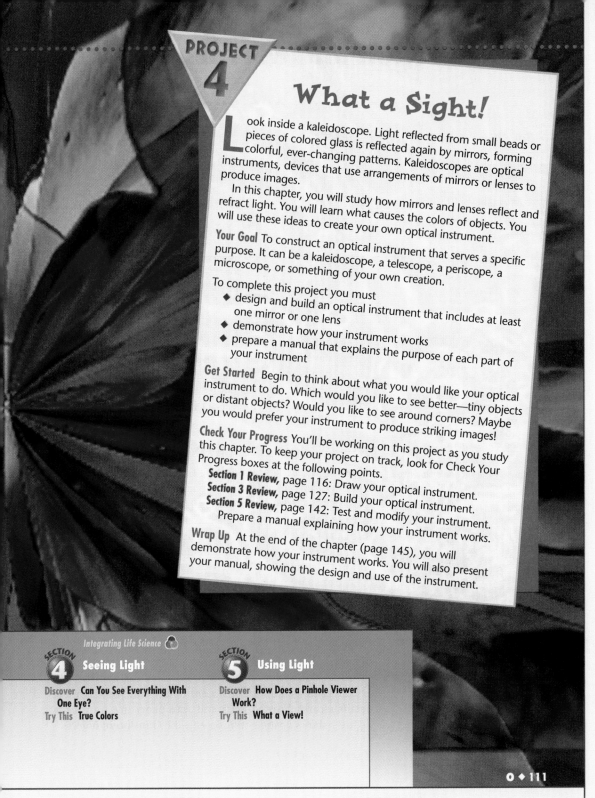

What a Sight!

Look inside a kaleidoscope. Light reflected from small beads or pieces of colored glass is reflected again by mirrors, forming colorful, ever-changing patterns. Kaleidoscopes are optical instruments, devices that use arrangements of mirrors or lenses to produce images.

In this chapter, you will study how mirrors and lenses reflect and refract light. You will learn what causes the colors of objects. You will use these ideas to create your own optical instrument.

Your Goal To construct an optical instrument that serves a specific purpose. It can be a kaleidoscope, a telescope, a periscope, a microscope, or something of your own creation.

To complete this project you must
- design and build an optical instrument that includes at least one mirror or one lens
- demonstrate how your instrument works
- prepare a manual that explains the purpose of each part of your instrument

Get Started Begin to think about what you would like your optical instrument to do. Which would you like to see better—tiny objects or distant objects? Would you like to see around corners? Maybe you would prefer your instrument to produce striking images!

Check Your Progress You'll be working on this project as you study this chapter. To keep your project on track, look for Check Your Progress boxes at the following points.

Section 1 Review, page 116: Draw your optical instrument.
Section 3 Review, page 127: Build your optical instrument.
Section 5 Review, page 142: Test and modify your instrument. Prepare a manual explaining how your instrument works.

Wrap Up At the end of the chapter (page 145), you will demonstrate how your instrument works. You will also present your manual, showing the design and use of the instrument.

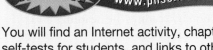

Integrating Life Science

4 Seeing Light

Discover **Can You See Everything With One Eye?**
Try This **True Colors**

5 Using Light

Discover **How Does a Pinhole Viewer Work?**
Try This **What a View!**

O ◆ 111

Program Resources

- **Teaching Resources** Chapter 4 Project Teacher Notes, pp. 94–95; Chapter 4 Project Overview and Worksheets, pp. 96–99; Chapter 4 Project Scoring Rubric, p. 100

Media and Technology

 Audio CDs and **Audiotapes** English-Spanish Section Summaries

WEB ACTIVITY www.phschool.com

You will find an Internet activity, chapter self-tests for students, and links to other chapter topics at this site.

of light before they design their optical instruments. You might want to demonstrate sample microscopes and periscopes. The microscope design would be similar to the telescope except that the distance between the lenses is greater than the sum of the focal lengths of the lenses. A periscope uses two mirrors and a cardboard tube with two windows cut in the side, one at the top and one in the bottom. The mirrors must be angled so that light entering through one window will exit through the other window. Make sure students experiment with their instruments and make necessary modifications prior to the class presentations.

Performance Assessment

The Chapter 4 Project Scoring Rubric on page 100 of Teaching Resources will help you evaluate how well students complete the Chapter 4 Project. Students will be assessed on
- how well they demonstrate their knowledge of reflection and refraction by constructing working optical instruments;
- how well they apply chapter concepts to the design, construction, and modification of their instruments;
- the thoroughness and organization of their presentations;
- the organization of their written manuals, including descriptions of all instrument parts.

By sharing the Chapter 4 Scoring Rubric with students at the beginning of the project, you will make it clear to them what they are expected to do.

O ◆ 111

Objectives

After completing the lesson, students will be able to

◆ describe what happens when light strikes opaque, transparent, and translucent objects;

◆ identify the ways in which images can be reflected.

Key Terms opaque, transparent, translucent, rays, regular reflection, diffuse reflection, image, plane mirror, virtual image, concave mirror, focal point, real image, convex mirror

1 Engage/Explore

Activating Prior Knowledge

Ask students to explain how the locations of the mirrors in a car, large truck, or bus help the driver. *(The rear-view and side mirrors allow drivers to see what is happening directly behind them. Large trucks usually have large, tilted mirrors on the side, and buses often have a mirror that allows the driver to see the passengers.)*

········· DISCOVER ·········

Skills Focus observing

Materials *2 plane mirrors, tape*

Time 10 minutes

Tips Use hand mirrors or cosmetic mirrors. Tape any sharp edges and caution students not to touch them.

Expected Outcome When the student looks into one mirror and winks the right eye, the left eye of the reflection winks. When the student looks into both mirrors and winks, the reflection's right eye winks.

Think It Over The reflection winks the opposite eye. The second reflection is a reflection of the first image, so it winks the same eye as the student.

SECTION
1 Reflection and Mirrors

DISCOVER •••••••••••••••••••••••••••••••••••••• ACTIVITY ••••

How Does Your Reflection Wink?

1. Look at your face in a mirror. Wink your right eye. Which eye does your reflection wink?

2. Tape two mirrors together so that they open and close like a book. Open them so they form a 90° angle with each other. **CAUTION:** *Be careful of any sharp edges.*

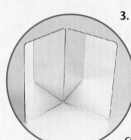

3. Looking into both mirrors at once, wink at your reflection again. Which eye does your reflection wink now?

Think It Over
Observing How does your reflection wink at you? How does the second reflection compare with the first reflection?

GUIDE FOR READING

◆ What happens when light strikes an object?

◆ What are the two kinds of reflection?

◆ What types of images are produced by plane, concave, and convex mirrors?

Reading Tip Before you read, preview the section and write down any new terms. As you read, find the meaning of each term.

◄ Glare on a window

Have you ever looked at a store window on a bright, sunny day? In order to see inside, you may have used your hands to block the glare. The glare is actually reflected light. The glare from the store window shows that glass can reflect light. But if you look at a clear glass window with no glare, you can see right through it.

When Light Strikes an Object

When light strikes an object, the light can be reflected, absorbed, or transmitted. Most objects reflect or absorb light. A material that reflects or absorbs all of the light that strikes it is **opaque** (oh PAYK). Most objects are opaque. You cannot see through opaque objects because light cannot pass through them. Examples of opaque materials include wood, metal, and cotton and wool fabrics.

A **transparent** material transmits light. When light strikes a transparent object, it passes right through, allowing you to see what is on the other side. Clear glass, water, and air are examples of transparent materials.

Other materials allow some light to pass through. This type of material is translucent. **Translucent** (trans LOO sunt) materials scatter light as it passes through. You can usually tell that there is something behind a translucent object, but you cannot see details clearly. Frosted glass and wax paper are translucent. Figure 1 shows opaque, transparent, and translucent objects.

READING STRATEGIES

Reading Tip Have students preview the section by reading the headings and subheadings and viewing the pictures and captions. Then instruct them to write all the new terms on a sheet of paper, leaving spaces between each term. As students read, have them take notes, using examples from the text to define the terms.

Study and Comprehension Have students write brief summaries of the information under each heading. Remind students to include only main ideas and key details in their summaries. Call on volunteers to read their summaries aloud. Students can use their summaries as study guides for the section.

Figure 1 The spools of thread are opaque. They reflect light of various colors. The pitcher and glass are transparent. They transmit light, allowing you to see the milk inside. The leaf is translucent. The frog can be seen through the leaf but lacks detail.

Kinds of Reflection

When you look at some objects, such as a shiny metal fixture or a mirror, you can see yourself. But when you look at other objects, such as a book, a wooden table, or your pencil, you see only the object itself. **You can see most objects because light reflects, or bounces, off them.** What you see when you look at an object depends on how its surface reflects light.

Regular Reflection To show how light travels and reflects, you can represent light waves as straight lines called **rays.** Light rays reflect from a surface according to the law of reflection: the angle of reflection equals the angle of incidence.

Regular reflection occurs when parallel rays of light hit a smooth surface. All the rays are reflected at the same angle. For example, if you look at a sheet of shiny metal, you can see your own reflection. The light rays coming from you strike the smooth surface and are reflected regularly.

Diffuse Reflection When parallel rays of light hit a bumpy, or uneven, surface, **diffuse reflection** occurs. Each ray obeys the law of reflection. But since each ray hits the surface at a different angle, the rays are reflected at different angles. Because the reflected rays travel in all directions, diffuse reflection allows you to see an object from any position.

Most objects reflect light diffusely. This is because most objects do not have smooth surfaces. Even surfaces that appear to be smooth, such as a freshly painted wall, have small bumps that scatter light. If you look at a wall through a magnifying glass, you will see that the surface is not really smooth.

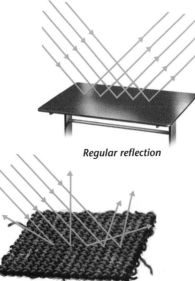

Regular reflection

Diffuse reflection

Figure 2 When light strikes a surface at an angle, it is reflected at the same angle. If the surface is smooth, the reflection is regular (top). If the surface is uneven, the reflection is diffuse (bottom).

Program Resources

◆ **Teaching Resources** 4-1 Lesson Plan, p. 101; 4-1 Section Summary, p. 102
◆ **Integrated Science Laboratory Manual** O-4, "Plane-Mirror Images"
◆ **Guided Study Workbook** Section 4-1

2 Facilitate

When Light Strikes an Object

Language Arts Connection

Explain that the prefix *trans-* means "to cross, or move through." Direct students to find the root meanings for *-lucent (To shine)* and *-parent (To appear, to see).* Then ask: **How can you combine the root meanings to recall the scientific definitions of these terms?** *(Light shines through translucent materials. You can see through a transparent object.)* **learning modality: verbal**

Building Inquiry Skills: Classifying

Materials *piece of tissue or rice paper, light source*
Time 5 minutes

Have students classify classroom objects as opaque, transparent, or translucent. Then hold the tissue or rice paper up to the light, and ask: **Which group does this belong to? Why?** *(Translucent; it allows some light through.)* **limited English proficiency**

Kinds of Reflection

Using the Visuals: Figure 2

For each light ray, have students identify the angle of incidence and the angle of reflection. *(Incidence—the angle between the incoming ray and the surface; reflection—the angle between the reflected ray and the surface)* Ask: **Why are the reflected rays going in different directions in the bottom diagram?** *(Because the surface is uneven, the rays hit the surface at different angles and are therefore reflected at different angles.)* **learning modality: visual**

Ongoing Assessment

Oral Presentation Ask students to describe what happens when light strikes different objects.

O ◆ 113

Mirrors

Classifying

Materials *shiny metal spoon*

Time 10 minutes

Tips Have students hold the spoon at a constant angle and move it farther away as they observe the images.

Answers The back of the spoon is a convex mirror, so the image is upright, smaller, and behind the mirror. The front is a concave mirror, so the image changes from upright to inverted as students vary the distance.

Extend Challenge students to produce a real image using the spoon. *(Real images are inverted and can be produced using the front of the spoon.)*

Building Inquiry Skills: Applying Concepts

Ask students: **Why would a room with a plane mirror covering one wall appear to be twice as large?** *(The images in the mirror would appear the same distance behind the mirror as the reflected objects were in front of the mirror.)* **learning modality: logical/mathematical**

Inquiry Challenge

Materials *concave mirror, white paper, flashlight, meter stick*

Time 25 minutes

Challenge small groups of students to produce real images of the flashlight bulb on the paper. Have them study the arrangements in Figure 5 to determine where to place the mirror, the flashlight, and the paper. Caution students to be careful with the mirrors, and not to shine the light in anyone's eyes. *(One student should hold the mirror while another student moves the flashlight away from the mirror. They will be able to identify the focal point as the location of the flashlight beyond which the image becomes inverted and real. Students should be able to locate the position at which the image of the flashlight bulb will appear on the paper. The meter stick may be used to measure the distances.)* **cooperative learning**

Sharpen your Skills

Classifying ACTIVITY
Look at the back of a shiny spoon. What kind of image do you see? How does changing the distance between your eyes and the spoon affect what you see? What kind of mirror does the back of the spoon represent? Now look at the front of the spoon. What kind of mirror is the front of the spoon? What kind of image do you see?

Mirrors

Did you look in a mirror this morning? Maybe you combed your hair or brushed your teeth in front of a mirror. A mirror is a sheet of glass that has a smooth, silver-colored coating on one side. When light passes through the glass, the coating on the back reflects the light regularly, allowing you to see an image. An **image** is a copy of an object formed by reflected or refracted rays of light.

Mirrors can be flat or curved. The shape of the surface determines how the image will look. Depending on the shape of the mirror, the image can be the same size as the object, or it can be larger or smaller.

Plane Mirrors Look into a flat mirror, or **plane mirror.** You will see an image that is the same size as you are. Your image will seem to be the same distance behind the mirror as you are in front of it. **A plane mirror produces an image that is right-side up and the same size as the object being reflected.**

The image you see when you look in a plane mirror is a virtual image. **Virtual images** are right-side up, or upright. "Virtual" describes something that you can see, but does not really exist. You can't reach behind a mirror and touch your image.

Why do you see a virtual image? Figure 3 shows how the image of the dancer is formed by a plane mirror. Light rays reflected from the dancer travel out in all directions. They strike the mirror and are reflected toward the eye. Even though the rays are reflected, the brain treats them as if they had come from behind the mirror. The dashed lines show the points from which the light rays appear to come. Since the light appears to come from behind the mirror, this is where the dancer's image appears to be located.

☑ *Checkpoint* What is a virtual image?

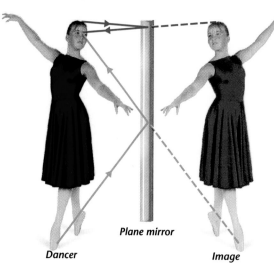

Plane mirror

Dancer   *Image*

Figure 3 A plane mirror forms a virtual image. When the dancer looks in the mirror, the rays of light reflected from her body are reflected back toward her. The rays appear to come from behind the mirror, where the image is formed.

Background

History of Science The study of mirrors and the reflection of light is quite ancient. Archimedes, the Greek scholar who lived over 2,000 years ago, was fascinated by *catoptrics*, the study of reflected light from mirrors. According to legend, Archimedes burned down the invading Roman ships by focusing light rays onto their sails with curved mirrors.

Curved mirrors greatly improved the effectiveness of lighthouses. In 1777, an Englishman, William Hutchinson, produced the first set of practical lighthouse mirrors, using small pieces of mirrored glass set in a curved piece of plaster. The mirrors increased the brightness of the light almost 400 times, but they had to be continually rotated so that the light could be seen from all directions. This produced the familiar "flashing" lighthouse beam.

Concave Mirrors A mirror with a surface that curves inward like the inside of a bowl is a **concave mirror.** Figure 4 shows how a concave mirror can reflect parallel rays of light so that they meet at a point. The point at which the rays meet is called the **focal point.**

Concave mirrors can form either virtual images or real images. The type of image formed by a concave mirror depends on the position of the object in relation to the focal point. Figure 5 shows how concave mirrors form images. If the object is farther away from the mirror than the focal point, the reflected rays form a real image. A **real image** is formed when rays actually meet at a point. Real images are upside down, or inverted. A real image may be larger or smaller than the object. If the object is between the focal point and the mirror, the image appears to be behind the mirror and is right-side up. Then it is a virtual image.

Some concave mirrors are used to project rays of light. For example, a car headlight has a bulb at the focal point of a concave mirror. When the light from the bulb spreads out and hits the mirror, the rays are reflected parallel to each other. This projects the light on the road ahead. Concave mirrors are also used to produce magnified images, as in makeup mirrors.

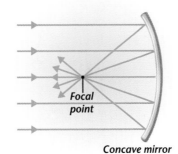

Figure 4 This concave mirror reflects parallel rays of light back through the focal point.

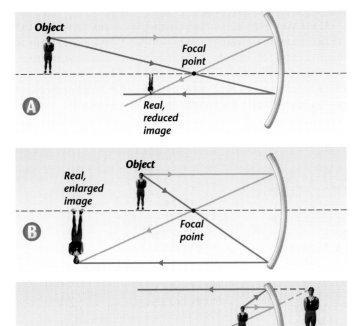

A Real, reduced image

B Real, enlarged image

C Focal point   Object   Virtual, enlarged image

Figure 5 The type of image formed by a concave mirror depends on the position of the object in relation to the focal point. **A,B.** If the object is farther from the mirror than the focal point, the image is real and inverted. **C.** If the object is between the mirror and the focal point, the image is virtual and upright. *Interpreting Diagrams How can you tell that the images in A and B are real?*

Materials *large, round bowl; water-filled squirt toy, paper towels*
Time 10 minutes

Ask students to predict what will happen to the stream of water if you spray it into the bowl, aiming directly at the center of the bottom. *(The water will bounce straight up into the center of the bowl.)* Have students observe what happens. Dry the bowl and have them predict what will happen if you aim at other locations inside the bowl. Demonstrate. *(Students should recognize that no matter where the stream is aimed, the water bounces back toward the center of the bowl.)* Have students infer what happens to light rays when they strike the concave surface of a mirror. *(The light rays bounce toward the mirror's focal point.)* **learning modality: kinesthetic**

Using the Visuals: Figure 5

Have students compare the three images formed by the concave mirror. Ask: **What two things do all real images have in common?** *(They are inverted, and they are formed when light rays meet at a point.)* Make sure students understand that real images are located on the same side of the mirror as the object. Point out that the reflected light rays do not always meet at the focal point. Have students trace the rays and identify the point at which the reflected rays meet. *(They meet at the point where the image is produced.)* Ask students to compare the real images to the virtual image. Ask: **How are virtual images different from real images?** *(Virtual images appear to come from behind the mirror, the image is upright, and the object comes between the mirror and the focal point.)* **learning modality: visual**

Answers to Self-Assessment

Caption Question

Figure 5 Because they are upside down and on the same side of the mirror as the object.

✓ *Checkpoint*

A virtual image is an image that is upright and appears to be behind the mirror.

Ongoing Assessment

Writing Have students describe how their images can change as they approach a plane mirror, a concave mirror, or a convex mirror.

3 Assess

Using the Visuals: Figure 6

Help students understand the statement that the image in a convex mirror looks farther away than the object. Point out that, although the image in the figure appears closer to the surface of the mirror than the object, it also appears much smaller. Ask: **How do we determine how far away something is?** *(By its size; distant objects look smaller than near objects.)* **learning modality: logical/mathematical**

Section 1 Review Answers

1. Sample: Transparent—glass, clear plastic, clear cellophane tape, eyeglass lenses; translucent—frosted glass, tracing paper, candle wax, wax paper; opaque—dark paper, cloth, rugs, books

2. In regular reflection, parallel light rays hit a smooth surface and are reflected at the same angle. In diffuse reflection, the rays hit an irregular surface. Because the rays hit the surface at different angles, they are reflected at different angles.

3. Plane mirror—virtual image; concave—real if the object is farther from the mirror than the focal point, virtual if the object is between the focal point and the mirror; convex—virtual

4. Sample: The image is real. The slide projector inverts the image from the slide; if the slide were placed right-side up in the projector, the image on the screen would appear upside down. Also, only a real image can be projected onto a screen.

....
CHAPTER
PROJECT
4

Check Your Progress

Encourage students to investigate the effects of different mirrors and lenses as they plan the materials they will need. Remind students to incorporate safety into their designs and to keep their instruments simple.

Performance Assessment

Writing Have students choose one type of mirror and explain how it forms images.

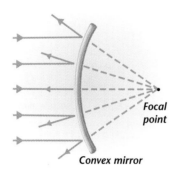

Focal point

Convex mirror

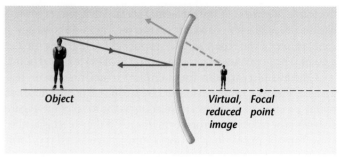

Object

Virtual, reduced image

Focal point

Figure 6 A convex mirror reflects parallel rays of light as though they came from the focal point behind the mirror. The image formed by a convex mirror is always virtual. *Applying Concepts What is a convex mirror?*

Convex Mirrors A mirror with a surface that curves outward is called a **convex mirror.** Figure 6 shows how some convex mirrors reflect parallel rays of light. The rays spread out but appear to come from a focal point behind the mirror. The focal point of a convex mirror is the point from which the rays appear to come. **Since the rays do not actually meet, images formed by convex mirrors are always virtual.**

Have you ever seen this warning on a rearview mirror? "Objects seen in the mirror are closer than they appear." Convex mirrors are used in cars as passenger-side rearview mirrors. Because a convex mirror spreads out rays of light, you can see a larger reflection area than you can with a plane mirror. Because you see more in the mirror, the images appear smaller and farther away than the objects themselves.

Section 1 Review

1. List four materials that are transparent, four that are translucent, and four that are opaque.

2. Describe two ways in which light can be reflected.

3. What types of images are produced by a plane mirror? A concave mirror? A convex mirror?

4. Thinking Critically Applying Concepts A slide projector projects an upright image onto a screen. The slides must be placed upside down in the projector. Is the image on the screen real or virtual? Give two reasons for your answer.

CHAPTER
PROJECT
4

Check Your Progress

Decide on the purpose of your optical instrument. How will you use it? Draw and label a sketch of the optical instrument you would like to build. Will you use mirrors, lenses, or a combination of both? Show how your instrument affects light rays that enter it. Gather the materials you will need to build your instrument.

Program Resources

◆ **Teaching Resources** 4-1 Review and Reinforce, p. 103; 4-1 Enrich, p. 104

Answers to Self-Assessment

Caption Question

Figure 6 A mirror with a surface that curves outward.

SECTION
Refraction and Lenses

DISCOVER

How Can You Make an Image Appear on a Sheet of Paper?

1. Hold a hand lens about 2 meters from a window. Look through the lens. What do you see? **CAUTION:** *Do not look at the sun.*

2. Move the lens farther away from your eye. What changes do you notice?

3. Now hold the lens between the window and a sheet of paper, but closer to the paper. Slowly move the lens away from the paper and toward the window. Keep watching the paper. What do you see? What happens as you move the lens?

Think It Over

Observing How do you think an image is formed on a sheet of paper? Describe the image. Is it real or virtual? How do you know?

A fish tank can play tricks on your eyes. If you look through the side, the fish seems closer than if you look over the top. If you look through the corner, you may see the same fish twice. You see one image of the fish through the front of the tank and another image through the side of the tank. The two images appear in different places!

Refraction of Light

As you look into a fish tank, you are seeing the light bend as it passes through three different mediums. The mediums are the water, the glass of the tank, and the air. As the light passes from one medium to the next, it refracts. **When light rays enter a new medium at an angle, the change in speed causes them to bend, or change direction.**

Refraction can cause you to see something that may not actually be there. For example, refraction can form a mirage. It can also cause a beautiful sight, a rainbow.

> **GUIDE FOR READING**
>
> ◆ What happens when light rays enter a medium at an angle?
>
> ◆ How do convex and concave lenses form images?
>
> *Reading Tip* As you read, draw diagrams to show how each type of lens refracts light.

Figure 7 There is only one fish in this tank, but the refraction of light makes it look as though there are two.

Chapter 4 **O ◆ 117**

Objectives

After completing the lesson, students will be able to
◆ explain refraction;
◆ describe how a lens forms an image and distinguish between concave and convex lenses.

Key Terms index of refraction, mirage, lens, concave lens, convex lens

1 Engage/Explore

Activating Prior Knowledge

Give students hand lenses and ask them what happens when they look through the lenses at the type in a book. *(The type looks bigger.)* Then ask: **Does the type itself get bigger or does something happen to the image of the type?** *(Something happens to the image of the type.)*

DISCOVER

Skills Focus observing
Materials *hand lens, white paper*
Time 10 minutes
Tips You may substitute a flashlight in place of sunlight from a window. Caution students never to look directly at the sun, even on a cloudy day. This activity will work best in a darkened room.
Expected Outcome Students should see an image of the window on the paper.
Think It Over The image is formed as the rays of light pass through the lens and onto the paper. The image is real. It is inverted and has been projected onto the paper.

---

2 Facilitate

Refraction of Light

Including All Students

Materials *wooden craft stick, large pan of water*
Time 5 minutes

Students who are visually impaired and those having difficulty mastering concepts can experience how a change of speed results from a change in medium. Have students grasp the craft stick between their thumb and index finger. Then have them rotate the stick so that the end travels from the air into a large pan of water. Ask: **What happened to the speed of the stick when it changed mediums?** *(It slowed down.)* Have students describe how this is similar to the way light behaves. *(When light moves from one medium to another, it changes speed.)* **learning modality: kinesthetic**

TRY THIS

Skills Focus inferring
Materials *small drinking glass, large drinking glass, water, vegetable oil*
Time 15 minutes
Tips Caution students to be careful handling wet or oily glasses. You may want to perform this as a demonstration.
Expected Outcome When the glasses are filled with oil, the small glass will be invisible.
Inferring Vegetable oil creates a different effect because it causes the light to refract at a different angle than water does.
Extend Tell students that the index of refraction of the oil is the same as the index of refraction of glass. Have them draw diagrams showing why this causes the glass to be invisible in oil. **learning modality: visual**

Disappearing Glass

Try this activity to see how different liquids refract light.

1. Place a small drinking glass inside a larger drinking glass. Can you see the small glass inside the larger one?
2. Fill both glasses with water. Look at the glasses from the side. Can you still see the smaller glass?
3. Empty and dry the glasses and refill them with vegetable oil. Describe what you see.

Inferring Why does the vegetable oil create an effect different from the water?

Figure 9 Passing white light through a prism causes the light to separate into its component colors. *Applying Concepts What determines the order in which the colors appear?*

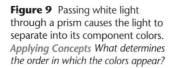

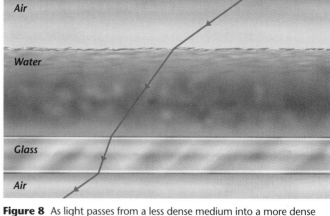

Figure 8 As light passes from a less dense medium into a more dense medium, it slows down and is refracted. *Inferring Why does the light leaving the glass and entering air travel in its original direction?*

Index of Refraction Some mediums cause light to bend more than others. Figure 8 shows how light passes from air into water, from water into glass, and from glass into air again. When light passes from air into water, the light slows down. Light slows down even more when it passes from water into glass. Light travels fastest in air, a little slower in water, and slower still in glass. When light passes from glass back into air, the light speeds up. Notice that the ray that leaves the glass is traveling in the same direction as it was before it entered the water.

Glass causes light to bend more than either air or water because glass refracts light more. Another way to say this is that glass has a higher index of refraction than either air or water. A material's **index of refraction** is a measure of how much a ray of light bends when it enters that material. The higher the index of refraction of a medium, the more it bends light. The index of refraction of a vacuum is 1. The index of refraction of diamond is 2.42.

Prisms Figure 9 shows that a beam of white light can be separated to show all the colors of the visible spectrum. Remember that white light is actually a mixture of many wavelengths of light, each with its own color. When white light enters a prism, each wavelength is refracted by a different amount. The longer the wavelength, the less the wave will be bent by a prism.

Background

History of Science In the late 1600s, the Danish scientist Erasmus Bartholin was investigating images seen through calcite when he discovered a phenomenon called double refraction. Double refraction takes place when light rays pass through most transparent crystals. When the ray of light enters the crystal, it splits into two rays. One ray, which Bartholin called the *extraordinary beam*, is refracted. The other, the *ordinary beam*, is not. If you look at an object through the crystal, you will see two images. If you turn the crystal, one image will appear to turn while the other will not. Crystals that demonstrate this optical phenomenon include calcite, mica, and quartz. Ice and sugar crystals also produce double refraction.

Rawbows When white light from the sun shines through tiny drops of water, a rainbow may appear. Raindrops act like tiny prisms, refracting and reflecting the light and separating the colors. The colors of the rainbow always appear in the same order because raindrops refract the shorter wavelengths the most. Red, with the longest wavelength, is refracted the least. Violet, with the shortest wavelength, is refracted the most. The result is that white light is separated into the colors of the visible spectrum: red, orange, yellow, green, blue, and violet.

Mirages Imagine that you are in a car moving down a road on a hot, sunny day. The road ahead looks wet. Yet when you get there, the road is perfectly dry. Did the puddles disappear just before you got there? No, they were never there at all! What you saw was a mirage. A **mirage** (mih RAHJ) is an image of a distant object caused by refraction of light.

Figure 11 shows how a mirage forms. The air higher up is cooler than the air near the road. Light travels faster when it reaches the warmer air. As a result, the rays bend as they travel downward. Near the ground, the rays are traveling almost parallel to the ground but continue to bend until they begin to travel upward. As they travel upward they bend in the other direction. Your brain assumes that the rays have traveled in a straight line. They look just like rays reflected off a smooth surface, such as water. The observer sees a mirage.

☑ *Checkpoint* **What causes a mirage?**

Figure 10 A rainbow forms when sunlight is refracted and reflected by tiny water droplets.

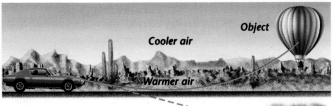

Object
Cooler air
Warmer air
Mirage

Figure 11 Light travels faster through hot air than through cool air. This causes light from the sky to curve as it approaches the ground. You see a mirage when refracted light appears to come from the ground.

Program Resources

🔵 **Science Explorer Series** *Weather and Climate,* Chapter 2

Answers to Self-Assessment

Caption Questions

Figure 8 The light rays refract again when they leave the glass and return to their original speed.

Figure 9 The colors appear in order of increasing wavelength.

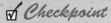
☑ *Checkpoint*

A mirage is caused by the refraction of light rays passing from cooler air to hot air.

Building Inquiry Skills: Observing

Materials *light source, 2 prisms, white paper*
Time 15 minutes

ACTIVITY

Have groups of students observe what happens when white light is passed through a prism. First, have them pass a beam of light through a prism and onto a piece of white paper. Ask: **What do you observe?** *(The light is separated into different colors.)* Then ask students to predict what will happen if the separated colors are passed through a second prism. *(Students answers will vary.)* Allow students to test their predictions by placing a second prism between the first prism and the white paper. *(Students should see that the second prism causes the separated colors to form white light again.)* **learning modality: visual**

🔵 **Integrating Earth Science**

Have students draw pictures showing the positions of the sun, the raindrops, and the rainbow. *(The rainbow will appear on the side of the sky opposite the sun.)* Ask students: **Do you think you are more likely to see a rainbow at noon, or in the late afternoon? Why?** *(Sample: Late afternoon. Sunlight needs to pass through the raindrops at an angle in order to separate the colors. When the sun is lower in the sky, in the late afternoon, it can pass through the raindrops at a greater angle than when the sun is higher in the sky at noon.)* **learning modality: logical/mathematical**

Addressing Naive Conceptions

Some students may confuse actual mirages with the mirages typically shown on television or in the movies. Explain that a mirage does not cause people to see objects that are not actually there, but it does make distant objects appear as if they were reflected in water. **learning modality: verbal**

Ongoing Assessment

Organizing Information Have students make concept maps describing how refraction affects the appearance of light.

Lenses

Using the Visuals: Figures 12 and 14

For each diagram shown in the figures, have students identify where the observer would have to be to see these images. (*On the side of the lens opposite the object; to the far right of each diagram*) Make sure students understand that these diagrams show the images that would be produced. The person would not actually see the images unless he or she was looking at the object through the lens. **learning modality: logical/mathematical**

Including All Students

Materials *concave and convex lenses*

Time 15 minutes

It may be difficult for students who are not fluent in English to keep the differences between concave and convex lenses straight. Encourage students to examine the lenses provided. Students can then work in pairs to make tables that compare and contrast concave and convex lenses. Students should use their observations and the text in developing the tables. Recommend that interested students draw diagrams that show how concave and convex lenses bend light rays. **limited English proficiency**

Portfolio Students can save their tables and their diagrams in their portfolios.

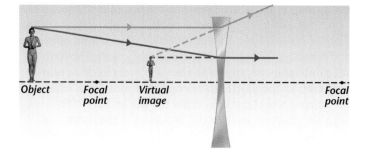

Figure 12 The ray that travels horizontally from the top of the object is refracted as though it is coming from the focal point on the same side of the concave lens as the object. The ray that travels toward the other focal point is refracted so it travels horizontally.
Interpreting Diagrams Why do the rays from a concave lens never meet?

Lenses

Have you ever looked through binoculars, used a microscope or a camera, or worn eyeglasses? If so, you have used a lens to bend light. A **lens** is a curved piece of glass or other transparent material that is used to refract light. A lens forms an image by refracting light rays that pass through it. Like mirrors, lenses can have different shapes. The type of image formed by a lens depends on the shape of the lens.

Concave lens

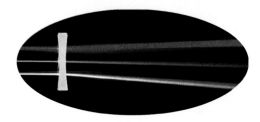

Convex lens

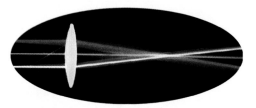

Figure 13 A concave lens refracts parallel rays of light so that they appear to come from one of the focal points. A convex lens refracts parallel rays of light so that they meet at the focal point.

Concave Lenses A **concave lens** is thinner in the center than at the edges. As parallel rays of light pass through a concave lens, they are bent away from the center of the lens. Figure 12 shows how the rays spread out, but appear to come from the focal point on the opposite side of the lens. **Because the light rays never meet, a concave lens can produce only a virtual image.**

Convex Lenses A **convex lens** is thicker in the center than at the edges. As parallel light rays pass through a convex lens, they are bent toward the center of the lens. The rays meet at the focal point of the lens and then continue on. The more curved the lens, the more it refracts light.

A convex lens acts somewhat like a concave mirror, because it focuses rays of light. **The type of image formed by a convex lens depends on the position of the object in relation to the focal point.** Figure 14 shows three examples. If the object is farther away than the focal point, the refracted rays form a real image on the other side of the lens. If the object is between the lens and the focal point, a virtual image forms on the same side of the lens as the object.

Background

Facts and Figures A single ray of light passing through a lens may be distorted, causing aberrations. A spherical aberration is produced when all the rays fail to meet at the focal point. This happens because rays that pass through the center and edges of the lens are focused at different distances. Another aberration, coma, produces a blurry, comet-shaped image. If one part of the lens fails to properly focus the image, another aberration called astigmatism is produced. Images can also appear to bulge or curve inward. A bulging image forms when the lens magnifies the center of the image more than the edges. When the edges are magnified more than the center, pincushion distortion occurs. In chromatic aberration, the lens fails to focus all the colors of light in the same plane. This forms two focal points—one for blue light and one for red.

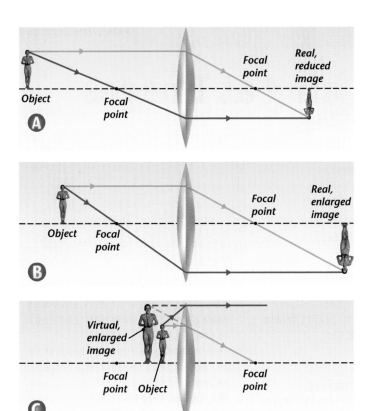

Figure A: Object, Focal point, Focal point, Real, reduced image

Figure B: Object, Focal point, Focal point, Real, enlarged image

Figure C: Virtual, enlarged image, Focal point, Object, Focal point

Figure 14 The type and size of image formed by a convex lens depend on the position of the object. **A, B.** If the object is farther from the focal point than the lens, the image is real and inverted. **C.** If the object is between the focal point and the lens, the image is virtual.

Section 2 Review

1. What happens to light rays as they pass from one medium into another medium?
2. What determines the type of image that is formed by a convex lens?
3. Why is it impossible for a concave lens to form a real image?
4. Explain why you sometimes see a rainbow during a rain shower or shortly afterward.
5. **Thinking Critically** **Problem Solving** Suppose you wanted to closely examine the leaf of a plant. Which type of lens would you use? Explain.

Science at Home

Here's how you can bend a pencil without touching it. Put a pencil in a glass of water, as shown in the photograph. Have your family members look at the pencil from the side. Using the idea of refraction, explain to your family why the pencil appears as it does.

Answers to Self-Assessment

Caption Question

Figure 12 Because the rays that pass through the lens are bent away from the center of the lens and spread out.

---

3 Assess

Section 2 Review Answers

1. Their speed changes; this causes them to change direction or bend.
2. The distance between the object and the lens
3. A concave lens cannot form a real image because it spreads out rays of light. A real image can be formed only when rays of light come together.
4. Raindrops act like tiny prisms that refract sunlight and separate it into its component colors.
5. You would use a convex lens because it can magnify the leaf. Convex lenses can form both real enlarged images and virtual enlarged images.

Science at Home

Materials *pencil, glass of water*

Students should explain to their families that the pencil appears to bend because the light bends when it travels between the air and the water. Because the brain assumes that light travels in a straight line from the image to the eye, this bending of light causes the pencil to appear as if it were located in a different place. Interested students may want to try using other liquids in the glass, such as vegetable oil, concentrated salt water, or rubbing alcohol, to find which liquid has the greatest index of refraction.

Performance Assessment

Drawing Have students draw diagrams showing how light rays change as they pass from a light source through a concave lens and then through a convex lens.
 Students can save their drawings in their portfolios.

O ◆ 121

Looking at Images

Preparing for Inquiry

Key Concept Images formed by a convex lens vary according to the distance between the object and the lens.

Skills Objectives Students will be able to
- control variables;
- observe images formed by a convex lens.

Time 45 minutes

Advance Planning Supply lenses with a variety of focal lengths. Make sure students choose lenses that will work. Obtain light bulbs and sockets, modeling clay, cardboard stands, tape, and meter sticks.

Guiding Inquiry

Invitation Inform students that a refracting telescope, a microscope, and a camera all use convex lenses. Ask students if they can infer what function(s) a convex lens serves in these instruments. *(Sample: They magnify very small or distant objects.)*

Introducing the Procedure
Demonstrate how to determine the focal length of the lens, if necessary.

Troubleshooting the Experiment
- Students can determine the position of the image by using a card to partially block some of the light at the top of the bulb and observing where the blockage occurs on the image.
- Lenses with very short focal lengths will not give good images at large distances.

Analyze and Conclude
1. No, only when the object is more than one focal length from the lens. When the object is placed between the focal point and the lens, the image is upright (virtual).
2. The image becomes larger, remains inverted, and moves farther from the lens.
3. When the bulb is between the focal

point and the lens, the image is a magnified virtual image on the same side of the lens as the object; it cannot be projected onto the paper.
4. Constant variable: focal length; manipulated variable: distance of the object from the lens; responding variables: image size and position.

Extending the Inquiry

Design an Experiment Students' experiments should repeat the procedure in this lab with lenses of varying focal length.

Skills Lab

Looking at Images

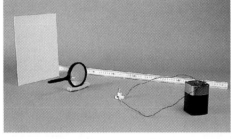

In this lab, you will control variables as you explore how images are formed by a convex lens.

Problem

How does the distance between an object and a convex lens affect the image formed?

Materials

tape
cardboard stand
light bulb and socket
battery and wires

convex lens
blank sheet of paper
clay, for holding the lens
meter stick

Procedure

1. Tape the paper onto the cardboard stand.
2. Place a lit bulb more than 2 m from the paper. Use the lens to focus light from the bulb onto the paper. Measure the distance from the lens to the paper. This is the approximate focal length of the lens you are using.
3. Copy the data table into your notebook.
4. Now place the bulb more than twice the focal length away from the lens. Record the position and size of the focused image on the paper. Measure the height of the bulb image.
5. Now, move the bulb so that it is just over one focal length away from the lens. Record the position and size of the image.

Analyze and Conclude

1. Is the image formed by a convex lens always upside down? If not, under what conditions is the image upright?
2. What happens to the size of the image as the bulb moves toward the lens? What happens to the position of the image?
3. What happens if the bulb is within one focal length of the lens? Explain.
4. **Think About It** Make a list of the variables in this experiment. Which variables did you keep constant? Which was the manipulated variable? Which was the responding variable?

Design an Experiment

With your teacher's approval and supervision, design an experiment to study images formed by convex lenses of various focal lengths. How does the focal length of the lens affect the position and size of the images produced?

DATA TABLE

Focal Length of Lens: _____ cm   Height of Bulb: _____ cm

Distance From Bulb to Lens (cm)	Distance From Lens to Cardboard (cm)	Image Orientation (upright or upside down)	Image Size (height in cm)

Program Resources

- **Teaching Resources** Skills Lab blackline masters, pp. 121–123

Media and Technology

 Lab Activity Videotape *Sound and Light,* 7

SECTION 3 Color

DISCOVER ⋯⋯⋯⋯⋯⋯⋯⋯⋯⋯⋯ ACTIVITY

How Do Colors Mix?

1. Carefully cut a disk with a diameter of about 10 cm out of a piece of sturdy white cardboard. Divide the disk into three equal-size segments. Use colored pencils to color one segment red, the next green, and the third blue.

2. Carefully punch two holes, about 2 cm apart, on opposite sides of the center of the disk.

3. Thread a string about 1 m long through the holes. Tie the ends of the string together so that the string forms a loop that passes through both holes.

4. With equal lengths of string on each side of the disk, turn the disk so that you are winding up the string. Predict what color(s) you will see if the disk spins fast.

5. Spin the disk by pulling and relaxing the string.

Think It Over
Observing What color do you see as the wheel spins fast? Was your prediction correct?

A s the morning sun slowly rises over the flower garden, the sunlight begins to reveal bright pink and orange poppies, purple pansies, and a striking display of many other colors. Each flower is beautiful, yet different. The light from the sun allows you to see each color clearly. But sunlight is white light. What makes each flower appear to be a different color?

The Color of Objects

The color of a flower depends on how it reflects light. Each flower absorbs some wavelengths of light and reflects other wavelengths. **The color of an object is the color of the light it reflects.**

GUIDE FOR READING

◆ What determines the color of an object?

◆ What are the primary colors of light?

◆ How is mixing pigments different from mixing light?

Reading Tip Before you read, use the section headings to make an outline about color. Leave space to take notes as you read.

O ◆ 123

READING STRATEGIES

Reading Tip Work as a class to outline the information under the first heading. Then have students work independently to complete the rest of the outline.
I. The Color of Objects
   A. Objects in white light
      1. objects absorb some light
      2. objects reflect different colors of light

Program Resources

◆ **Teaching Resources** 4-3 Lesson Plan, p. 109; 4-3 Section Summary, p. 110
◆ **Guided Study Workbook** Section 4-3

SECTION 3 Color

Objectives

After completing the lesson, students will be able to
◆ identify the factors that determine the color of an object;
◆ explain and compare how colors are combined in light and in pigments.

Key Terms primary color, secondary color, complementary color, pigment

1 Engage/Explore

Activating Prior Knowledge

Place a piece of yellow cellophane on an overhead projector. Then ask students what will happen if you place a piece of blue cellophane over the yellow. (*Most will say that it will turn green.*) Demonstrate that this is true. Explain that this section will increase students' understanding of how colors mix.

⋯⋯⋯ DISCOVER ⋯⋯⋯

Skills Focus observing
Materials *white cardboard, crayons or markers, 1 m string, compass*
Time 15 minutes
Tips You may want to prepare the cardboard circles before the activity and just have students color them in. Use the pointed end of the compass to carefully make the two holes on the opposite sides of the circle.
Expected Outcome As students spin the disc, it will look grayish-white. All the colors are reflected and reach the eye at the same time; they combine to form white light.
Think It Over The disc looks white. Answers will vary based on students' predictions.

O ◆ 123

2 Facilitate

The Color of Objects

Building Inquiry Skills: Making Models

Materials *paper, colored pencils or markers*
Time 15 minutes

Have students draw a red object, such as an apple, and use the pencils or markers to represent white light striking and being reflected from the object. *(Students should show all colors of light striking the object and only red light being reflected.)* Have students draw objects of different colors, including black and white.

limited English proficiency

 Students can save their drawings in their portfolios.

Using the Visuals: Figure 17

Ask: **What colors of light would a white object reflect in the first picture? What color would it appear to be?** *(All colors; white)* Then ask: **What colors of light would a white object reflect in the second picture? What color would it appear to be?** *(Green; green)* **learning modality: visual**

Real-Life Learning

Ask: **Why does the sky appear blue?** *(Students probably will not be able to answer this question. Some may suggest the sky is blue because it reflects blue light.)* Tell students that sunlight in the atmosphere is scattered by dust particles and by oxygen and nitrogen molecules. Explain that shorter wavelengths of light, such as blue, are scattered to a greater degree than the longer, red wavelengths of light. When the particles that do the scattering are shorter than the visible wavelengths of light, such as O_2 and N_2 molecules, the effect is even more pronounced. The sky appears blue when you look up at it during the daytime because of the scattering effect of sunlight. **learning modality: verbal**

Figure 15 The petals of this lily appear orange because they reflect orange light. The stems and leaves appear green because they reflect green light.

Objects in White Light Flowers and other objects reflect different colors of light. For example, when white light strikes the orange petals of a lily, the petals reflect mostly orange wavelengths. The petals absorb the other wavelengths. You see the petals as orange because orange wavelengths of light bounce off them and enter your eyes. On the other hand, the stem and leaves appear green. They reflect mostly green wavelengths and absorb the other colors.

What happens with black and white objects? A skunk looks black and white because some parts of it reflect all wavelengths of light while other parts do not reflect any light. When white light strikes the skunk's stripe, all the colors are reflected. The colors combine, so you see white light. When white light strikes the black parts of the skunk, all the light is absorbed and none is reflected. Your eyes see black.

Even colored and white objects can appear black if there is no light to reflect off them. Imagine being in a dark room. If there is no light present, then no light can reflect off the things in the room. No light enters your eyes, so you see nothing. If there is a small amount of light in the room, you may be able to make out the shapes of objects. However, you will not be able to tell their colors.

Objects in Colored Light Objects can look a different color depending on the color of light in which they are seen. Figure 17 shows two photographs of a desktop, each taken under different light. The first picture was taken under ordinary white light. In it, the keyboard is blue and the folder is red. The second picture was taken under green light. When green light shines on an object,

Figure 16 The white part of this skunk reflects all colors of light. *Applying Concepts Why do the skunk's legs look black?*

Background

Integrating Science Astronomers use the colors of the light produced by stars to categorize them. Many stars that we see at night are blue-white stars. Other stars produce yellow or red light. A star's color indicates its temperature. Blue and blue-white stars are hotter than yellow or red stars. However, a star may appear red because it is relatively cool and faint, or its light may have changed color as it passed through interstellar

materials. To account for such variables, scientists also evaluate a star's absolute magnitude—the amount of light it produces. Giant stars have yellow, red, and orange light; they are about 100 times as bright as our sun. Supergiants are even brighter, and can be any color. Main sequence stars, including the sun and most stars we see in the night sky, range from cool, faint red stars to hot, blue stars. Sirius is a hot, white star.

Figure 17 In white light, objects appear in many different colors (left). If viewed under green light, the same objects appear in shades of green or black (right). *Predicting How would these objects look under blue light?*

the object either reflects or absorbs the green light. Since red and blue objects reflect only red and blue light, they absorb all of the green light. The binder looks black.

Objects Seen Through Filters Some transparent materials allow only certain colors of light to pass through them. They reflect or absorb the other colors. Such materials are called color filters. For example, a red filter is a piece of glass or plastic that allows only red light to pass through. Spotlights on theater stages often use color filters to produce different color effects. Photographic slides are color filters, too. A slide projector shines white light through a combination of color filters. The image you see on the screen shows the colors that each part of the slide allows through.

☑ *Checkpoint* What is a color filter?

Combining Colors

An understanding of color is very useful in photography, art, theater lighting, and printing. People who work with color must know how to produce a wide range of colors from just a few basic colors. It is possible to produce any color by mixing colors of the spectrum in varying amounts. Three colors that can be used to make any other color are called **primary colors.** Any two primary colors combined in equal amounts produce a **secondary color.**

Mixing Colors of Light The primary colors of light are red, green, and blue. When combined in equal amounts, the primary colors produce white light. But if they are combined in varying amounts, they can produce any other color. For example, red and green combine to form yellow light. Yellow is a secondary color of light because it is produced from two primary colors.

Sharpen your Skills

Developing Hypotheses

1. Carefully make a color wheel with eight segments. Use colored pencils to color alternate blue and yellow segments.

2. Predict what color you will see if you spin the wheel. Write a hypothesis of what you think the outcome will be. Be sure to write your hypothesis as an "If . . . then . . ." statement.

3. Spin the wheel. What do you see? Does it confirm your hypothesis?

4. Repeat the activity with color wheels that have different pairs of colors.

Answers to Self-Assessment

Caption Questions

Figure 16 They absorb all colors of light.
Figure 17 Objects that reflect blue light would appear blue; objects that absorb blue light would appear black.

☑ *Checkpoint*

A transparent material that allows certain colors of light to pass through it and reflects or absorbs other colors.

Combining Colors

Sharpen your Skills

Developing Hypotheses
Materials *white cardboard, colored pencils or markers, string, compass*
ACTIVITY
Time 15 minutes
Tips You may want to prepare the materials as you did for the Discover, except divide the circle into 8 parts.
Expected Outcome Students should see green light as a result of mixing blue and yellow.
Sample Hypothesis If blue and red are mixed, then I will see purple.
Extend Challenge students to find out what happens when the color wheel consists of one color and black. *(Students will see a darker shade of that color.)*

Ongoing Assessment

Oral Presentation Ask students to describe what they would see if they looked at a white shirt through a red filter. *(The shirt would appear red.)*

O ◆ 125

Combining Colors, continued

Visual Arts CONNECTION

Tell students that all paints are made of pigments that are powdered and mixed with a liquid. Throughout history, pigments have been mixed with egg white, gelatin, beeswax, linseed oil, water, and synthetic materials such as latex. Early pigments were mostly made from metal ores, such as the reddish pigment made from iron oxide. Most pigments today are made from petroleum chemicals.

In Your Journal Students may identify colors originally made from minerals such as gold, silver, zinc oxide, cobalt, brick red, and others. Interested students may want to research how early artists used plants and other materials to produce colored pigments. **learning modality: verbal**

Integrating Technology

Have students refer to the primary colors of light shown in Figure 18. Ask: **How can only three colors make all the colors that you see on television or on a computer screen?** *(Sample: The colors combine in different ways to make the different colors.)* **learning modality: visual**

Inquiry Challenge

Materials *water color paints, paintbrush, water color paper*

Time 10 minutes

Allow students to predict how combining pigments will produce different colors. Place students in groups of four or five. Give each student a specific color of paint. Then challenge each group to match the color found on an object in the classroom. Have students complete a list of all the colors that they used to create a specific shade. **cooperative learning**

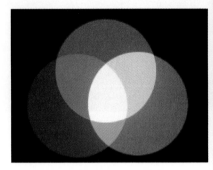
Overlapping primary colors of light

Visual Arts CONNECTION

Ever since the first cave artists painted about 20,000 years ago, pigments made from natural materials have been used to create pictures. In the 1400s, Renaissance painters such as Leonardo da Vinci and Raphael used many more colorful pigments to create their vivid paintings. Pigments were derived from minerals, plants, and animals.

In Your Journal

Look at the color names for markers, paints, or crayons. Do you see vermilion (red), azure (blue) or ochre (brown)? These colors were all originally made from minerals. Now these colors are made from chemicals. Can you find the names of other colors that may have originally come from minerals?

Figure 18 The primary colors of light are red, green, and blue (left). When combined in equal amounts, the primary colors of light form white light. A color television produces all colors of light by combining red, green, and blue light in varying amounts. *Interpreting Photographs How does a television show black?*

The secondary colors of light are yellow (red + green), cyan (green + blue), and magenta (red + blue). Figure 18 shows the primary and secondary colors of light.

A primary color and a secondary color can combine to make white. Any two colors that combine to form white light are called **complementary colors.** Yellow and blue are complementary colors, as are cyan and red, and magenta and green.

INTEGRATING TECHNOLOGY A color television screen produces only three colors of light. Figure 18 shows a magnified portion of a color television screen. Notice that the picture on the screen is made up of little groups of red, green, and blue lights. By varying the brightness of each colored light, the television produces pictures of many different colors.

Mixing Pigments How do artists produce the many shades of colors you see in paintings? Paints and dyes have different colors because of the pigments they contain. **Pigments** are substances that are used to color other materials. Color pigments are opaque substances that reflect particular colors. The color you see is the color that particular pigment reflects.

Mixing colors of pigments is different from mixing colors of light. **As pigments are added together, fewer colors of light are reflected and more are absorbed.** The more pigments that are combined, the darker the mixture looks.

Background

History of Science Adding colored pigment to cloth is called dyeing. Once the molecules of the dye are deposited onto the fabric, it is impossible to remove them using the solvent that first dissolved them. Dyes were first used at least 4,000 years ago in Egypt and China. The ancient Romans valued printed and dyed cloths. Indigo, woad, and madder plants were used to create purple and blue colors. Dyed fabrics were so valuable that rulers in the Dark Ages passed regulations about which citizens were entitled to wear certain colors. By the 1400s, the first European book on dyeing was released. By this time, some insects were used to create different colors, such as bright red. The first synthetic dye, aniline purple, or mauve, was invented by Sir William Perkin, an English chemist, in 1856. Most modern dyes are made from petrochemicals and coal tar.

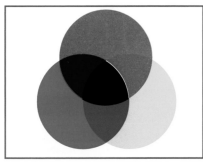
Overlapping primary colors of pigments

Figure 19 The primary colors of pigments are cyan, yellow, and magenta (left). The photograph shows a printed image and the round inset shows an enlargement of part of it. Four-color printing uses the three primary colors of pigments, plus black.

The primary colors of pigments are cyan, yellow, and magenta. If you combine all three primary colors of pigments in equal amounts, you get black. If you combine two primary colors of pigments in equal amounts, you get a secondary color. The secondary colors of pigments are red (magenta + yellow), green (cyan + yellow), and blue (magenta + cyan). By combining pigments in varying amounts, you can produce any other color. Figure 19 shows the primary and secondary colors of pigments.

If you use a magnifying glass to look at color pictures in this book, you will see that the pictures are made up of tiny dots of different colors of ink. The colors used are cyan, yellow, and magenta. Black ink is also used to make pictures darker. Because of the four colors of ink used, the process that produced this book is called four-color printing.

Section 3 Review

1. Why do objects have different colors?
2. What are the primary colors of light? What happens when the primary colors of light are mixed in equal amounts?
3. What happens when the primary colors of pigments are mixed in equal amounts?
4. What colors are used in the four-color printing process?
5. **Thinking Critically Comparing and Contrasting** Make a table that compares and contrasts the primary and secondary colors of light and those of pigments.

Check Your Progress

CHAPTER PROJECT 4

Build your optical instrument according to the sketch you prepared. How does your instrument use reflection or refraction to produce and clarify images? Do you need to be able to change the focus of the image? Does your instrument have moving parts? How will you combine the different parts of the instrument?

Program Resources

◆ **Teaching Resources** 4-3 Review and Reinforce, p. 111; 4-3 Enrich, p. 112

Media and Technology

Transparencies "The Primary Colors of Light and Pigment," Transparency 18

Answers to Self-Assessment

Caption Question

Figure 18 By switching off all the colored lights in the area of the screen that appears black.

Demonstration

Materials *computer with color controls*
Time 10 minutes

Use the color controls to demonstrate how primary colors of pigments combine to form different colors. (Macs have a color control located in the Control Panel, under Date & Time/ Clock Options/Use Custom Clock Color/Select Color. Windows computers have a similar control under the "Settings" option on the Task Bar.) Explain that the computer is programmed to show how pigments combine to help people see what their color documents will look like. Allow students to change the combinations of colors. **learning modality: visual**

3 Assess

Section 3 Review Answers

1. Objects reflect the colors you see and absorb the other colors of light.
2. Red, green, and blue. They produce white light.
3. They produce black.
4. Cyan, yellow, magenta, black
5. Primary colors of light—red, green, and blue; secondary colors of light— cyan, yellow, and magenta. Primary colors of pigment—cyan, yellow, and magenta; secondary colors of pigment— red, green, and blue

Check Your Progress

CHAPTER PROJECT 4

Answer students' questions and address any design difficulties they may be having. If students are having trouble because their design is too elaborate, guide them in simplifying the design.

Performance Assessment

Writing Have students explain how they would produce the color violet if they were a painter using primary colors of paint and if they were a stage director using primary colors of light filters.

Changing Colors

Preparing for Inquiry

Key Concept Objects seen through filters can appear a different color.

Skills Objectives Students will be able to

◆ observe the effect of color filters on white light;

◆ predict the color of light that passes through different filters;

◆ infer how the filter affects white light.

Time 45 minutes

Advance Planning Supply colored objects and cellophane. Collect flashlights and shoe boxes.

Guiding Inquiry

Invitation Ask students how they can tell what color an object is. *(Under white light, the object will be the color of the light it reflects.)* Ask students what color of light a white object reflects. *(All colors of light)*

Troubleshooting the Experiment
Pair students who are colorblind with students who are not.

Analyze and Conclude

1. Red object: looked red; object reflected mostly red, red cellophane transmitted red. Yellow object: looked orange; object reflected mostly yellow, red cellophane transmitted some yellow. Blue object: looked purple; object reflected mostly blue, red cellophane transmitted some blue.

2. Red object: looked purple, object reflected mostly red, blue cellophane transmitted some red. Yellow object: looked green; object reflected mostly yellow, blue cellophane transmitted some yellow. Blue object: looked blue; object reflected mostly blue, blue cellophane transmitted blue.

3. Red—red; green—green; blue—blue

4. White reflects all colors of light, so the white object would appear to be the same color as the cellophane.

5. Students' diagrams should show all colors of light being reflected or absorbed except the color of the filter.

6. More like pigments. Most of the light would be absorbed.

Changing Colors

Stage lighting in theaters uses color filters to control the colors of light on stage. In this lab you will study the effect of color filters on white light.

Problem

How do color filters affect the appearance of white light?

Skills Focus

observing, predicting, inferring

Materials

shoe box   scissors
flashlight   removable tape
red object (such as a ripe tomato)
yellow object (such as a ripe lemon)
blue object (such as blue construction paper)
red, green, and blue cellophane, enough to
    cover the top of the shoe box

Procedure

1. Carefully cut a large rectangular hole in the lid of the shoe box.
2. Carefully cut a small, round hole in the center of one of the ends of the shoe box.
3. Tape the red cellophane under the lid of the shoe box, covering the hole in the lid.
4. Place the objects in the box and put the lid on.
5. In a darkened room, shine the flashlight into the shoe box through the side hole. Note the apparent color of each object in the box.
6. Repeat Steps 3–5 using the other colors of cellophane.

Analyze and Conclude

1. What did you see when you looked through the red cellophane? Explain why each object appeared as it did.
2. What did you see when you looked through the blue cellophane? Explain.
3. What color of light does each piece of cellophane allow through?
4. Predict what you would see under each piece of cellophane if you put a white object in the box. Test your prediction.
5. Use diagrams to show how each color of cellophane affects the white light from the flashlight.
6. **Think About It** Do color filters work more like pigments or like colors of light? What would happen if you shined a flashlight through both a red and a green filter? Explain.

Getting Involved

Visit a local theater or talk to a lighting designer to find out how color filters are used to produce different stage effects.

Extending the Inquiry

Getting Involved Encourage students to prepare a list of questions before the visit. Have them watch a performance in which filtered lights are used.

Safety

Caution students to take care when using the scissors. Review the safety guidelines in Appendix A.

Program Resources

◆ **Teaching Resources** Real-World Lab blackline masters, pp. 124–125

Media and Technology

Lab Activity Videotape
Sound and Light, 8

SECTION 4 Seeing Light

DISCOVER ·· ACTIVITY····

Can You See Everything With One Eye?

1. Write an X and an O on a sheet of paper. They should be about 5 cm apart.
2. Hold the sheet of paper at arm's length.
3. Close or cover your left eye. Stare at the X with your right eye.
4. Slowly move the paper toward your face while staring at the X. What do you notice?

5. Repeat the activity, keeping both eyes open. What difference do you notice?

Think It Over
Posing Questions Write two questions about vision that you could investigate using the X and the O.

The excitement mounts as the pitcher goes into his windup. As he goes through his motion, he keeps his eye on the strike zone. The batter watches the pitcher release the ball, then swings. Crack! The batter hits the ball, drops the bat, and sprints toward first base. From your seat behind home plate, you watch the ball travel toward the outfield. Will it be a base hit? The left fielder watches the ball leave the bat and travel toward him. It goes over his head—a double!

Everyone involved has been following the first rule of baseball: Keep your eye on the ball. As the ball moves, the eyes must adjust continuously to keep it in focus. Fortunately, this change in focus happens automatically.

GUIDE FOR READING

◆ How do your eyes allow you to see?

◆ What kinds of lenses are used to correct vision problems?

Reading Tip As you read, make a flowchart that shows how light travels through the eye and how the brain interprets the image.

Figure 20 As the ball moves through the air, your eyes must continuously adjust their focus to see the ball.

Chapter 4 O ◆ 129

 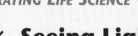

SECTION 4 Seeing Light

Objectives

After completing the lesson, students will be able to
◆ describe how light waves are sensed and interpreted as images by humans;
◆ identify types of vision problems and kinds of lenses that can be used to correct the problems.

Key Terms cornea, iris, pupil, retina, rod, cone, optic nerve, nearsighted, farsighted

1 Engage/Explore

Activating Prior Knowledge

Ask students to hold an index finger close to their faces, with their eyes focused on the tip of the finger. Students should move their fingers slowly away from their faces, noticing the change in focus of the background.

········ **DISCOVER** ·········

Skills Focus posing questions
Materials *white paper, pencil*
Time 5 minutes
Tips Suggest students repeat the activity at least twice to be certain of their results.
Expected Outcome As the student moves the paper toward his or her face, the O disappears. This does not happen when the activity is done with both eyes open.
Think It Over Sample questions: If I repeat the activity staring at the O, will the X behave as the O did? At what distance does the letter O disappear?

The Human Eye

Using the Visuals: Figure 21

Direct students to use their fingers to trace the path of light as it enters the eye. Ask: **Which two parts of the eye refract light?** *(The cornea and the lens)* Tell students to look at the lens. Ask: **What holds the lens in place?** *(The ciliary muscles)* **learning modality: visual**

Building Inquiry Skills: Observing

Materials *mirror, drawing paper*
Time 5 minutes

Pair students and have them observe each other's eyes, or have students observe their own eyes in a mirror. Students should make detailed drawings of their observations. Direct students to note the colors of different parts of the eye. Ask: **What parts of the eye do you see? What colors are those parts?** *(Iris— brown, blue, green, or gray; white of the eye, pupil—black; and blood vessels—red or pink)* Have students observe their partner's eyes as the partner moves from dim into bright light. Ask: **How do your partner's eyes change?** *(The pupils widen in dim light and narrow in bright light.)* **learning modality: visual**

Including All Students

Some students may find it difficult to remember all the parts of the eye and the functions of each of the parts. Suggest that students work in pairs to develop flowcharts that explain the role and function of each of the parts of the eye in helping them to see. The flowcharts should begin with light entering the cornea and end with signals leaving the eye via the optic nerve. **cooperative learning**

 Students can save their flowcharts in their portfolios.

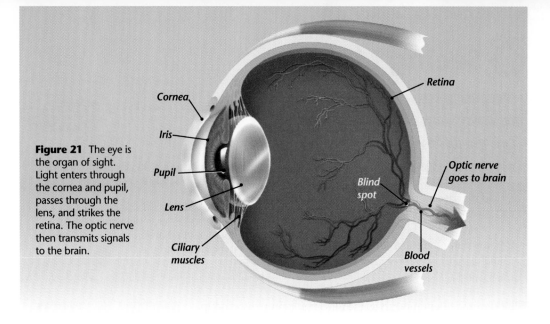

Figure 21 The eye is the organ of sight. Light enters through the cornea and pupil, passes through the lens, and strikes the retina. The optic nerve then transmits signals to the brain.

The Human Eye

Your eyes are complicated organs, with each part playing its own role in helping you see. **You see objects because of a series of steps that involve the structures of the eye and the brain.**

The Cornea Light enters the eye through the transparent front surface called the **cornea.** The cornea protects the eye. It also acts as a lens, bending rays of light as they enter the eye. Each time you blink, your eyelids act like little windshield wipers, cleansing and moistening the cornea.

The Iris The **iris** is a ring of muscle that contracts and expands to change the amount of light that enters the eye. The iris gives the eye its color. In most people the iris is brown; in others it is blue or green.

The Pupil The **pupil** is the part of the eye that looks black. It is actually a hole, covered by the clear cornea. The pupil looks black because it is an opening into the dark inside of the eye. Figure 22 shows how the size of the pupil depends on whether the iris is contracted or expanded. In dim light, the pupil becomes larger, allowing more light in. In very bright light, the pupil becomes smaller, reducing the amount of light that enters the eye.

Figure 22 In dim light, the iris contracts. The pupil gets bigger and allows more light into the eye. *Relating Cause and Effect What happens in bright light?*

Background

Facts and Figures Stereoscopic, or 3-D, movies trick the eyes into seeing a flat image as three-dimensional. When a 3-D movie is made, two cameras, or one camera with two lenses, film the action simultaneously. The camera lenses are spaced about as far apart as human eyes. After the two films are edited and prepared for viewing, they are projected onto the screen using two projectors running at exactly the same speed. People watching the movie wear special glasses that have different-colored filters for each eye, or different polarizations. The result is that one eye sees only the images filmed by one lens, and the other eye sees only the images filmed by the other lens. When the two images are merged together by the brain, the viewer perceives these differences as depth.

The Lens Just behind the pupil is the lens. The lens of your eye is a convex lens. The lens refracts light, forming an image on the lining of your eyeball. Figure 23 shows how the lens changes its focus. When you focus on a distant object, the ciliary muscles holding the lens relax, making the lens longer and thinner. When you focus on a nearby object, the muscles contract and the lens becomes shorter and fatter.

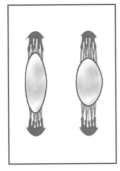

Figure 23 The ciliary muscles holding the lens in place contract or relax to change the shape of the lens.

The Retina The layer of cells lining the inside of the eyeball is the **retina.** As the cornea and the lens refract light, an upside-down image is formed on the retina. The retina is made up of millions of tiny, light-sensitive cells called rods and cones. The rods and cones generate small nerve signals when they are hit by light.

The **rods** contain a pigment that reacts to small amounts of light. The rods distinguish among black, white, and shades of gray. They allow you to see in dim light, so they are important for night vision.

The **cones** respond to colors. There are three types of cones: those that detect red light, those that detect green light, and those that detect blue light. The cone cells function only in bright light. This is why it is difficult to distinguish colors in dim light.

The Optic Nerve and the Brain The signals generated by the rods and cones travel to your brain along a short, thick nerve called the **optic nerve.** When the signals reach your brain, it automatically turns the image right-side up. Your brain also combines the two images, one from each eye, into a single three-dimensional image.

There is one spot on the retina that does not have any rods or cones. This blind spot is the part of the retina where the optic nerve begins. You cannot see light that falls on the blind spot. However, an object whose light falls on the blind spot of one eye can usually be seen with the other eye. If you keep both eyes open, you do not notice the effect of the blind spots.

✓ *Checkpoint* *Where in the eye is the image formed?*

Correcting Vision

In some people, the eyeball is slightly too long or too short, so the image on the retina is slightly out of focus. Fortunately, wearing glasses or contact lenses can usually correct this type of vision problem. **Some lenses in eyeglasses are convex and some are concave. The type of lens used depends on whether the eyeball is too long or too short.**

True Colors ACTIVITY

When you stare too long at a color, the cones in your eyes get tired.

1. Stare at the bottom right star of the flag for at least 60 seconds. Do not move your eyes or blink during that time.

2. Now stare at a sheet of blank white paper.

Observing What do you see when you look at the white paper? How are the colors you see related to the colors in the original art?

Answers to Self-Assessment

Caption Question

Figure 22 The iris muscle expands, and the pupil grows smaller, letting in less light.

✓ *Checkpoint*
On the retina

Building Inquiry Skills: Observing

Turn off the lights in the classroom and close the blinds to darken the classroom. When students' eyes have adjusted to the dark, ask them to describe the colors they see. *(Students will see mostly black, white, and shades of gray.)* Turn the lights back on. Have students compare the colors they see to the colors they saw in the dark. Ask: **Can humans see colors in the dark? Why or why not?** *(No. The cones, which respond to colors, only function in bright light.)* **learning modality: visual**

Addressing Naive Conceptions

Students may think that people who are colorblind can see black and white but not colors. Explain that colorblind people have a condition that affects the cones of their eyes so they cannot see one or more of the three primary colors of light. Because white is seen when all colors are reflected, colorblind people see white only as the reflection of the colors they can see. For example, a person who cannot see red sees white as bluish-green because they can only see the blue and green reflected rays. **learning modality: verbal**

TRY THIS

Skills Focus observing
Materials *white paper*
Time 10 minutes
Tips Set a timer for 80 seconds and tell students when to start staring and when to look away.
Observing Students will see the flag as red, white, and blue. These are the complementary colors of the page.
Extend Have students find out what colors they will see if they stare at a red, white, and blue flag. **learning modality: visual**

Correcting Vision

Demonstration

Materials *prescription eyeglasses, overhead projector, small print*

Time 5 minutes

Place the small print on the projector and hold the lenses above it. Have students infer whether the lens is concave or convex. *(Concave lenses magnify the image. Convex lenses distort or blur the image.)* **learning modality: visual**

3 Assess

Section 4 Review Answers

1. Cornea: bends light as it enters the eye; pupil: controls amount of light entering the eye; lens: forms image inside eye; retina: has rods and cones that react to light; optic nerve: transmits signals to brain; brain: interprets signals as images.
2. In dim light, the pupil grows larger to allow more light in. In bright light, the pupil grows smaller and lets less light in.
3. Nearsightedness: eyeball is too long, image of distant object falls in front of retina; corrected with concave lens to spread out light rays and focus image on retina. Farsightedness: eyeball is too short, image of near object falls behind retina; corrected with convex lens to focus image on retina.
4. Rods help you distinguish between black, white, and shades of gray. Cones need a lot of light to detect red, green, and blue.

Science at Home

Materials *sheet of paper*

Students see an image of their left hand with a hole in it, a combination of images from both eyes.

Performance Assessment

Organizing Information Have students create flowcharts showing how a nearsighted person wearing glasses sees a distant object.

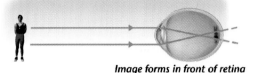

Nearsightedness (eyeball too long)
Image forms in front of retina

Farsightedness (eyeball too short)
Image forms behind retina

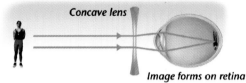

Correction
Concave lens
Image forms on retina

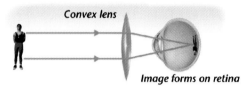

Correction
Convex lens
Image forms on retina

Figure 24 Nearsightedness and farsightedness are caused when the eyeball is a little too long or too short. Both can be corrected by wearing lenses.

Nearsightedness A **nearsighted** person can see nearby things clearly, but objects at a distance appear blurry. This happens because the eyeball is a little too long. The lens focuses the image in front of the retina. A nearsighted person can wear eyeglasses with concave lenses to see more clearly. A concave lens spreads out the rays a little before they enter the lens of the eye. This causes the image to form a little farther back, on the retina.

Farsightedness A **farsighted** person can see distant objects clearly, but nearby objects appear blurry. This happens when the eyeball is a little too short. The lens focuses the rays of light so that they would meet behind the retina. The image that falls on the retina is out of focus. A farsighted person can wear glasses with convex lenses. A convex lens makes the rays bend toward each other a little before they enter the eye. A clear image is then formed on the retina.

Section 4 Review

1. Describe briefly the function of each of these structures in allowing a person to see: cornea, pupil, lens, retina, optic nerve, brain.
2. How and why does the pupil change size?
3. What causes nearsightedness? Farsightedness? How can each be corrected?
4. **Thinking Critically** **Comparing and Contrasting** Compare and contrast the functions of the rods and the cones.

Science at Home

Roll a sheet of paper into a tube and hold one end up to your right eye. Hold your left hand against the left side of the far end of the tube with your palm facing toward you. Keeping both eyes open, look at a distant object. Draw and label a diagram of what you see. What do you think causes this optical illusion?

Program Resources

◆ **Teaching Resources** 4-4 Review and Reinforce, p. 115; 4-4 Enrich, p. 116

DISCOVER .... ACTIVITY

How Does a Pinhole Viewer Work?

1. ✂ Carefully use a pin to make a tiny hole in the center of the bottom of a paper cup.
2. Place a piece of wax paper over the open end of the cup. Hold the paper in place with a rubber band.
3. Turn off the room lights. Point the end of the cup with the hole in it at a bright window. **CAUTION:** *Do not look directly at the sun.*
4. Look at the image formed on the wax paper.

Think It Over

Classifying Describe the image you see. Is it upside down or right-side up? Is it smaller or larger than the actual object? What type of image is it?

H ave you ever seen photos of the moons of Jupiter? Have you ever thought it would be exciting to fly close to the rings of Saturn? Of course you know that traveling in space has been done for only a few decades. But you might be surprised to know that the moons of Jupiter and the rings of Saturn had not been seen by anyone before the year 1600. It was only about 1609 that a new invention, the telescope, made those objects visible to people on Earth.

Since the 1600s, astronomers have built more powerful telescopes that allow them to see objects in space that are very far from Earth. The Trifid Nebula, for example, is a cloud of gas and dust in space 28,000 trillion kilometers from Earth. It took about 3,000 years for light from this nebula to travel to Earth.

In this section you will learn how simple a device the telescope is. You may wonder why no one invented it sooner!

GUIDE FOR READING

◆ How do telescopes and microscopes work?
◆ How does a camera work?
◆ How is laser light different from ordinary light?

Reading Tip Before you read, preview the section to identify devices that use light. As you read, make notes about how each device is commonly used.

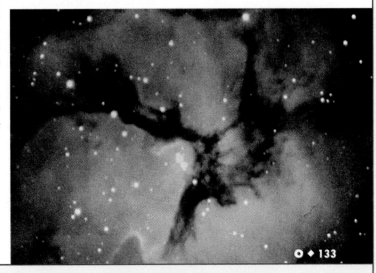

The Trifid Nebula ▶

O ◆ 133

Objectives

After completing the lesson, students will be able to

◆ explain how telescopes, cameras, and microscopes use light;
◆ describe the differences between laser light and ordinary light and list uses of lasers;
◆ identify and cite uses for optical fibers.

Key Terms telescope, refracting telescope, objective lens, eyepiece lens, reflecting telescope, microscope, camera, laser, hologram, optical fiber, total internal reflection

1 Engage/Explore

Activating Prior Knowledge

Ask students: **Can you use a camera to take pictures in the dark?** (*Answers may vary. Students may say "no" or they may suggest using a flash or a type of camera that amplifies light, such as an infrared camera or a night vision camera.*) Ask: **How does a flash help a camera take pictures?** (*It illuminates the room or the subject so that a picture can be taken.*)

.... DISCOVER ....

Skills Focus classifying
Materials *paper cup, pin, rubber band, wax paper*
Time 15 minutes
Tips You may wish to make the holes in the cups prior to the activity. Make sure students do not crumple the cup with the rubber band. As an alternative to a bright window in a darkened room, use a burning candle or light bulb to form the image. If using a light bulb, place a mark on the bulb so that students can better determine whether the image is erect or inverted.
Expected Outcome Students will see an image on the wax paper.
Think It Over The image is upside down, smaller than the actual object, and real.

2 Facilitate

Telescopes

Skills Focus classifying
Materials *2 hand lenses of different strengths*
Time 10 minutes
Tips You may wish to use a burning candle or a flashlight bulb to help students form an image. Caution students not to look directly at the sun. Have students look at a book or other object to determine which lens is stronger.
Classifying The image is a real, inverted, smaller image. This combination of lenses is similar to a refracting telescope.
Extend Challenge students to use two mirrors and one or two lenses to produce an image. Students should recognize that this is similar to a reflecting telescope.
learning modality: visual

Using the Visuals: Figure 25

As students examine Figure 25, have them recall the meanings of the terms *reflect* and *refract*. Ask: **What does *reflect* mean? What optical instruments reflect light?** (*Reflect means to bounce back. Mirrors reflect.*) Then ask: **What does *refract* mean? What optical instruments refract light?** (*Refract means to bend. Lenses refract.*) Then direct students to examine both figures and point out the lenses and mirrors in each. Students should recognize that the reflecting telescope uses mirrors and lenses, while the refracting telescope uses lenses.
learning modality: verbal

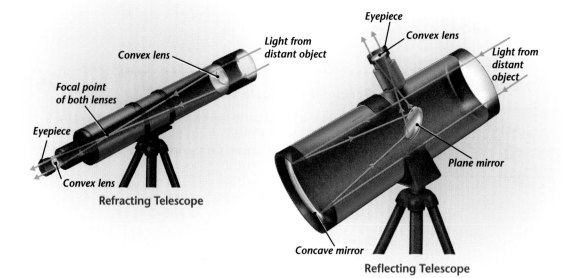

Figure 25 A refracting telescope (left) uses a combination of lenses to form an image. A reflecting telescope (right) uses a combination of lenses and mirrors to form an image.

What a View!

You can use two hand lenses of different strengths to form an image.
1. Hold the stronger lens close to your eye.
2. Hold the other lens at arm's length.
3. Use your lens combination to view a distant object. **CAUTION:** *Do not look at the sun.* Adjust the distance of the farther lens until the image is clear.

Classifying What type of image do you see? What type of telescope is similar to this lens combination?

Telescopes

Distant objects are difficult to see because light from them has spread out by the time it reaches your eyes. Your eyes are too small to gather much light. A **telescope** forms enlarged images of distant objects. **Telescopes use lenses or mirrors to collect and focus light from distant objects.** The most common use of telescopes is to collect light from space. This allows astronomers to see objects they could not see with their eyes alone.

There are two main types of telescopes: refracting telescopes and reflecting telescopes. Both types are shown in Figure 25. A **refracting telescope** consists of two convex lenses, one at each end of a long tube. The larger lens is the objective lens. The **objective lens** gathers the light coming from an object and focuses the rays to form a real image. The lens close to your eye is the eyepiece lens. The **eyepiece lens** magnifies the image so you can see it clearly. The image you see through a refracting telescope is upside down.

A **reflecting telescope** uses a large concave mirror to gather light. The mirror collects light from distant objects and focuses the rays to form a real image. A small mirror inside the telescope reflects the image to the eyepiece lens. The eyepiece can be replaced by a camera to record the image. The image you see through a reflecting telescope is upside down also.

✓ *Checkpoint* What are the two main types of telescopes?

Background

History of Science The most controversial finding of the Italian scientist Galileo Galilei (1564–1642) came from observations he made with a telescope. In 1609 and 1610, Galileo studied the Moon's surface, the moons of Jupiter, the planet Saturn, and the movements of Venus. His observations led him to conclude that Earth was not the center of the universe and that Earth revolved around the sun. This conflicted with traditional Church teachings that placed Earth at the universe's center. So threatened were the religious and political powers by Galileo's assertions, the Inquisition brought him to trial in Rome. Galileo was forced to withdraw his ideas. He was sentenced to house arrest, where he spent the last eight years of his life.

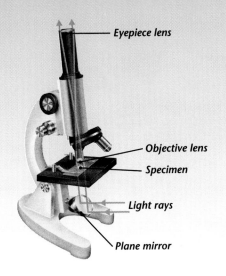

- Eyepiece lens
- Objective lens
- Specimen
- Light rays
- Plane mirror

Figure 26 A microscope uses a combination of lenses to form enlarged images of tiny objects. You can use a microscope to look at microorganisms such as these single-celled algae.

Microscopes

What would happen if you used a telescope to look at small objects close up? The principle of a refracting telescope can also be used to enlarge very small objects. A **microscope** forms enlarged images of tiny objects. **A microscope uses a combination of lenses to produce and magnify an image.**

Figure 26 shows how a microscope works. The specimen to be viewed is placed on a glass or plastic slide and covered with a coverslip. The slide is then placed on the platform of the microscope. A light source or a mirror illuminates the slide from below. The objective lens, placed very close to the slide, forms a real, but enlarged, image of the tiny object. The eyepiece lens enlarges the image even more. The image can be hundreds of times larger than the object itself. Most microscopes have two or three objective lenses so you can change the magnifying power.

Cameras

A **camera** uses lenses to focus light and record an image of an object. Cameras range from simple pinhole cameras to high-tech models used by professional photographers. They all work in basically the same way.

In a pinhole camera, rays of light from an object enter a small box through a tiny pinhole. This light forms an upside down, real image on the back of the box. However, most cameras are more complex.

Answers to Self-Assessment

☑ *Checkpoint*
Refracting and reflecting

Microscopes

Building Inquiry Skills: Observing

Materials *microscope, slide, coverslip, letter A (regular size) from a newspaper* **ACTIVITY**
Time 20 minutes

🔧 Allow students to examine and use a microscope. Begin by having them identify the objective lens, eyepiece, platform, and light source or mirror. Ask: **How many objective lenses does the microscope have? How are they different?** *(Sample: three objective lenses; they have different strengths of magnification.)* Direct students to place the letter A on a slide and cover it with a coverslip. Students should then view the letter through the lowest magnification. Ask: **Is the image erect or inverted? Smaller or larger?** *(The image is inverted and larger.)* **learning modality: kinesthetic**

Cameras

Building Inquiry Skills: Classifying

Have students draw a picture of a pinhole camera based on the description in the text, or draw one on the board. Challenge students to draw the light rays entering the camera and forming an image. Ask: **What purpose does the pinhole serve in this design?** *(The pinhole focuses the light on the back of the box so that an image forms.)* **learning modality: logical/mathematical**

Ongoing Assessment

Writing Have students write paragraphs that describe how two lenses can be arranged to enlarge an image of something that is either very distant or very small.

Cameras, continued

Including All Students

Materials *light-sensitive paper, small objects such as a leaf, coin, or comb*

ACTIVITY

Time 10 minutes, with observation after 30 minutes

Some students may need extra help to understand how light can cause an image to form on film. Have students create images of objects on light-sensitive paper by placing an object on the paper, then exposing it to bright sunlight. Students may want to use objects to create designs or pictures. After about 30 minutes, students can remove the objects and examine the paper. Ask: **What happened?** (*Where light hit the paper, it darkened. This left an outline of the object.*) Then ask: **How is this similar to what happens in a camera?** (*In a camera, film is exposed to light, and the film darkens when developed to form an image.*) **learning modality: visual**

Portfolio Students can save their images in their portfolios.

Using the Visuals: Figure 27

Have students trace the path of light through the camera, identifying each part of the camera. (*Light passes through the shutter, then the aperture, then the lens, and finally reaches the film.*) Ask students to infer whether the image on the film is inverted or upright and explain their answers. (*Inverted; it passes through a convex lens.*) **learning modality: visual**

Real-Life Learning

Explain that photographers can control the shutter speed of their cameras. A slower speed allows more light to enter the camera. A faster speed allows light into the camera briefly. Ask: **When would you be likely to use a slow shutter speed?** (*When taking an image indoors or in a darkened area.*) **learning modality: logical/mathematical**

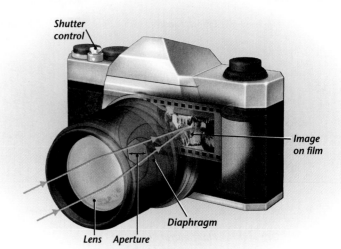

Figure 27 A camera uses a lens to project an image onto film. *Comparing and Contrasting Compare the lens, diaphragm, aperture, and film of the camera to the corresponding parts of the eye.*

Figure 27 shows the structure of a camera. The shutter is a little door behind an aperture, or hole. **When you press the button of a camera to take a photograph, you briefly open the shutter. This allows light to hit the film.** The shutter speed is the amount of time the shutter is open, or the exposure time. The diaphragm controls the amount of light that enters the camera by changing the size of the aperture. This is similar to the way that the iris of your eye controls the amount of light that enters your eye through the pupil.

Inside the camera, light passes through a convex lens or a combination of lenses. The lens focuses the light to form a real image on the film. To get a clear, properly focused image, the lens must move closer to or away from the film, depending on whether the object is close or far away. Most cameras allow you to move the lens by turning a ring on the front of the camera. An automatic camera moves the lens itself until the image is focused.

Photographic film is a material that undergoes a chemical change when exposed to light. The film is developed into negatives by treating it with chemicals. The negative is used to print the image on paper. The result is a photograph.

☑ *Checkpoint* What part of a camera controls the amount of light that enters the camera?

Lasers

In a laser show, thin beams of light flash across the walls and ceiling. These are not ordinary beams of light. The light can be focused into a narrow beam with very little spread. It can produce a clear, sharp image on a flat surface. The properties of these beams of light allow them to have many different uses.

Background

History of Science In 1953, an American scientist named Charles Townes and two colleagues produced the first device to amplify microwave radiation. They called it a *maser,* which stood for "microwave amplification by stimulated emission of radiation." In 1958, Townes and another American scientist, A.L. Schawlow, showed that it was possible to make a similar device that used light.

The first successful laser was operated in 1960 by Theodore Maiman, an American physicist who had heard of Townes and Schawlow's maser.

In 1964, Townes and two Soviet physicists (who had proposed related ideas independently) were awarded the Nobel Prize for Physics.

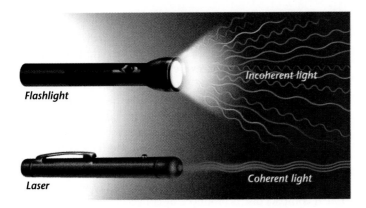

Flashlight

Incoherent light

Laser

Coherent light

Figure 28 White light is made up of many different wavelengths, or colors. Laser light consists of light of only one wavelength. All the crests of laser light are in step with one another.

When you turn on an ordinary light bulb, the light spreads out and is visible around the room. Ordinary white light is made up of light of many different colors and wavelengths. **A laser beam consists of waves that all have the same wavelength, or color. The waves are coherent, or in step.** All the crests of the waves align with one another, as do all the troughs.

The word **laser** comes from the first letters of the words that describe how it works: **l**ight **a**mplification by **s**timulated **e**mission of **r**adiation. *Light amplification* means that the light is strengthened, or given more energy. *Stimulated emission* means that the atoms emit light when exposed to radiation.

A laser consists of a tube that contains a material such as ruby or a helium-neon mixture. The material used determines the wavelength of the light produced.

Electricity, a light flash, or a chemical reaction causes the material in the tube to emit light. The light travels up and down the tube. One end of the tube is covered with a mirror. This mirror reflects all the photons that hit it. The photons then travel to a partially reflecting mirror at the other end of the tube. As the photons travel in the tube, they bump into other atoms. The atoms then emit more photons with the same amount of energy as the one that caused the collision. The photons then travel together in step with one another. This process continues until there is a stream of in-step photons traveling up and down the tube. Some of the light "leaks" through the partially reflecting mirror. The light that comes out of the tube is the laser beam.

Figure 29 This diagram of a ruby laser shows photons moving up and down the tube. The light that comes out of the tube is the laser beam.

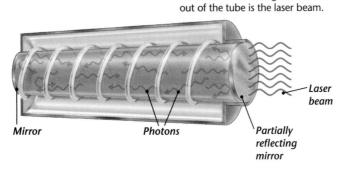

Mirror **Photons** **Partially reflecting mirror** **Laser beam**

Answers to Self-Assessment

Caption Question

Figure 27 The camera lens is similar to the cornea and lens of the eye; the diaphragm is similar to the iris; the aperture is similar to the pupil; and the film is similar to the retina.

☑ *Checkpoint*

The diaphragm

Lasers

Including All Students

Students who need additional help may benefit from translating into simpler terms the words represented by the letters that spell *laser*. Have students write the meaning of each term in their own words. Conclude by having students formulate a definition for a laser based on the meanings of each individual word. (*Sample: A laser beam is amplified light waves caused by atoms that have been excited by radiation.*) **learning modality: verbal**

Demonstration

Materials *laser pointer*
Time 5 minutes

Have students read the description of how a laser works in the text. Ask: **When I turn on the switch on this laser pointer, what happens inside the pointer?** (*Sample: The electricity will cause the material inside to release photons.*) Ask: **What happens to the photons after they are released?** (*They move up and down the tube. They have collisions with atoms and the atoms release photons. These photons combine to form a stream of light that exits the tube.*) Ask students to predict how long the photons will take to move up and down the tube before the laser beam is produced. Turn on the laser pointer to test their predictions. The beam will emerge immediately. Ask student to infer how fast the photons move inside the tube. (*At the speed of light*) Indicate to students that most laser pointers use diode or solid state technology. **learning modality: kinesthetic**

Ongoing Assessment

Writing Have students describe either how a camera uses light or how a laser produces light.

Uses of Lasers

Building Inquiry Skills: Applying Concepts

Ask a volunteer to describe a universal product code. *(A series of black bars on a white background)* Challenge students to apply what they know about color and light to explain how lasers can be used to read universal product codes. *(Answers will vary. Students should realize that the black parts of the code will absorb the light and the white spaces will reflect it. The scanner can detect the reflected light to read the code.)* Ask: **How does having only one wavelength of light make lasers a good light source to use in universal product code scanners?** *(Students should infer that the scanner can be set to look for a specific wavelength of light so outside light sources will not affect it.)* Explain that this is why scanners can be used in brightly lit stores; if they relied on white light, they could only be used in the dark. **learning modality: logical/mathematical**

SCIENCE & History

Have students make sketches that indicate how light is used by each invention. Then ask them to identify whether the invention reflects or refracts light. *(Refracts—spectacles, microscope, telescope, camera; reflects—telescope, Hubble Space Telescope, the inside of a laser)*

Extend Challenge students to identify specific ways in which their lives have been affected by each of these inventions.

In Your Journal Provide resources for students to research the early photographic process. Bring to class old photos, or copies of photos such as Matthew Brady's Civil War photographs, for students to examine and compare. **learning modality: visual**

Uses of Lasers

Lasers have many practical applications. Lasers are widely used by surveyors and engineers. A laser beam is so straight that it can be used to make sure that surfaces are level and that bridges and tunnels are properly aligned. For example, a laser beam was used to guide the tunnel diggers who dug the Channel Tunnel between England and France. Some very powerful lasers can even cut through steel. Many stores and supermarkets use lasers. A laser scans the universal product code, or bar code. The store's computer then displays the price of the object.

Compact Discs Lasers can be used to store and read information. A compact disc is produced by converting data into electrical signals. The electrical signals are converted to a laser beam, which cuts a pattern of pits on a blank disc. When you play a compact disc or read one with a computer, a laser beam shines on the surface and is reflected. The reflection patterns vary because

SCIENCE & History

Optical Instruments

The development of optical instruments has changed the way we look at the world and beyond. It has allowed major scientific discoveries.

1595 THE NETHERLANDS
Microscopes

The first useful microscope is thought to have been constructed by Zacharias Jansen or his father, Hans. The Jansen microscope could magnify images up to nine times the size of the object. By the mid-1600s, microscopes looked like the one shown here.

| 1300 | 1400 | 1500 | 1600 |

1350 ITALY
Spectacles

Craftsmen made small disks of glass that could be framed and worn in front of the eyes. Early spectacles consisted of convex lenses. They were used as reading glasses.

138 ◆ O

1607 THE NETHERLANDS
Telescopes

The first telescope was made of two convex lenses. It was from this simple invention that the Italian scientist Galileo developed his more powerful telescopes shown here.

Background

Integrating Science Photorefractive Keratectomy, or PRK, is laser surgery done to correct vision. PRK can be performed in the office of a trained opthalmologist. This form of surgery involves a computer-guided laser that makes extremely precise alterations to the shape of the cornea. A small portion of the cornea is removed; the newly shaped cornea alters the refraction of light entering the eye. This can correct nearsightedness because it alters how the light focuses on the retina. Many individuals can obtain perfect or near-perfect vision after this surgery. However, there may be complications, including hazing or scarring of the cornea, over- or under-correction, or infection. The long-term effects of the procedure are not known.

of the pits. The compact disc player or disc drive changes these patterns into electrical signals. The signals are sent to speakers and you hear sound.

Surgery Doctors can use lasers instead of scalpels to make incisions. The beam of light can be powerful enough to cut through flesh. As the laser makes the incision, it seals the cut blood vessels. This reduces the amount of blood a patient loses. Laser incisions usually heal faster than scalpel cuts, so the patient's recovery time is reduced.

INTEGRATING HEALTH

Eye doctors use lasers to repair detached retinas. If the retina falls away from the inside of the eye, the rods and cones can no longer send signals to the brain. This can lead to total or partial blindness. The doctor can use a laser to "weld" or burn the retina back onto the eyeball. Lasers can also be used to destroy or remove skin blemishes and cancerous growths.

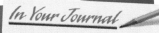
In Your Journal

Find out more about early photography and people's reactions to it. Then imagine you are an early photographer explaining photography to someone who has never seen a photo. Create a two-page dialog in which you answer that person's questions on the process and possible uses of photography.

1990 UNITED STATES
Hubble Space Telescope

This large reflecting telescope was launched by the crew of the space shuttle *Discovery*. It can detect infrared, visible, and ultraviolet rays in space and send pictures back to Earth.

| 1700 | 1800 | 1900 | 2000 |

1826 FRANCE
Cameras

The earliest camera, the pinhole camera, was adapted to form and record permanent images by Joseph Nicéphore Niepce and Louis-Jacques-Mandé Daguerre of France. This is one of Nicéphore Niepce's earliest photographic images.

1960 UNITED STATES
Lasers

The first laser, built by American Theodore Maiman, used a rod of ruby to produce light. Since then, lasers have been used in numerous ways, including in engineering, medicine, and communications.

Chapter 4 **O ◆ 139**

Media and Technology

Exploring Physical Science Videodisc
Unit 6, Side 2,
"The Nova Laser"

Chapter 10

Music Connection

ACTIVITY

Materials *compact disc and cassette recording of same piece of music, CD player, cassette player*
Time 10 minutes

Play the song first on the cassette player and then on the CD player. Instruct students to listen carefully to each. Then ask: **Which had the best quality of sound—the cassette or the CD?** *(Most students will say the CD.)* If possible, play a phonograph record of the same song. Direct students to listen for scratches and popping. Ask: **Why don't CDs make scratching and popping sounds?** *(On a compact disc, only light touches the surface. The light cannot scratch or damage the compact disc.)* Inform students that when CDs become scratched or pitted from rough handling, the sound may "skip." This happens because the laser beam is not reflected back to the detector in the CD player, so no sound is produced. **learning modality: verbal**

Integrating Health

Ask students to identify the advantages of laser surgery. *(Reduction in blood loss, quicker recovery time)* Then ask them to speculate why all surgical cuts are not yet made with lasers. *(Samples: Lasers are expensive, some tissues do not respond well to lasers, not all doctors are trained to use lasers.)* **learning modality: verbal**

Ongoing Assessment

Oral Presentation Have students choose one optical instrument from Science and History and explain how current models of each instrument work.

O ◆ 139

Uses of Lasers, continued

Using the Visuals: Figure 30

Have students trace the path of each laser light beam in the figure and indicate where the beam touches the film. Then ask: **After the beams are split, at what point do they meet again?** *(When they reach the film)* Then ask: **How does the interference pattern differ from the initial path of the beams?** *(The interference pattern is uneven; the initial path is smooth.)* **learning modality: visual**

Building Inquiry Skills: Observing

Materials *hologram*
Time 5 minutes

Allow students to see a hologram on a sticker or other object. This will help them compare the image formed to the process shown in Figure 30. Ask: **How can you alter the way the hologram looks?** *(By tilting it or viewing it from an angle)* **learning modality: visual**

Optical Fibers

Demonstration

Materials *plastic optical fiber, penlight*
Time 10 minutes

Darken the room. Hold the optical fiber in a straight line and place the penlight at one end. Show students the opposite end; they will notice the bright light. Ask students: **What do you predict will happen if I bend the optical fiber into a spiral and shine the penlight into one end?** *(Sample: The light will travel in a straight line and won't travel through the fiber.)* Then bend the fiber; the light will shine through. Ask students to infer why this is a useful property of optical fibers. *(Optical fibers can transmit light even when bent, so they can be used in narrow or curved spaces.)* **learning modality: visual**

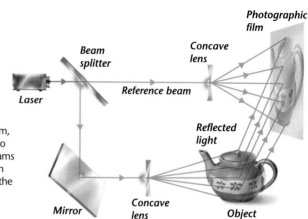

Figure 30 To form a hologram, the light from a laser is split into two beams. When the two beams strike the photographic film, an interference pattern produces the image, or hologram.

Holography Check out your local video store or newsstand. Some videos and magazines have pictures that appear to move as you walk by. A **hologram** is a three-dimensional photograph created by using the light from a laser. The process is called holography.

Figure 30 shows how a hologram is produced. A laser beam is split into two beams. One beam passes through a concave lens, behind which is a piece of photographic film. The concave lens spreads out the rays of light before they hit the film. The second beam is sent to a mirror and reflected toward another concave lens, behind which is the object being photographed. Again, the rays are spread out by the lens before they hit the object. The object then reflects these rays toward the film, where they interfere with rays from the first beam. The interference pattern between the two beams of light creates a three-dimensional image that is recorded on the film.

☑ *Checkpoint* *What are four uses of lasers?*

Figure 31 Optical fibers are thin strands of glass or plastic that carry light.

Optical Fibers

Lasers are also used in communications. A laser beam is electromagnetic radiation of a single wavelength. It is similar to radio waves and so can carry signals by modulation. Unlike radio waves, laser beams are not usually sent through the air. Instead, they are sent through optical fibers. **Optical fibers** are long, thin strands of glass or plastic that can carry light for long distances without allowing the light to fade out. You may have seen optical fibers in lamps or in the small hand-held lights that are sometimes sold at circuses and other shows.

EXPLORING Uses of Lasers

The invention of the laser has led to many developments in technology and communication.

▲ A laser beam reads information from tiny pits on a compact disc.

▲ Civil engineers use laser beams to ensure that buildings are straight.

▼ Optical fibers carry beams of laser light great distances. One tiny fiber can carry thousands more phone conversations than the traditional copper wire cable.

Small, hand-held lasers are commonly used as pointers in lectures and presentations.

▲ A supermarket scanner reflects a laser off a set of lines known as a universal product code, or UPC. Each product has a unique code. This code represents a number that is programmed into the store's computer. The computer then displays the name of the object and the price on a screen near the cash register.

◀ Banks now commonly put small holograms on credit cards for security reasons. The hologram makes credit cards difficult to copy.

▶ Laser surgery can correct vision by reshaping the cornea of the eye.

Answers to Self-Assessment

✓ Checkpoint

Lasers can be used for cutting through steel, making holograms, scanning bar codes, and storing and reading information on a compact disc.

EXPLORING
Uses of Lasers

Ask students to classify the uses of lasers as Medical, Consumer Services and Products, and Communication. *(Medical—laser surgery; Consumer Services and Products—holograms on credit cards, compact discs, and supermarket scanners; Communication—optical fibers in telephones)* Then have them calculate how many hours each day they rely on laser technology. *(Answers will vary. Many students will say that they spend several hours talking on the telephone, shopping, or listening to CDs.)*
Extend Ask students to choose one application shown and make a concept map that describes how the properties of lasers make it possible for them to be used in the application. **learning modality: logical/mathematical**

Building Inquiry Skills: Observing

Materials *glass of water, penlight or laser pointer*

Time 15 minutes

Challenge students to shine a penlight into a glass of water so that all the light is reflected and none leaves the water. Students should place their eyes level with the surface of the water, then shine the light into the side of the glass from beneath the water's surface. Allow students time to experiment to find the correct angle. If they have difficulty, they can add a few drops of watercolor paint or milk to the glass. Ask: **What happened to the light beam when total internal reflection took place?** *(It bounced back down into the water.)* **learning modality: kinesthetic**

Ongoing Assessment

Drawing Have students sketch a device that uses laser beams and draw the path traveled by the beams.

3 Assess

Section 5 Review Answers

1. Both form enlarged images of distant objects, and both eyepieces contain a convex lens. Reflecting telescopes use a large concave mirror to collect and focus rays of light. Refracting telescopes use a lens to collect and focus rays of light.

2. A microscope uses a combination of lenses to produce and magnify an image of a tiny object. A light source or mirror illuminates the object from below.

3. The light that enters a camera passes through a convex lens and forms a real, inverted image.

4. A laser beam is composed of coherent light made up of waves of all the same wavelength that are in step.

5. Any two: transmit messages in communications systems; used in medical instruments to allow doctors to examine internal organs; used in lamps and decorative lighting devices.

6. Yes. Laser beams can have enough energy to cut flesh. Because the eye allows light to enter, high-energy light can easily damage the eye.

Check Your Progress

CHAPTER PROJECT 4

As students test their instruments, coach them to identify and make any necessary changes. Have students keep a design log to keep track of modifications they make and how they affect the instrument. Students can use the information in their design logs to help them write their manuals.

Performance Assessment

Writing Have students write two short paragraphs describing the role of reflection and refraction in technological applications of light.

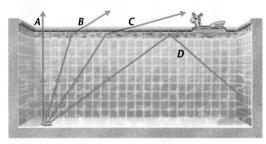

Figure 32 The angle of the light beam determines whether or not the light can leave the medium. If the angle is great enough, the light is reflected back into the water.

Figure 33 Light travels through an optical fiber by total internal reflection.

Figure 32 shows how light can stay inside a medium and not pass through the surface to the outside. When a light beam hits a surface at a 0° angle of incidence, it goes through the surface without being bent. As the angle of incidence gets larger, the light is bent more and more. When it travels nearly parallel to the surface, all of the light is reflected. This complete reflection of light by the inside surface of a medium is called **total internal reflection.** Figure 33 shows how a laser beam reflects off the inside of an optical fiber and keeps going, even if the optical fiber is curved or curled up.

Communications To send signals through optical fibers, the electrical signals that start out over copper wires are changed into pulses of light by tiny lasers. Then the signals can travel over long ranges in the optical fiber. Optical fibers have led to great improvements in telephone service, computer networks, and cable television systems. Signals sent over optical fibers are usually faster and clearer than those sent over copper wire. One tiny optical fiber can carry thousands of phone conversations at the same time. Optical fibers are so much thinner than copper wire that more fibers can be placed in the same space underground.

Medicine Optical fibers are commonly used in medical instruments. Doctors can insert a thin optical fiber inside various parts of the body, such as the heart or the stomach. The optical fiber can be attached to a microscope or a camera. In this way, doctors can examine internal organs without having to perform surgery.

Section 5 Review

1. Compare and contrast refracting telescopes and reflecting telescopes.
2. How does a microscope work?
3. Why does a camera produce an upside-down image?
4. What is a laser beam composed of?
5. Describe two uses of optical fibers.
6. Thinking Critically Making Judgments Do you think it would be dangerous to look into a laser beam? Explain your answer.

Check Your Progress

CHAPTER PROJECT 4

Now it is time to test your optical instrument. Does it work as you designed it to? Can you adjust the mirror or lenses to change the focus of the image? Do moving parts move smoothly and easily? Modify any parts of your instrument to help it work better. Prepare a manual that describes and explains each part of the instrument.

Program Resources

◆ **Teaching Resources** 4-5 Review and Reinforce, p. 119; 4-5 Enrich, p. 120

SECTION 1 Reflection and Mirrors

Key Ideas

◆ Light that strikes an object can be reflected, absorbed, or transmitted.

◆ A plane mirror produces an image that is right-side up and the same size as the object.

◆ Concave mirrors can form either virtual images or real images. Images formed by convex mirrors are always virtual.

Key Terms

opaque	plane mirror
transparent	virtual image
translucent	concave mirror
ray	focal point
regular reflection	real image
diffuse reflection	convex mirror
image	

SECTION 2 Refraction and Lenses

Key Ideas

◆ When light rays hit the surface of a medium at an angle, they bend, or change direction.

◆ The type of image formed by a convex lens depends on the position of the object in relation to the focal point.

◆ Concave lenses produce only virtual images.

Key Terms

index of refraction	concave lens
mirage	convex lens
lens	

SECTION 3 Color

Key Ideas

◆ You see an object as the color of the light it reflects. The primary colors of light are red, green, and blue.

◆ As pigments are added together, fewer colors of light are reflected and more are absorbed.

Key Terms

primary color	complementary color
secondary color	pigment

SECTION 4 Seeing Light

INTEGRATING LIFE SCIENCE

Key Ideas

◆ You see objects because of a series of steps that involve the structures of the eye and the brain.

◆ Lenses can correct some vision problems.

Key Terms

cornea	retina	optic nerve
iris	rod	nearsighted
pupil	cone	farsighted

SECTION 5 Using Light

Key Ideas

◆ A telescope uses lenses or mirrors to gather light.

◆ A laser beam consists of waves that all have the same wavelength. The waves are coherent.

Key Terms

telescope	camera
refracting telescope	laser
objective lens	hologram
eyepiece lens	optical fiber
reflecting telescope	total internal reflection
microscope	

Organizing Information

Compare/Contrast Table Copy the tables about mirrors and lenses onto a sheet of paper. Then fill in the empty spaces and add a title to each table. (For more on compare/contrast tables, see the Skills Handbook.)

Type of Mirror	How It Affects Light	Type of Image Formed
Plane	Reflects	a. __?__
b. __?__	c. __?__	Real or virtual
Convex	Reflects	d. __?__

Type of Lens	How It Affects Light	Type of Image Formed
Convex	e. __?__	f. __?__
g. __?__	h. __?__	Virtual

Organizing Information

Compare/Contrast Table
Sample title for the first table: *Mirrors;*
a. Virtual **b.** Concave **c.** Reflects
d. Virtual
Sample title for the second table: *Lenses;*
e. Refracts **f.** Real or virtual **g.** Concave
h. Refracts

Program Resources

◆ **Teaching Resources** Chapter 4 Project Scoring Rubric, p. 100; Chapter 4 Performance Assessment Teacher Notes, pp. 159–160; Chapter 4 Performance Assessment Student Worksheet, p. 161; Chapter 4 Test, pp. 162–165; Book Test, pp. 166–169

Media and Technology

Interactive Student Tutorial CD-ROM O-4

Computer Test Bank *Sound and Light*, Chapter 4 Test

Reviewing Content
Multiple Choice
1. b 2. c 3. a 4. c 5. d

True or False
6. virtual 7. true 8. black 9. true
10. Optical fibers

Checking Concepts
11. A transparent object, such as clear glass, transmits light. A translucent object, such as frosted glass, scatters light that passes through it. An opaque object, such as wood, reflects or absorbs light, but does not transmit light.

12. Both are produced when light is reflected or refracted. Virtual images are right-side up and real images are upside down. A virtual image appears where rays of light seem to focus or come from, but the rays never actually meet. A real image is formed where reflected rays actually meet at a point. It can be projected onto a screen.

13. The index of refraction is higher in materials in which light travels slowly.

14. A mirage is caused by light rays refracting as they pass through layers of air with different temperatures. The rays bend, but the eye assumes that the light has traveled in a straight line and so the image produced is a mirage.

15. The rose petals reflect red light and absorb all other colors. The leaves reflect green light and absorb all other colors.

16. To adjust the focus for near and distant objects, the ciliary muscles in the eye change the tension on the lens, which changes the shape of the lens. The lens is thicker to focus on near objects and thinner to focus on distant objects.

17. The shutter of a camera opens to allow light to enter the camera. The light from the object passes through a lens and is focused onto the photographic film, where it produces an image. The film undergoes a chemical change wherever it is exposed to light.

18. Answers will vary. Samples: Telescope, microscope, corrective lenses, or optical fibers. Students' speeches should list the instrument's contribution to society, science, technology, medicine, and entertainment.

Reviewing Content

 For more review of key concepts, see the Interactive Student Tutorial CD-ROM.

Multiple Choice
Choose the letter of the best answer.

1. A substance that does not transmit light is
   a. translucent.
   b. opaque.
   c. transparent.
   d. polarized.
2. The scattering of light off an uneven surface is called
   a. regular reflection.
   b. refraction.
   c. diffuse reflection.
   d. total internal reflection.
3. A convex lens can form
   a. either a real image or a virtual image.
   b. a virtual image.
   c. a real image.
   d. a reflection.
4. The colored part of the eye is the
   a. retina.
   b. cornea.
   c. iris.
   d. pupil.
5. A laser produces light that
   a. has many colors.
   b. spreads out in many directions.
   c. is incoherent.
   d. is coherent.

True or False
If the statement is true, write true. If it is false, change the underlined word or words to make the statement true.

6. An image that only seems to be where it is seen is a <u>real</u> image.
7. A lens that is thinner in the middle than at the edges is a <u>concave</u> lens.
8. Under green light a red object appears <u>blue</u>.
9. <u>Farsightedness</u> can be corrected by a convex lens.
10. <u>Holograms</u> are long, thin strands of glass or plastic that can carry light for long distances.

Checking Concepts
11. Explain the differences among transparent, translucent, and opaque materials. Give an example of each type of material.
12. Describe the differences and similarities between real and virtual images. How can each type of image be formed?
13. How is the index of refraction of a substance related to the speed of light in the substance?
14. Explain how mirages form.
15. Why do you see the petals of a rose as red and the leaves as green?
16. Explain how the lenses in your eyes adjust to focus on near and distant objects.
17. Explain how a camera works.
18. Writing to Learn You have been asked to nominate an optical instrument for an award. Choose the instrument that you think has played the most significant role in society. Write a nomination speech that describes several reasons for your choice.

Thinking Critically
19. Applying Concepts Can a plane mirror ever produce a real image? Explain.
20. Comparing and Contrasting How is mixing colors of light different from mixing pigments?
21. Relating Cause and Effect Explain why you can only see shades of gray in dim light.
22. Comparing and Contrasting How is a microscope similar to a refracting telescope? How is it different?
23. Problem Solving A telescope produces a real, upside-down image. If you want to see a boat that is far out to sea, how could you modify your telescope so the boat appears right-side up?
24. Making Generalizations Explain why laser light can never be white.

Thinking Critically
19. No. The image is always virtual and right-side up. A plane mirror cannot actually focus rays of light.
20. Primary light colors are red, green, and blue. Primary pigment colors are cyan, yellow, and magenta. When the primary colors of light are mixed in equal amounts, white light is produced. When the primary colors of pigment are mixed in equal amounts, they produce black.
21. Tiny light-sensitive cells in the retina called rods enable the eye to see in dim light. The rods only distinguish between black, white and shades of gray. The cones, which are sensitive to colors, only operate in bright light.
22. Similar—both use a combination of lenses to form images; different—refracting telescopes collect light from distant objects; microscopes produce enlarged images of tiny objects.
23. You could add another convex lens to invert the image again.
24. Laser light is coherent light made up of only one wavelength. White light is a combination of all the different wavelengths of light.

Applying Skills

Use the diagram to answer Questions 25–27.

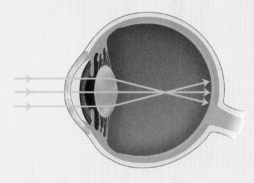

25. Classifying Which type of vision problem does this eye have?

26. Problem Solving What type of lens can correct this vision problem?

27. Communicating Copy the diagram into your notebook. Add a correcting lens to your diagram and show how the lens makes the image focus on the retina.

Project Wrap Up Demonstrate your optical instrument to your class. Explain how your instrument works and how it can be used. Present diagrams that show how the mirrors or lenses in your instrument reflect or refract light.

Reflect and Record Consider the design and performance of your instrument. What parts of the instrument worked as expected? What improvements could you make? What are the similarities and differences between your instrument and other students' instruments?

Test Preparation

Use these questions to prepare for standardized tests.

Read the passage. Then answer Questions 28–31.

As the sun sets, it is still visible for several minutes after it has really sunk below the horizon. This is because light is refracted by Earth's atmosphere. The density of the atmosphere gradually decreases as its altitude above Earth's surface increases. For this reason, the refracted rays bend gradually to produce a curved path.

Refraction can also cause the shape of the sun to appear different just before it rises or sets. When the sun is near the horizon, the rays from the lower edge are bent more than the rays from the upper edge. This makes the sun look oval rather than round.

28. What would be a good title for this passage?
   a. The Sun Sets Earlier Each Day
   b. Why Light Lingers After the Sunset
   c. How the Atmosphere Lights Earth
   d. How Sunlight Travels Through the Atmosphere

29. According to this passage, what happens to sunlight as it passes through the atmosphere?
   a. It is separated into colors.
   b. Its path curves because of reflection.
   c. Its path curves because of refraction.
   d. It is absorbed and does not reach Earth's surface.

30. How does the fact that the atmosphere is denser in some places than in others affect sunlight?
   a. It causes the light to curve.
   b. It causes the light to be reflected.
   c. It causes the light to stay in the atmosphere.
   d. It causes rainbows to form.

31. What is the result of refraction of sunlight?
   a. Daytimes are several minutes longer.
   b. Daytimes are several minutes shorter.
   c. The shape of the sun can be seen even after it has set.
   d. The sun appears round when it is really oval in shape.

Applying Skills

25. nearsightedness
26. concave
27. Students' diagrams should show how a concave lens spreads out the rays of light a little before they pass into the eye. The light passing through the lens of the eye should focus on the retina.

Project Wrap Up Students should demonstrate their optical instruments, explaining their designs and uses. Students' presentations should be accompanied by the manuals they created. Manuals should contain diagrams and descriptions of the instrument. If desired, students may base their presentations on their manuals. Each student should describe how light is reflected and refracted as it moves through the instrument, and how the instrument is affected when different components are changed. They might compare their instrument to one that is commercially available.

Reflect and Record Each student should relate the characteristics of his or her design to the instrument's performance, then explain in detail how the improvements he or she suggests will improve its performance. Similarities and differences between students' designs will mostly involve the shape and number of the mirrors and lenses they use.

Test Preparation

28. d **29.** c **30.** a **31.** a

Program Resources

◆ **Inquiry Skills Activity Book** Provides teaching and review of all inquiry skills
◆ **Standardized Test Preparation Book** Provides standardized test practice
◆ **Reading in the Content Area** Provides strategies to improve science reading skills
◆ **Teacher's ELL Handbook** Provides multiple strategies for English language learners

The Magic of the Movies

This interdisciplinary feature presents the central theme of motion pictures by connecting four different disciplines: language arts, science, mathematics, and social studies. The four explorations are designed to capture students' interest and help them see how the content they are studying in science relates to other school subjects and to real-world events. The unit is particularly suitable for team teaching.

1 Engage/Explore

Activating Prior Knowledge

Help students recall what they learned in Chapter 4, Light, by asking questions such as: **Film is loaded into a projector upside down. Is the image on a movie screen virtual or real?** *(real)* **How do you know?** *(The image is upside down compared to what was in the projector and it can be projected onto a screen.)* **What is the purpose of a lens in a movie camera?** *(A lens forms an image by refracting light.)* **What is the purpose of a shutter in a movie camera?** *(To allow light to expose the film for a brief amount of time)* **If a movie is filmed at a rate of 24 exposures per second, what does that tell you about the shutter?** *(The shutter exposes 24 frames of film every second.)*

Introducing the Unit

Have students think about what they know about how movies are made. Ask: **In what ways do movie makers need to be aware of sound and light?** *(Accept all reasonable answers. Samples: Actors must speak loudly and clearly enough to be recorded. Sound engineers make sure that unwanted background sounds don't end up on the soundtrack. Background sounds added later must match what the audience sees. Makeup artists must know how bright lights make actors appear on film.)*

THE MAGIC OF THE MOVIES

LIGHTS! CAMERA! ACTION!

• A dinosaur, 12 feet tall, roars from the forest.

• An alien spaceship lands in Washington, D.C.

• A pig calls out orders to a herd of sheep.

When you go to the movies, you expect to be entertained. You want a movie to make you laugh or cry or shiver. A movie is simply a series of pictures shown at tremendous speed on a flat screen. Even so, millions of people go to the movies every week.

Movies have been around for about 100 years. Until 1927, movies were silent and filmed in black and white. Then in the late 1920s and 1930s, the movie industry changed. Moviemakers added sound to make the first "talking pictures." Not long after that, they added color.

What makes movies so special? Much of the magic of the movies comes from the different ways in which directors use light, color, special effects, camera angles, editing, and computer wizardry. These techniques help to make a movie scene scary or exciting or romantic.

146 ◆ O

Program Resources

◆ **Teaching Resources** Interdisciplinary Explorations: Language Arts, pp. 126-128; Science, pp. 129-131; Mathematics, pp. 132-134; Social Studies, pp. 135-137

Picking a Point of View

A screenwriter writes the script or story for a movie from a certain point of view. For example, when a movie tells a story from the point of view of one main character, the audience shares that character's thoughts and feelings. The person may tell parts of the story as a "voice-over." If you were the main character telling the story, you might say, "As my wagon reached the top of the hill, I saw the beautiful sunrise." In contrast, the voice-over sometimes is given by a narrator who you don't see in the movie. The narrator tells the same story, but from a different point of view. For example, the narrator might describe the scene with the wagon by saying, "As the wagon reached the top of the hill, the light of the rising sun revealed a tired horse and an even more tired driver."

The movie *Babe* begins with a narrator's voice describing what happens to pigs when they leave

the farm. Then the camera zooms in on Babe, a pig who has the ability to carry on conversations with his animal friends. The movie alternates between Babe's point of view and the narrator's.

Often, the point of view shifts from character to character as the camera moves. In a hospital scene, for instance, the camera may look up from the patient's point of view. Then the camera may look down at the patient, representing the point of view of doctors, nurses, or family members.

Editing is key to the moviemaking process. The film editors, as well as the director, decide what the audience will see in each shot. They also plan actions and conversations that make people like or admire certain characters and dislike others.

These camera operators are filming a movie that takes place in France during the 1830s.

Language Arts Activity

Think of a story or book you have read that you would like to see as a movie. In one or two paragraphs, write a summary of the plot of the movie. Then explain what point of view you would use to tell the story as a movie. Why would you choose that point of view?

○ ◆ 147

2 Facilitate

◆ Ask students to name movies they have seen that contained voice-overs. Ask: **Did a character in the movie narrate or was the narrator an unknown person? Why did they use a voice-over?** (*Accept all answers. Sample: to tell you what happened before the story began*)

◆ Ask: **Have you ever read a book and then seen the story told on film? Did you like the film?** (*Answers may vary. Students may dislike the film because it was different from the book. Others may like seeing characters brought to life.*)

◆ Show a short portion of a G-rated movie. Try to find a portion that shows a scene shot using multiple camera angles. Most scenes are filmed this way. Show the scene once. Then discuss how directors change camera angles repeatedly to give you different perspectives on a scene.

Lead students to recognize that an editor must take thousands of pieces of film and paste them together to make the movie. Most scenes in a movie are filmed several times and the editor chooses the scene that he or she most likes.

Language Arts Activity

Students may have difficulty summarizing the plot. Suggest that students work in pairs. Partners can help each other condense the plot into two paragraphs.
Teaching Resources The following worksheets correlate with this page: Write a Script, page 126; Read a Script, page 127; and Write a Cover Letter That Sells, page 128.

3 Assess

Activity Assessment

Students' plots should be clear and concise. Students should explain what point of view they chose and why.

Background

Facts and Figures The producer of a movie is responsible for finding investors to pay for the movie's production. The producer also arranges for the movie to be distributed when it is finished.

The screenwriter describes in a script what the audience will see and hear. During production, however, the director and other personnel make changes to the script.

The director visualizes how best to make

the movie and guides the rest of the team to create a product that matches the director's vision of how the finished work should look.

Assistant directors arrange for cast, sets, and props to be in the right places at the right times according to the shooting schedule.

Casting directors select and hire performers for the different roles.

2 Facilitate

- ◆ Point out that blinking demonstrates persistence of vision.
- ◆ Explain that a motion picture is not displayed continuously. It is actually flickering on and off 24 times a second. This is faster than we can perceive, so we see it as continuous motion. If we were able to perceive that fast, we would see a constant flicker. Students who have seen footage of the earliest movies may recall noticing that they flickered because the frame rate was slower.
- ◆ If any students have a "flip book", ask them to bring it to class for other students to see. By looking at each picture, students can see how little the scene changes from page to page.

Science Activity

Urge students to read through all the instructions before they begin. Have students make 8 equal frames by measuring; students should not fold the strip.

The white strip should fit inside the black and should slide to the bottom.

If possible, bring a lazy susan to class for students to test their zoetropes.

To extend the activity, students can design their own zoetropes. Remind them that the first and last frames must be similar otherwise the zoetrope will appear jumpy.

Teaching Resources The following worksheets correlate with this page: Make a Flip Book, page 129; Make Sugar Glass, page 130; and Make a Miniature Movie Set, page 131.

3 Assess

Activity Assessment

Zoetropes will appear to animate only if they are measured correctly. If students' zoetropes do not work, show them a working one and challenge them to deduce why theirs doesn't work.

How Pictures Seem to Move

The movie opens. The film rolls, and the action begins. What is happening? A movie is a fast-moving series of small photographs projected onto a screen. The pictures appear so fast—at about 24 pictures per second—that your eyes blend them together in continuous motion. But your eyes are tricking you. You are seeing an optical illusion.

When you watch a movie, your eyes see each picture for just a fraction of a second. Then the picture is replaced by the next one. The pictures move so fast that even when one image is gone, your brain continues to see it. Seeing this after-image is called "persistence of vision." It creates the illusion of motion.

Many discoveries and inventions in the 1800s combined to make the first motion picture. For example, in 1834, a toy called a zoetrope was invented. The zoetrope contained pictures inside a drumlike device with slits. People could spin the drum while looking through the slits. The motion of the zoetrope made the pictures appear to move.

By the late 1800s, American inventor Thomas Edison was working on a movie camera. It used a plastic called celluloid to coat film. Edison made the film 35 millimeters wide, a width still used today. Edison punched holes along the edge of the film so it would wind on a spool. If you've loaded film into a camera, you may have seen these holes. In the late 1920s, moviemakers added another strip to the film that gave sound to movies.

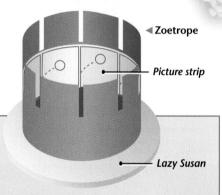

◄ Zoetrope

Picture strip

Lazy Susan

Science Activity

Make your own moving picture by building a zoetrope.

- ◆ Cut a strip of white paper 45.5 cm by 7.5 cm. Mark the strip to make 8 equal picture frames.
- ◆ Near the center of the first frame, draw a picture. Your picture should be a simple outline of an object such as an animal or person.
- ◆ Draw your object again in the second frame, but change its position slightly. Repeat the step until you have drawn the object in every frame. Remember to change its position a bit each time, as shown in the illustration below.
- ◆ Cut a piece of black construction paper to measure 45.5 cm by 15 cm.

- ◆ Mark 8 vertical slits on the top half of the black paper, each 5.5 cm apart. Cut the slits, making each 4 mm wide and 7.5 cm deep.
- ◆ Tape the black paper into a circle with the slits on top.
- ◆ Tape the picture strip into a circle with the pictures on the inside. Slide the strip inside the black circle to create your zoetrope.
- ◆ Place your zoetrope on a record player or Lazy Susan. Center it. Look through the slits as you spin the zoetrope. What do you see?

Background

Integrating Science and Technology

When a camera and projector both operate at a speed of 24 frames per second, the film is seen at the same rate at which the event occurred when it was filmed. However, occasionally scenes are filmed faster or slower.

When a scene is filmed faster than 24 frames a second and is projected at a normal rate later, the action appears in slow motion.

This effect is often useful for studying some phenomenon, such as a chameleon catching a fly, that occurs too fast for the human eye to perceive.

When a scene is filmed slower than 24 frames a second, the action will appear speeded up when projected at a normal rate. This effect is useful for studying something, such as how a plant sprouts, that occurs very slowly.

Model makers built a number of small-scale ship models to use in the movie *TITANIC*®.

Making Models

A sinking luxury liner, a fiery train crash, a city devastated by an earthquake—these scenes look real on the screen. But moviemakers don't sink ships or destroy cities. They use models.

Often a movie uses several models in different sizes. The makers of the movie *TITANIC*, for example, built a nearly full-size model of one side of the huge ship. It floated in a tank big enough to hold 65 million liters of water. Another large tank held full-size models of different rooms and decks on the ship. These models were used for scenes with actors.

The movie also used smaller *Titanic* models that were built to scale. Scale is a ratio that compares the measurements of a model to the actual size of the object. One *Titanic* model was built to a scale of 1 : 20 (1 meter in the model to 20 meters in actual size). Even so, it was still almost 14 meters long. Interior curtains and furniture were added to make the model look real. After scenes were filmed with this model, computer-generated images added water, smoke curling from smokestacks, and passengers.

Models must be to scale. For example, if a car is 3.5 meters (350 centimeters) long, a model at a scale of 1 : 16 would be almost 22 centimeters long. A larger model of the car, at 1 : 4, would be about 87.5 centimeters long.

Camera tricks make models look more real. Because miniatures weigh less than actual objects, they move differently. Instead of crashing through a wall, a model car might bounce off it. To solve this problem, directors often photograph miniatures moving slowly. This makes the models appear to move like larger, heavier objects. Other camera tricks can make a tiny model look larger and farther away.

Math Activity

Sketch a simple scene, such as a room interior or a city scene. Pick four objects in the scene and estimate or measure the actual size of each. The objects could include a chair, a person, a car, or a skyscraper. (*Note:* One story in a modern building equals about 4 meters.) Decide on a scale for your model, such as 1 : 4, 1 : 12, or 1 : 16. After determining the actual sizes of the objects, calculate the size of each scale model.

O ◆ 149

Background

Integrating Science and Technology For the movie *Mouse Hunt*, model makers and mechanical engineers used animatronics, electronic puppets. The puppet mouse had to be about four times larger than a real mouse because all the mechanical components could not fit inside the body of a model the size of a real mouse. The mouse puppet took five months to build and was operated by six puppeteers, one with a hand inside the mouse and five using radio controls. The puppet designers found that fur was very difficult to make look realistic because of the size of the model. Hair technicians spent months experimenting with different kinds of fur to find one that made the puppet look realistic on film.

2 Facilitate

◆ Expect some students to have very strong opinions about the movie *TITANIC* and to be keen to discuss issues not related to the math topic. Point out that this section is about making the models. Stress that discussions about the merits of the movie or its stars should be saved until after class.

◆ Ask: **Do you think it is easier to make full-size props or miniatures? Explain.** (*Both sizes have pros and cons. Accept all reasonable answers.*)

◆ Point out that the models described in this unit are all smaller than the original. Ask: **Can you think of a model made for a movie that was larger than the original?** (*Accept all reasonable answers. Samples: props for movies such as* Godzilla *and* Honey, I Shrunk the Kids.) Ask: **A scale of 1 : 4 means that the model is one quarter the size of the actual object. What scale would you use for a model that is twice the size of the actual object?** (*1 : 0.5 or 2 : 1*)

Math Activity

Remind students that the scale chosen must be applied to both the height and the width of the objects. The same scale must be applied in all dimensions.
Teaching Resources The following worksheets correlate with this page: The Making of *Toy Story*, page 132; Opening Weekend, page 133; and Cost of Buying Film, page 134.

3 Assess

Activity Assessment

Check that students' measures of objects and models match the scale they chose.

2 Facilitate

◆ As students look at the pictures on these pages, they may be surprised that the early movies were at all convincing. Explain that audiences were not used to special effects in those days and were as impressed by giant insects as we are with a giant lizard in *Godzilla*.

◆ Ask students: **What kinds of movies do you think people most like to see currently?** *(Answers will vary. Samples: action movies, science fiction adventures, comedies)*

◆ If you have time, you might wish students to explore how movies have influenced history. A history teacher may wish to introduce how propaganda movies were used to motivate people in good and bad ways during wartime.

Social Studies Activity

Students may have difficulty appreciating how movies today are affected by the latest social and technological developments because they cannot remember how movies in the recent past were different. Share with students the movie facts in the background below to help prompt student thinking.

Teaching Resources The following worksheets correlate with this page: Be a Location Scout, page 135; Animation in the World, page 136; and Stereotypes in Movies, page 137.

3 Assess

Activity Assessment

Examine students' lists and check that they recognize the social issues on which popular movies are based.

◆ To extend this activity, challenge students to think about what technological or social changes are likely to occur in the future and the kinds of movies that might be based on those changes.

A Trip to the Moon, 1902
This early French movie represents an astronomer's dream. In the dream, men travel to the moon inside a capsule shot from a giant cannon.

Them!, 1954
In this 1954 movie, nuclear tests in the American southwest create mutant giant ants.

Reflecting the Times

When moviemakers look for an idea for a new movie, they think first about what people are interested in seeing. Moviemakers want to know what's important to people. Advances in science and technology and recent events in history all influence people. Movies often reflect changes in people's lives.

In the early 1900s, people were just beginning to fly airplanes. Early science fiction movies of the 1920s and 1930s were pure fantasy.

By the 1950s, space flight technology was developing. In 1957, the Soviet Union sent the first satellite, *Sputnik,* into orbit. Soon after, the United States and the Soviet Union were competing in space exploration. Both nations also were making powerful nuclear weapons. The idea of nuclear war frightened people. Many movies of the 1950s and 1960s reflected these fears. Giant insects and other monsters appeared on movie screens. Science fiction movies featured alien invasions.

The "space race" continued in the 1960s. American astronauts and Soviet cosmonauts orbited Earth. In July 1969, three American astronauts became the first people to reach the moon. Later, space probes sent back pictures of other planets. These space flights made people dream about space travel. About the same time, people began using computers. Some people were afraid the new machines would control them. In the 1968 movie *2001: A Space Odyssey,* the computer HAL did just that.

Interest in space kept science fiction movies popular in the 1980s and 1990s. By that time, computers were part of everyday life. They were

Background

Facts and Figures The top three grossing movies for each year from 1990 to 1998 were:

◆ 1990: *Home Alone, Ghost, Dances With Wolves*

◆ 1991: *Terminator 2: Judgment Day, Robin Hood: Prince of Thieves, Beauty and the Beast*

◆ 1992: *Aladdin, Home Alone 2, Batman Returns*

◆ 1993: *Jurassic Park, Mrs. Doubtfire, The Fugitive*

◆ 1994: *Forrest Gump, The Lion King, True Lies*

◆ 1995: *Toy Story, Batman Forever, Apollo 13*

◆ 1996: *Independence Day, Twister, Mission: Impossible*

◆ 1997: *TITANIC, Men in Black, The Lost World: Jurassic Park*

◆ 1998: *Saving Private Ryan, Armageddon, There's Something About Mary*

E.T., 1982
E.T. is an alien stranded on Earth. He is found by a 10-year-old boy, and they become friends.

not instruments to be feared. Tension between the United States and the Soviet Union was relaxing. Movies seemed more optimistic about the future than in the 1950s. In popular movies such as *E.T.* and *Close Encounters of the Third Kind*, the human characters showed more curiosity than fear about aliens—even those that visited Earth. The movie *Men in Black* featured aliens who were more often humorous than threatening.

Social Studies Activity

Think of some recent movies that you and others may have seen. With your classmates, organize a panel discussion on the links between movies and current events. Think about the changes that have occurred in the world around you. How have space probes, planet explorations, computers, video games, the Internet, and political events influenced these movies?

Tie It Together

Making a Movie

Put your movie ideas into action. With your classmates, plan a short (10–15 minute) movie. If possible, use a video camera to make your movie. Use what you've learned about point of view, the use of scale models, and editing.

- Think of a subject or event for your movie. As a class, outline the script for the movie.
- Work in small groups to make storyboards—drawings showing key scenes in the movie.

- Choose a director, actors, a camera operator, and a film editor.
- Assign groups to plan lights, sound effects, model-building, props, background painting, and photography.
- After shooting and editing your movie, present it for other students in your school.

Time 5 days (1 day to choose roles and plan the overview; 1 day to plan each task; 2 days to rehearse; 1 day to tape the scenes)

Tips Consider performing this activity as a whole class. There are enough tasks for all students.

- Have students choose the subject of their video on the first day. Suggest that students depict on video a 10–15 minute movie from a story that they have all studied in school. Then have students brainstorm for a list of all the roles and tasks that will be needed. Record the roles and tasks on the board. To avoid conflict, assign roles to students using your best judgment of what each would be most suitable for. If students wish to exchange roles with each other, allow them to do so.
- Urge students to make their video as thriftily as possible. Students may be tempted to have excessively elaborate plans for props, backgrounds, and so on.
- Urge different groups to keep checking with each other to ensure that their goals are compatible in the areas in which they overlap. Lead students to appreciate how much communication and cooperation is required in the making of feature-length films with budgets of millions of dollars.

Extend If possible, find a video producer to talk to the class about aspects of his or her work.

Developing scientific thinking in students is important for a solid science education. To learn how to think scientifically, students need frequent opportunities to practice science process skills, critical thinking skills, as well as other skills that support scientific inquiry. The *Science Explorer* Skills Handbook introduces the following key science skills:

◆ Science Process Skills
◆ SI Measuring Skills
◆ Skills for Conducting a Scientific Investigation
◆ Critical Thinking Skills
◆ Information Organizing Skills
◆ Data Table and Graphing Skills

The Skills Handbook is designed as a reference for students to use whenever they need to review a science skill. You can use the activities provided in the Skills Handbook to teach or reinforce the skills.

Think Like a Scientist

Observing

ACTIVITY

Before students look at the photograph, remind them that an observation is what they can see, hear, smell, taste, or feel. Ask: **Which senses will you use to make observations from this photograph?** *(Sight is the only sense that can be used to make observations from the photograph.)* **What are some observations you can make from the photograph?** *(Answers may vary. Sample answers: The boy is wearing sneakers, sports socks, shorts, and a T-shirt; the boy is sitting in the grass holding something blue against his knee; the boy is looking at his knee; there is a soccer ball laying beside the boy.)* List the observations on the board. If students make any inferences or predictions about the boy at this point, ask: **Can you be sure your statement is accurate from just observing the photograph?** Help students understand how observations differ from inferences and predictions.

Inferring

ACTIVITY

Review students' observations from the photograph. Then ask: **What inferences can you make from your observations?** *(Students may*

Think Like a Scientist

Although you may not know it, you think like a scientist every day. Whenever you ask a question and explore possible answers, you use many of the same skills that scientists do. Some of these skills are described on this page.

Observing

When you use one or more of your five senses to gather information about the world, you are **observing.** Hearing a dog bark, counting twelve green seeds, and smelling smoke are all observations. To increase the power of their senses, scientists sometimes use microscopes, telescopes, or other instruments that help them make more detailed observations.

An observation must be an accurate report of what your senses detect. It is important to keep careful records of your observations in science class by writing or drawing in a notebook. The information collected through observations is called evidence, or data.

Inferring

When you interpret an observation, you are **inferring,** or making an inference. For example, if you hear your dog barking, you may infer that someone is at your front door. To make this inference, you combine the evidence—the barking dog—and your experience or knowledge—you know that your dog barks when strangers approach—to reach a logical conclusion.

Notice that an inference is not a fact; it is only one of many possible interpretations for an observation. For example, your dog may be barking because it wants to go for a walk. An inference may turn out to be incorrect even if it is based on accurate observations and logical reasoning. The only way to find out if an inference is correct is to investigate further.

Predicting

When you listen to the weather forecast, you hear many predictions about the next day's weather—what the temperature will be, whether it will rain, and how windy it will be. Weather forecasters use observations and knowledge of weather patterns to predict the weather. The skill of **predicting** involves making an inference about a future event based on current evidence or past experience.

Because a prediction is an inference, it may prove to be false. In science class, you can test some of your predictions by doing experiments. For example, suppose you predict that larger paper airplanes can fly farther than smaller airplanes. How could you test your prediction?

 Use the photograph to answer the questions below.

Observing Look closely at the photograph. List at least three observations.

Inferring Use your observations to make an inference about what has happened. What experience or knowledge did you use to make the inference?

Predicting Predict what will happen next. On what evidence or experience do you base your prediction?

say that the boy hurt his knee playing soccer and is holding a coldpack against his injured knee.) **What experience or knowledge helped you make this inference?** *(Students may have experienced knee injuries from playing soccer, and they may be familiar with coldpacks like the one the boy is using.)* **Can anyone suggest another possible interpretation for these observations?** *(Answers may vary. Sample answer: The boy hurt his knee jogging, and he just happened to sit beside a soccer ball his sister left in the yard.)* **How can you find out whether an inference is correct?** *(by further investigation)*

Predicting

ACTIVITY

After students come to some consensus about the inference that the boy hurt his knee, encourage them to make predictions about what will happen next. *(Students' predictions may vary. Sample answers: The boy will go to the doctor. A friend will help the boy home. The boy will get up and continue playing soccer.)*

Classifying

Could you imagine searching for a book in the library if the books were shelved in no particular order? Your trip to the library would be an all-day event! Luckily, librarians group together books on similar topics or by the same author. Grouping together items that are alike in some way is called **classifying.** You can classify items in many ways: by size, by shape, by use, and by other important characteristics.

Like librarians, scientists use the skill of classifying to organize information and objects. When things are sorted into groups, the relationships among them become easier to understand.

Classify the objects in the photograph into two groups based on any characteristic you choose. Then use another characteristic to classify the objects into three groups.

Making Models

Have you ever drawn a picture to help someone understand what you were saying? Such a drawing is one type of model. A model is a picture, diagram, computer image, or other representation of a complex object or process. **Making models** helps people understand things that they cannot observe directly.

Scientists often use models to represent things that are either very large or very small, such as the planets in the solar system, or the parts of a cell. Such models are physical models—drawings or three-dimensional structures that look like the real thing. Other models are mental models—mathematical equations or words that describe how something works.

This student is using a model to demonstrate what causes day and night on Earth. What do the flashlight and the tennis ball in the model represent?

Communicating

Whenever you talk on the phone, write a letter, or listen to your teacher at school, you are communicating. **Communicating** is the process of sharing ideas and information with other people. Communicating effectively requires many skills, including writing, reading, speaking, listening, and making models.

Scientists communicate to share results, information, and opinions. Scientists often communicate about their work in journals, over the telephone, in letters, and on the Internet. They also attend scientific meetings where they share their ideas with one another in person.

On a sheet of paper, write out clear, detailed directions for tying your shoe. Then exchange directions with a partner. Follow your partner's directions exactly. How successful were you at tying your shoe? How could your partner have communicated more clearly?

O ♦ 153

On what did you base your prediction? *(Scientific predictions are based on knowledge and experience.)* Point out that in science, predictions can often be tested with experiments.

Classifying ACTIVITY

Encourage students to think of other common things that are classified. Then ask: **What things at home are classified?** *(Clothing might be classified in order to place it in the appropriate dresser drawer; glasses, plates, and silverware are grouped in different parts of the kitchen; screws, nuts, bolts, washers, and nails might be separated into small containers.)* **What are some things that scientists classify?** *(Scientists classify many things they study, including organisms, geological features and processes, and kinds of machines.)* After students have classified the different fruits in the photograph, have them share their criteria for classifying them. *(Some characteristics students might use include shape, color, size, and where they are grown.)*

Making Models ACTIVITY

Ask students: **What are some models you have used to study science?** *(Students may have used human anatomical models, solar system models, maps, stream tables.)* **How did these models help you?** *(Models can help you learn about things that are difficult to study, because they are either too big, too small, or complex.)* Be sure students understand that a model does not have to be three-dimensional. For example, a map in a textbook is a model. Ask: **What do the flashlight and tennis ball represent?** *(The flashlight represents the sun, and the ball represents Earth.)* **What quality of each item makes this a good model?** *(The flashlight gives off light, and the ball is round and can be rotated by the student.)*

Communicating ACTIVITY

Challenge students to identify the methods of communication they've used today. Then ask: **How is the way you communicate with a friend similar to and different from the way scientists communicate about their work to other scientists?** *(Both may communicate using various methods, but scientists must be very detailed and precise, whereas communication between friends may be less detailed and precise.)* Encourage students to communicate like a scientist as they carry out the activity. *(Students' directions should be detailed and precise enough for another person to successfully follow.)*

O ♦ 153

Making Measurements

Measuring in SI

Review SI units in class with students. Begin by providing metric rulers, graduated cylinders, balances, and Celsius thermometers. Use these tools to reinforce that the meter is the unit of length, the liter is the unit of volume, the gram is the unit of mass, and the degree Celsius is the unit for temperature. Ask: **If you want to measure the length and width of your classroom, which SI unit would you use?** *(meter)* **Which unit would you use to measure the amount of matter in your textbook?** *(gram)* **Which would you use to measure how much water a drinking glass holds?** *(liter)* **When would you use the Celsius scale?** *(To measure the temperature of something)* Then use the measuring equipment to review SI prefixes. For example, ask: **What are the smallest units on the metric ruler?** *(millimeters)* **How many millimeters are there in 1 cm?** *(10 mm)* **How many in 10 cm?** *(100 mm)* **How many centimeters are there in 1 m?** *(100 cm)* **What does 1,000 m equal?** *(1 km)*

Length *(Students should state that the shell is 4.6 centimeters, or 46 millimeters, long.)* If students need more practice measuring length, have them use meter sticks and metric rulers to measure various objects in the classroom.

Liquid Volume *(Students should state that the volume of water in the graduated cylinder is 62 milliliters.)* If students need more practice measuring liquid volume, have them use a graduated cylinder to measure different volumes of water.

Making Measurements

When scientists make observations, it is not sufficient to say that something is "big" or "heavy." Instead, scientists use instruments to measure just how big or heavy an object is. By measuring, scientists can express their observations more precisely and communicate more information about what they observe.

Measuring in SI

The standard system of measurement used by scientists around the world is known as the International System of Units, which is abbreviated as SI (in French, *Système International d'Unités*). SI units are easy to use because they are based on multiples of 10. Each unit is ten times larger than the next smallest unit and one tenth the size of the next largest unit. The table lists the prefixes used to name the most common SI units.

Common SI Prefixes		
Prefix	**Symbol**	**Meaning**
kilo-	k	1,000
hecto-	h	100
deka-	da	10
deci-	d	0.1 (one tenth)
centi-	c	0.01 (one hundredth)
milli-	m	0.001 (one thousandth)

Length To measure length, or the distance between two points, the unit of measure is the **meter (m).** The distance from the floor to a doorknob is approximately one meter. Long distances, such as the distance between two cities, are measured in kilometers (km). Small lengths are measured in centimeters (cm) or millimeters (mm). Scientists use metric rulers and meter sticks to measure length.

Common Conversions
1 km = 1,000 m
1 m = 100 cm
1 m = 1,000 mm
1 cm = 10 mm

The larger lines on the metric ruler in the picture show centimeter divisions, while the smaller, unnumbered lines show millimeter divisions. How many centimeters long is the shell? How many millimeters long is it?

ACTIVITY

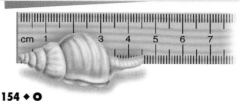

Liquid Volume To measure the volume of a liquid, or the amount of space it takes up, you will use a unit of measure known as the **liter (L).** One liter is the approximate volume of a medium-size carton of milk. Smaller volumes are measured in milliliters (mL). Scientists use graduated cylinders to measure liquid volume.

Common Conversion
1 L = 1,000 mL

The graduated cylinder in the picture is marked in milliliter divisions. Notice that the water in the cylinder has a curved surface. This curved surface is called the *meniscus.* To measure the volume, you must read the level at the lowest point of the meniscus. What is the volume of water in this graduated cylinder?

ACTIVITY

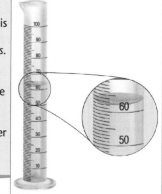

Mass To measure mass, or the amount of matter in an object, you will use a unit of measure known as the **gram (g)**. One gram is approximately the mass of a paper clip. Larger masses are measured in kilograms (kg). Scientists use a balance to find the mass of an object.

Common Conversion

1 kg = 1,000 g

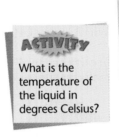

The mass of the apple in the picture is measured in kilograms. What is the mass of the apple? Suppose a recipe for applesauce called for one kilogram of apples. About how many apples would you need?

Temperature
To measure the temperature of a substance, you will use the **Celsius scale**. Temperature is measured in degrees Celsius (°C) using a Celsius thermometer. Water freezes at 0°C and boils at 100°C.

What is the temperature of the liquid in degrees Celsius?

Converting SI Units

To use the SI system, you must know how to convert between units. Converting from one unit to another involves the skill of **calculating**, or using mathematical operations. Converting between SI units is similar to converting between dollars and dimes because both systems are based on multiples of ten.

Suppose you want to convert a length of 80 centimeters to meters. Follow these steps to convert between units.

1. Begin by writing down the measurement you want to convert—in this example, 80 centimeters.
2. Write a conversion factor that represents the relationship between the two units you are converting. In this example, the relationship is *1 meter = 100 centimeters.* Write this conversion factor as a fraction, making sure to place the units you are converting from (centimeters, in this example) in the denominator.

3. Multiply the measurement you want to convert by the fraction. When you do this, the units in the first measurement will cancel out with the units in the denominator. Your answer will be in the units you are converting to (meters, in this example).

Example

80 centimeters = ___?___ meters

$$80 \text{ centimeters} \times \frac{1 \text{ meter}}{100 \text{ centimeters}} = \frac{80 \text{ meters}}{100}$$

$$= 0.8 \text{ meters}$$

Convert between the following units.
1. 600 millimeters = _?_ meters
2. 0.35 liters = _?_ milliliters
3. 1,050 grams = _?_ kilograms

O ◆ 155

Conducting a Scientific Investigation

Posing Questions

Before students do the activity on the next page, walk them through the steps of a typical scientific investigation. Begin by asking: **Why is a scientific question important to a scientific investigation?** *(It is the reason for conducting a scientific investigation.)* **What is the scientific question in the activity at the bottom of the next page?** *(Is a ball's bounce affected by the height from which it is dropped?)*

Developing a Hypothesis

Emphasize that a hypothesis is a possible explanation for a set of observations or answer to a scientific question, but it is *not* a guess. Ask: **On what information do scientists base their hypotheses?** *(Their observations and previous knowledge or experience)* Point out that a hypothesis does not always turn out to be correct. Ask: **In that case, do you think the scientist wasted his or her time? Explain your answer.** *(No, because the scientist probably learned from the investigation and may be able to develop another hypothesis that could be supported.)*

Designing an Experiment

Have a volunteer read the Experimental Procedure in the box. Then call on students to identify the manipulated variable *(amount of salt added to water)*, the variables that are kept constant *(amount and starting temperature of water, placing containers in freezer)*, the responding variable *(time it takes water to freeze)*, and the control *(Container 3)*.

Ask: **How might the experiment be affected if Container 1 had only 100 mL of water?** *(It wouldn't be a fair comparison with the containers that have more water.)* **What if Container 3 was not included in the experiment?** *(You wouldn't have anything to compare the other two containers with to know if their freezing times were faster or slower than normal.)* Help students understand the importance of keeping all variables constant except the manipulated variable. Also, be sure

Conducting a Scientific Investigation

In some ways, scientists are like detectives, piecing together clues to learn about a process or event. One way that scientists gather clues is by carrying out experiments. An experiment tests an idea in a careful, orderly manner. Although experiments do not all follow the same steps in the same order, many follow a pattern similar to the one described here.

Posing Questions

Experiments begin by asking a scientific question. A scientific question is one that can be answered by gathering evidence. For example, the question "Which freezes faster— fresh water or salt water?" is a scientific question because you can carry out an investigation and gather information to answer the question.

Developing a Hypothesis

The next step is to form a hypothesis. A **hypothesis** is a possible explanation for a set of observations or answer to a scientific question. In science, a hypothesis must be something that can be tested. A hypothesis can be worded as an *If…then…* statement. For example, a hypothesis might be *"If I add salt to fresh water, then the water will take longer to freeze."* A hypothesis worded this way serves as a rough outline of the experiment you should perform.

156 ◆ O

they understand the role of the control. Then ask: **What operational definition is used in this experiment?** *("Frozen" means the time at which a wooden stick can no longer move in a container.)*

Designing an Experiment

Next you need to plan a way to test your hypothesis. Your plan should be written out as a step-by-step procedure and should describe the observations or measurements you will make.

Two important steps involved in designing an experiment are controlling variables and forming operational definitions.

Controlling Variables In a well-designed experiment, you need to keep all variables the same except for one. A **variable** is any factor that can change in an experiment. The factor that you change is called the **manipulated variable.** In this experiment, the manipulated variable is the amount of salt added to the water. Other factors, such as the amount of water or the starting temperature, are kept constant.

The factor that changes as a result of the manipulated variable is called the **responding variable.** The **responding variable** is what you measure or observe to obtain your results. In this experiment, the responding variable is how long the water takes to freeze.

An experiment in which all factors except one are kept constant is a **controlled experiment.** Most controlled experiments include a test called the control. In this experiment, Container 3 is the control. Because no salt is added to Container 3, you can compare the results from the other containers to it. Any difference in results must be due to the addition of salt alone.

Forming Operational Definitions
Another important aspect of a well-designed experiment is having clear operational definitions. An **operational definition** is a statement that describes how a particular variable is to be measured or how a term is to be defined. For example, in this experiment, how will you determine if the water has frozen? You might decide to insert a stick in each container at the start of the experiment. Your operational definition of "frozen" would be the time at which the stick can no longer move.

EXPERIMENTAL PROCEDURE

1. Fill 3 containers with 300 milliliters of cold tap water.

2. Add 10 grams of salt to Container 1; stir. Add 20 grams of salt to Container 2; stir. Add no salt to Container 3.

3. Place the 3 containers in a freezer.

4. Check the containers every 15 minutes. Record your observations.

Interpreting Data

The observations and measurements you make in an experiment are called data. At the end of an experiment, you need to analyze the data to look for any patterns or trends. Patterns often become clear if you organize your data in a data table or graph. Then think through what the data reveal. Do they support your hypothesis? Do they point out a flaw in your experiment? Do you need to collect more data?

Drawing Conclusions

A conclusion is a statement that sums up what you have learned from an experiment. When you draw a conclusion, you need to decide whether the data you collected support your hypothesis or not. You may need to repeat an experiment several times before you can draw any conclusions from it. Conclusions often lead you to pose new questions and plan new experiments to answer them.

Is a ball's bounce affected by the height from which it is dropped? Using the steps just described, plan a controlled experiment to investigate this problem. **ACTIVITY**

Interpreting Data

Emphasize the importance of collecting accurate and detailed data in a scientific investigation. Ask: **What if you forgot to record some data during your investigation?** (*They wouldn't be able to completely analyze their data to draw valid conclusions.*) Then ask: **Why are data tables and graphs a good way to organize data?** (*They often make it easier to compare and analyze data.*) You may wish to have students review the Skills Handbook pages on Creating Data Tables and Graphs at this point.

Drawing Conclusions

Help students understand that a conclusion is not necessarily the end of a scientific investigation. A conclusion about one experiment may lead right into another experiment. Point out that in scientific investigations, a conclusion is a summary and explanation of the results of an experiment.

Tell students to suppose that for the Experimental Procedure described on this page, they obtained the following results: Container 1 froze in 45 minutes, Container 2 in 80 minutes, and Container 3 in 25 minutes. Ask: **What conclusions can you draw about this experiment?** (*Students might conclude that the more salt that is added to fresh water, the longer it takes the water to freeze. The hypothesis is supported, and the question of which freezes faster is answered—fresh water.*)

You might wish to have students work in pairs to plan the controlled experiment. **ACTIVITY** (*Students should develop a hypothesis, such as "If I increase the height from which a ball is dropped, then the height of its bounce will increase." They can test the hypothesis by dropping balls from varying heights (the manipulated variable). All trials should be done with the same kind of ball and on the same surface (constant variables). For each trial, they should measure the height of the bounce (responding variable).*) After students have designed the experiment, provide rubber balls and invite them to carry out the experiment so they can collect and interpret data and draw conclusions.

Thinking Critically

Comparing and Contrasting

Emphasize that the skill of comparing and contrasting often relies on good observation skills, as in this activity. *(Students' answers may vary. Sample answer: Similarities—both are dogs and have four legs, two eyes, two ears, brown and white fur, black noses, pink tongues; Differences—smooth coat vs. rough coat, more white fur vs. more brown fur, shorter vs. taller, long ears vs. short ears.)*

Applying Concepts

Point out to students that they apply concepts that they learn in school in their daily lives. For example, they learn to add, subtract, multiply, and divide in school. If they get a paper route or some other part-time job, they can apply those concepts. Challenge students to practice applying concepts by doing the activity. *(Antifreeze lowers the temperature at which the solution will freeze, and thus keeps the water in the radiator from freezing.)*

Interpreting Illustrations

Again, point out the need for good observation skills. Ask: **What is the difference between "interpreting illustrations" and "looking at the pictures"?** *("Interpreting illustrations" requires thorough examination of the illustrations, captions, and labels, while "looking at the pictures" implies less thorough examination.)* Encourage students to thoroughly examine the diagram as they do the activity. *(Students' paragraphs will vary, but should describe the internal anatomy of an earthworm, including some of the organs in the earthworm.)*

Thinking Critically

*H*as a friend ever asked for your advice about a problem? If so, you may have helped your friend think through the problem in a logical way. Without knowing it, you used critical-thinking skills to help your friend. Critical thinking involves the use of reasoning and logic to solve problems or make decisions. Some critical-thinking skills are described below.

Comparing and Contrasting

When you examine two objects for similarities and differences, you are using the skill of **comparing and contrasting.** Comparing involves identifying similarities, or common characteristics. Contrasting involves identifying differences. Analyzing objects in this way can help you discover details that you might otherwise overlook.

Compare and contrast the two animals in the photo. First list all the similarities that you see. Then list all the differences.

Applying Concepts

When you use your knowledge about one situation to make sense of a similar situation, you are using the skill of **applying concepts.** Being able to transfer your knowledge from one situation to another shows that you truly understand a concept. You may use this skill in answering test questions that present different problems from the ones you've reviewed in class.

You have just learned that water takes longer to freeze when other substances are mixed into it. Use this knowledge to explain why people need a substance called antifreeze in their car's radiator in the winter.

Interpreting Illustrations

Diagrams, photographs, and maps are included in textbooks to help clarify what you read. These illustrations show processes, places, and ideas in a visual manner. The skill called **interpreting illustrations** can help you learn from these visual elements. To understand an illustration, take the time to study the illustration along with all the written information that accompanies it. Captions identify the key concepts shown in the illustration. Labels point out the important parts of a diagram or map, while keys identify the symbols used in a map.

Upper blood vessel
Reproductive organs
Arches
Brain
Mouth
Bristles
Digestive tract
Lower blood vessel
Waste-removal organs
Nerve cord
Intestine

▲ Internal anatomy of an earthworm

Study the diagram above. Then write a short paragraph explaining what you have learned.

Relating Cause and Effect

If one event causes another event to occur, the two events are said to have a cause-and-effect relationship. When you determine that such a relationship exists between two events, you use a skill called **relating cause and effect.** For example, if you notice an itchy, red bump on your skin, you might infer that a mosquito bit you. The mosquito bite is the cause, and the bump is the effect.

It is important to note that two events do not necessarily have a cause-and-effect relationship just because they occur together. Scientists carry out experiments or use past experience to determine whether a cause-and-effect relationship exists.

You are on a camping trip and your flashlight has stopped working. List some possible causes for the flashlight malfunction. How could you determine which cause-and-effect relationship has left you in the dark?

Making Generalizations

When you draw a conclusion about an entire group based on information about only some of the group's members, you are using a skill called **making generalizations.** For a generalization to be valid, the sample you choose must be large enough and representative of the entire group. You might, for example, put this skill to work at a farm stand if you see a sign that says, "Sample some grapes before you buy." If you sample a few sweet grapes, you may conclude that all the grapes are sweet—and purchase a large bunch.

A team of scientists needs to determine whether the water in a large reservoir is safe to drink. How could they use the skill of making generalizations to help them? What should they do?

Making Judgments

When you evaluate something to decide whether it is good or bad, or right or wrong, you are using a skill called **making judgments.** For example, you make judgments when you decide to eat healthful foods or to pick up litter in a park. Before you make a judgment, you need to think through the pros and cons of a situation, and identify the values or standards that you hold.

Should children and teens be required to wear helmets when bicycling? Explain why you feel the way you do.

Problem Solving

When you use critical-thinking skills to resolve an issue or decide on a course of action, you are using a skill called **problem solving.** Some problems, such as how to convert a fraction into a decimal, are straightforward. Other problems, such as figuring out why your computer has stopped working, are complex. Some complex problems can be solved using the trial and error method—try out one solution first, and if that doesn't work, try another. Other useful problem-solving strategies include making models and brainstorming possible solutions with a partner.

O ◆ 159

Emphasize that not all events that occur together have a cause-and-effect relationship. For example, tell students that you went to the grocery and your car stalled. Ask: **Is there a cause-and-effect relationship in this situation? Explain your answer.** *(No, because going to the grocery could not cause a car to stall. There must be another cause to make the car stall.)* Have students do the activity to practice relating cause and effect. *(Students should identify that the flashlight not working is the effect. Some possible causes include dead batteries, a burned-out light bulb, or a loose part.)*

Making Generalizations

Point out the importance of having a large, representative sample before making a generalization. Ask: **If you went fishing at a lake and caught three catfish, could you make the generalization that all fish in the lake are catfish? Why or why not?** *(No, because there might be other kinds of fish you didn't catch because they didn't like the bait or they may be in other parts of the lake.)* **How could you make a generalization about the kinds of fish in the lake?** *(By having a larger sample)* Have students do the activity in the Student Edition to practice making generalizations. *(The scientists should collect and test water samples from a number of different parts of the reservoir.)*

Making Judgments

Remind students that they make a judgment almost every time they make a decision. Ask: **What steps should you follow to make a judgment?** *(Gather information, list pros and cons, analyze values, make judgment)* Invite students to do the activity, and then to share and discuss the judgments they made. *(Students' judgments will vary, but should be supported by valid reasoning. Sample answer: Children and teens should be required to wear helmets when bicycling because helmets have been proven to save lives and reduce head injuries.)*

Problem Solving

Challenge student pairs to solve a problem about a soapbox derby. Explain that their younger brother is building a car to enter in the race. The brother wants to know how to make his soapbox car go faster. After student pairs have considered the problem, have them share their ideas about solutions with the class. *(Most will probably suggest using trial and error by making small changes to the car and testing the car after each change. Some students may suggest making and manipulating a model.)*

Organizing Information

Concept Maps

Challenge students to make a concept map with at least three levels of concepts to organize information about types of transportation. All students should start with the phrase *types of transportation* at the top of the concept map. After that point, their concept maps may vary. *(For example, some students might place* private transportation *and* public transportation *at the next level, while other students might have* human-powered *and* gas-powered. *Make sure students connect the concepts with linking words. Challenge students to include cross-linkages as well.)*

Compare/Contrast Tables

Have students make their own compare/contrast tables using two or more different sports or other activities, such as playing musical instruments. Emphasize that students should select characteristics that highlight the similarities and differences between the activities. *(Students' compare/contrast tables should include several appropriate characteristics and list information about each activity for every characteristic.)*

Organizing Information

As you read this textbook, how can you make sense of all the information it contains? Some useful tools to help you organize information are shown on this page. These tools are called *graphic organizers* because they give you a visual picture of a topic, showing at a glance how key concepts are related.

Concept Maps

Concept maps are useful tools for organizing information on broad topics. A concept map begins with a general concept and shows how it can be broken down into more specific concepts. In that way, relationships between concepts become easier to understand.

A concept map is constructed by placing concept words (usually nouns) in ovals and connecting them with linking words. Often, the most general concept word is placed at the top, and the words become more specific as you move downward. Often the linking words, which are written on a line extending between two ovals, describe the relationship between the two concepts they connect. If you follow any string of concepts and linking words down the map, it should read like a sentence.

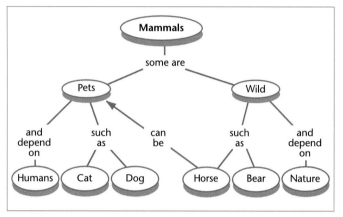

Some concept maps include linking words that connect a concept on one branch of the map to a concept on another branch. These linking words, called cross-linkages, show more complex interrelationships among concepts.

Compare/Contrast Tables

Compare/contrast tables are useful tools for sorting out the similarities and differences between two or more items. A table provides an organized framework in which to compare items based on specific characteristics that you identify.

To create a compare/contrast table, list the items to be compared across the top of a table. Then list the characteristics that will form the basis of your comparison in the left-hand

Characteristic	Baseball	Basketball
Number of Players	9	5
Playing Field	Baseball diamond	Basketball court
Equipment	Bat, baseball, mitts	Basket, basketball

column. Complete the table by filling in information about each characteristic, first for one item and then for the other.

Venn Diagrams

Another way to show similarities and differences between items is with a Venn diagram. A Venn diagram consists of two or more circles that partially overlap. Each circle represents a particular concept or idea. Common characteristics, or similarities, are written within the area of overlap between the two circles. Unique characteristics, or differences, are written in the parts of the circles outside the area of overlap.

To create a Venn diagram, draw two over-lapping circles. Label the circles with the names of the items being compared. Write the

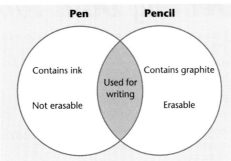

Pen   Pencil

Contains ink   Contains graphite

Used for writing

Not erasable   Erasable

unique characteristics in each circle outside the area of overlap. Then write the shared characteristics within the area of overlap.

Flowcharts

A flowchart can help you understand the order in which certain events have occurred or should occur. Flowcharts are useful for outlining the stages in a process or the steps in a procedure.

To make a flowchart, write a brief description of each event in a box. Place the first event at the top of the page, followed by the second event, the third event, and so on. Then draw an arrow to connect each event to the one that occurs next.

Preparing Pasta

Boil water
↓
Cook pasta
↓
Drain water
↓
Add sauce

Cycle Diagrams

A cycle diagram can be used to show a sequence of events that is continuous, or cyclical. A continuous sequence does not have an end because, when the final event is over, the first event begins again. Like a flowchart, a cycle diagram can help you understand the order of events.

To create a cycle diagram, write a brief description of each event in a box. Place one event at the top of the page in the center. Then, moving in a clockwise direction around an imaginary circle, write each event in its proper sequence. Draw arrows that connect each event to the one that occurs next, forming a continuous circle.

Steps in a Science Experiment

Pose a question → Develop a hypothesis → Design an experiment → Interpret data → Draw conclusions → (back to Pose a question)

O ◆ 161

Creating Data Tables and Graphs

Data Tables

Have students create a data table to show how much time they spend on different activities during one week. Suggest that students first list the main activities they do every week. Then they should determine the amount of time they spend on each activity each day. Remind students to give this data table a title. *(Students' data tables will vary. A sample data table is shown below.)*

Bar Graphs

Students can use the data from the data table they created to make a bar graph showing how much time they spend on different activities during a week. The vertical axis should be divided into units of time, such as hours. Remind students to label both axes and give their graph a title. *(Students' bar graphs will vary. A sample bar graph is shown below.)*

Creating Data Tables and Graphs

How can you make sense of the data in a science experiment? The first step is to organize the data to help you understand them. Data tables and graphs are helpful tools for organizing data.

Data Tables

You have gathered your materials and set up your experiment. But before you start, you need to plan a way to record what happens during the experiment. By creating a data table, you can record your observations and measurements in an orderly way.

Suppose, for example, that a scientist conducted an experiment to find out how many Calories people of different body masses burn while doing various activities. The data table shows the results.

Notice in this data table that the manipulated variable (body mass) is the heading of one column. The responding variable (for Experiment 1, the number of Calories burned while bicycling) is the heading of the next column. Additional columns were added for related experiments.

CALORIES BURNED IN 30 MINUTES OF ACTIVITY			
Body Mass	Experiment 1 Bicycling	Experiment 2 Playing Basketball	Experiment 3 Watching Television
30 kg	60 Calories	120 Calories	21 Calories
40 kg	77 Calories	164 Calories	27 Calories
50 kg	95 Calories	206 Calories	33 Calories
60 kg	114 Calories	248 Calories	38 Calories

Bar Graphs

To compare how many Calories a person burns doing various activities, you could create a bar graph. A bar graph is used to display data in a number of separate, or distinct, categories. In this example, bicycling, playing basketball, and watching television are three separate categories.

To create a bar graph, follow these steps.

1. On graph paper, draw a horizontal, or *x*-, axis and a vertical, or *y*-, axis.
2. Write the names of the categories to be graphed along the horizontal axis. Include an overall label for the axis as well.
3. Label the vertical axis with the name of the responding variable. Include units of measurement. Then create a scale along the axis by marking off equally spaced numbers that cover the range of the data collected.
4. For each category, draw a solid bar using the scale on the vertical axis to determine the

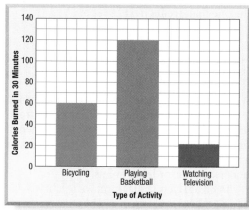

Calories Burned by a 30-kilogram Person in Various Activities

appropriate height. For example, for bicycling, draw the bar as high as the 60 mark on the vertical axis. Make all the bars the same width and leave equal spaces between them.
5. Add a title that describes the graph.

Time Spent on Different Activities in a Week

	Going to Classes	Eating Meals	Playing Soccer	Watching Television
Monday	6	2	2	0.5
Tuesday	6	1.5	1.5	1.5
Wednesday	6	2	1	2
Thursday	6	2	2	1.5
Friday	6	2	2	0.5
Saturday	0	2.5	2.5	1
Sunday	0	3	1	2

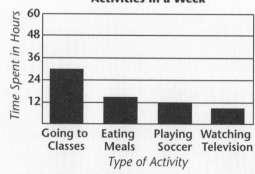

Time Spent on Different Activities in a Week

Line Graphs

To see whether a relationship exists between body mass and the number of Calories burned while bicycling, you could create a line graph. A line graph is used to display data that show how one variable (the responding variable) changes in response to another variable (the manipulated variable). You can use a line graph when your manipulated variable is *continuous*, that is, when there are other points between the ones that you tested. In this example, body mass is a continuous variable because there are other body masses between 30 and 40 kilograms (for example, 31 kilograms). Time is another example of a continuous variable.

Line graphs are powerful tools because they allow you to estimate values for conditions that you did not test in the experiment. For example, you can use the line graph to estimate that a 35-kilogram person would burn 68 Calories while bicycling.

To create a line graph, follow these steps.

1. On graph paper, draw a horizontal, or *x-*, axis and a vertical, or *y-*, axis.
2. Label the horizontal axis with the name of the manipulated variable. Label the vertical axis with the name of the responding variable. Include units of measurement.
3. Create a scale on each axis by marking off equally spaced numbers that cover the range of the data collected.
4. Plot a point on the graph for each piece of data. In the line graph above, the dotted lines show how to plot the first data point (30 kilograms and 60 Calories). Draw an imaginary vertical line extending up from the horizontal axis at the 30-kilogram mark. Then draw an imaginary horizontal line extending across from the vertical axis at the 60-Calorie mark. Plot the point where the two lines intersect.

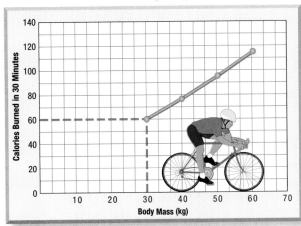

Effect of Body Mass on Calories Burned While Bicycling

5. Connect the plotted points with a solid line. (In some cases, it may be more appropriate to draw a line that shows the general trend of the plotted points. In those cases, some of the points may fall above or below the line. Also, not all graphs are linear. It may be more appropriate to draw a curve to connect the points.)
6. Add a title that identifies the variables or relationship in the graph.

> Create line graphs to display the data from Experiment 2 and Experiment 3 in the data table. **ACTIVITY**

> You read in the newspaper that a total of 4 centimeters of rain fell in your area in June, 2.5 centimeters fell in July, and 1.5 centimeters fell in August. What type of graph would you use to display these data? Use graph paper to create the graph. **ACTIVITY**

Line Graphs

Walk students through the steps involved in creating a line graph using the example illustrated on the page. For example, ask: **What is the label on the horizontal axis? On the vertical axis?** *(Body Mass (kg); Calories Burned in 30 Minutes)* **What scales are used on each axis?** *(3 squares per 10 kg on the x-axis and 2 squares per 20 calories on the y-axis)* **What does the second data point represent?** *(77 Calories burned for a body mass of 40 kg)* **What trend or pattern does the graph show?** *(The number of Calories burned in 30 minutes of cycling increases with body mass.)*

Have students follow the steps to carry out the first activity. **ACTIVITY** *(Students should make a different graph for each experiment with different y-axis scales to practice making scales appropriate for data. See sample graphs below.)*

Have students carry out the second activity. **ACTIVITY** *(Students should conclude that a bar graph would be best for displaying the data. A sample bar graph for these data is shown below.)*

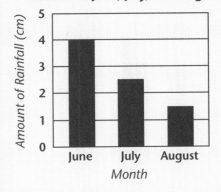

Rainfall in June, July, and August

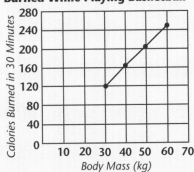

Effect of Body Mass on Calories Burned While Playing Basketball

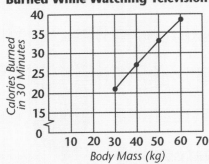

Effect of Body Mass on Calories Burned While Watching Television

Circle Graphs

Emphasize that a circle graph has to include 100 percent of the categories for the topic being graphed. For example, ask: **Could the data in the bar graph titled "Calories Burned by a 30-kilogram Person in Various Activities" (on the previous page) be shown in a circle graph? Why or why not?** (*No, because it does not include all the possible ways a 30-kilogram person can burn Calories.*) Then walk students through the steps for making a circle graph. Help students to use a compass and a protractor. Use the protractor to illustrate that a circle has 360 degrees. Make sure students understand the mathematical calculations involved in making a circle graph.

You might wish to have students work in pairs to complete the activity. (*Students' circle graphs should look like the graph below.*)

ACTIVITY

Circle Graphs

Like bar graphs, circle graphs can be used to display data in a number of separate categories. Unlike bar graphs, however, circle graphs can only be used when you have data for *all* the categories that make up a given topic. A circle graph is sometimes called a pie chart because it resembles a pie cut into slices. The pie represents the entire topic, while the slices represent the individual categories. The size of a slice indicates what percentage of the whole a particular category makes up.

The data table below shows the results of a survey in which 24 teenagers were asked to identify their favorite sport. The data were then used to create the circle graph at the right.

Sports That Teens Prefer

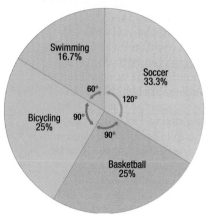

FAVORITE SPORTS	
Sport	Number of Students
Soccer	8
Basketball	6
Bicycling	6
Swimming	4

To create a circle graph, follow these steps.

1. Use a compass to draw a circle. Mark the center of the circle with a point. Then draw a line from the center point to the top of the circle.
2. Determine the size of each "slice" by setting up a proportion where x equals the number of degrees in a slice. (NOTE: A circle contains 360 degrees.) For example, to find the number of degrees in the "soccer" slice, set up the following proportion:

$$\frac{\text{students who prefer soccer}}{\text{total number of students}} = \frac{x}{\text{total number of degrees in a circle}}$$

$$\frac{8}{24} = \frac{x}{360}$$

Cross-multiply and solve for x.

$$24x = 8 \times 360$$
$$x = 120$$

The "soccer" slice should contain 120 degrees.

3. Use a protractor to measure the angle of the first slice, using the line you drew to the top of the circle as the 0° line. Draw a line from the center of the circle to the edge for the angle you measured.
4. Continue around the circle by measuring the size of each slice with the protractor. Start measuring from the edge of the previous slice so the wedges do not overlap. When you are done, the entire circle should be filled in.
5. Determine the percentage of the whole circle that each slice represents. To do this, divide the number of degrees in a slice by the total number of degrees in a circle (360), and multiply by 100%. For the "soccer" slice, you can find the percentage as follows:

$$\frac{120}{360} \times 100\% = 33.3\%$$

6. Use a different color to shade in each slice. Label each slice with the name of the category and with the percentage of the whole it represents.
7. Add a title to the circle graph.

ACTIVITY

In a class of 28 students, 12 students take the bus to school, 10 students walk, and 6 students ride their bicycles. Create a circle graph to display these data.

Ways Students Get to School

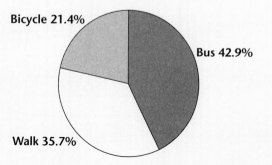

Bicycle 21.4%

Bus 42.9%

Walk 35.7%

Laboratory Safety

Safety Symbols

These symbols alert you to possible dangers in the laboratory and remind you to work carefully.

Safety Goggles Always wear safety goggles to protect your eyes in any activity involving chemicals, flames or heating, or the possibility of broken glassware.

Lab Apron Wear a laboratory apron to protect your skin and clothing from damage.

Breakage You are working with materials that may be breakable, such as glass containers, glass tubing, thermometers, or funnels. Handle breakable materials with care. Do not touch broken glassware.

Heat-resistant Gloves Use an oven mitt or other hand protection when handling hot materials. Hot plates, hot glassware, or hot water can cause burns. Do not touch hot objects with your bare hands.

Heating Use a clamp or tongs to pick up hot glassware. Do not touch hot objects with your bare hands.

Sharp Object Pointed-tip scissors, scalpels, knives, needles, pins, or tacks are sharp. They can cut or puncture your skin. Always direct a sharp edge or point away from yourself and others. Use sharp instruments only as instructed.

Electric Shock Avoid the possibility of electric shock. Never use electrical equipment around water, or when the equipment is wet or your hands are wet. Be sure cords are untangled and cannot trip anyone. Disconnect the equipment when it is not in use.

Corrosive Chemical You are working with an acid or another corrosive chemical. Avoid getting it on your skin or clothing, or in your eyes. Do not inhale the vapors. Wash your hands when you are finished with the activity.

Poison Do not let any poisonous chemical come in contact with your skin, and do not inhale its vapors. Wash your hands when you are finished with the activity.

Physical Safety When an experiment involves physical activity, take precautions to avoid injuring yourself or others. Follow instructions from your teacher. Alert your teacher if there is any reason you should not participate in the activity.

Animal Safety Treat live animals with care to avoid harming the animals or yourself. Working with animal parts or preserved animals also may require caution. Wash your hands when you are finished with the activity.

Plant Safety Handle plants in the laboratory or during field work only as directed by your teacher. If you are allergic to certain plants, tell your teacher before doing an activity in which those plants are used. Avoid touching harmful plants such as poison ivy, poison oak, or poison sumac, or plants with thorns. Wash your hands when you are finished with the activity.

Flames You may be working with flames from a lab burner, candle, or matches. Tie back loose hair and clothing. Follow instructions from your teacher about lighting and extinguishing flames.

No Flames Flammable materials may be present. Make sure there are no flames, sparks, or other exposed heat sources present.

Fumes When poisonous or unpleasant vapors may be involved, work in a ventilated area. Avoid inhaling vapors directly. Only test an odor when directed to do so by your teacher, and use a wafting motion to direct the vapor toward your nose.

Disposal Chemicals and other laboratory materials used in the activity must be disposed of safely. Follow the instructions from your teacher.

Hand Washing Wash your hands thoroughly when finished with the activity. Use antibacterial soap and warm water. Lather both sides of your hands and between your fingers. Rinse well.

General Safety Awareness You may see this symbol when none of the symbols described earlier appears. In this case, follow the specific instructions provided. You may also see this symbol when you are asked to develop your own procedure in a lab. Have your teacher approve your plan before you go further.

Laboratory Safety

Laboratory safety is an essential element of a successful science class. It is important for you to emphasize laboratory safety to students. Students need to understand exactly what is safe and unsafe behavior, and what the rationale is behind each safety rule.

Review with students the Safety Symbols and Science Safety Rules listed on this and the next two pages. Then follow the safety guidelines below to ensure that your classroom will be a safe place for students to learn science.

◆ Post safety rules in the classroom and review them regularly with students.

◆ Familiarize yourself with the safety procedures for each activity before introducing it to your students.

◆ Review specific safety precautions with students before beginning every science activity.

◆ Always act as an exemplary role model by displaying safe behavior.

◆ Know how to use safety equipment, such as fire extinguishers and fire blankets, and always have it accessible.

◆ Have students practice leaving the classroom quickly and orderly to prepare them for emergencies.

◆ Explain to students how to use the intercom or other available means of communication to get help during an emergency.

◆ Never leave students unattended while they are engaged in science activities.

◆ Provide enough space for students to safely carry out science activities.

◆ Keep your classroom and all science materials in proper condition. Replace worn or broken items.

◆ Instruct students to report all accidents and injuries to you immediately.

Laboratory Safety

Additional tips are listed below for the Science Safety Rules discussed on these two pages. Please keep these tips in mind when you carry out science activities in your classroom.

General Precautions

- For open-ended activities such as Chapter Projects, go over general safety guidelines with students. Have students submit their procedures or design plans in writing and check them for safety considerations.
- In an activity where students are directed to taste something, be sure to store the material in clean, *nonscience* containers. Distribute the material to students in *new* plastic or paper dispensables, which should be discarded after the tasting. Tasting or eating should never be done in a lab classroom.
- During physical activity, make sure students do not overexert themselves.
- Remind students to handle microscopes and telescopes with care to avoid breakage.

Heating and Fire Safety

- No flammable substances should be in use around hot plates, light bulbs, or open flames.
- Test tubes should be heated only in water baths.
- Students should be permitted to strike matches to light candles or burners *only* with strict supervision. When possible, you should light the flames, especially when working with younger students.
- Be sure to have proper ventilation when fumes are produced during a procedure.
- All electrical equipment used in the lab should have GFI switches.

Using Chemicals Safely

- When students use both chemicals and microscopes in one activity, microscopes should be in a separate part of the room from the chemicals so that when students remove their goggles to use the microscopes, their eyes are not at risk.

Science Safety Rules

To prepare yourself to work safely in the laboratory, read over the following safety rules. Then read them a second time. Make sure you understand and follow each rule. Ask your teacher to explain any rules you do not understand.

Dress Code

1. To protect yourself from injuring your eyes, wear safety goggles whenever you work with chemicals, burners, glassware, or any substance that might get into your eyes. If you wear contact lenses, notify your teacher.
2. Wear a lab apron or coat whenever you work with corrosive chemicals or substances that can stain.
3. Tie back long hair to keep it away from any chemicals, flames, or equipment.
4. Remove or tie back any article of clothing or jewelry that can hang down and touch chemicals, flames, or equipment. Roll up or secure long sleeves.
5. Never wear open shoes or sandals.

General Precautions

6. Read all directions for an experiment several times before beginning the activity. Carefully follow all written and oral instructions. If you are in doubt about any part of the experiment, ask your teacher for assistance.
7. Never perform activities that are not assigned or authorized by your teacher. Obtain permission before "experimenting" on your own. Never handle any equipment unless you have specific permission.
8. Never perform lab activities without direct supervision.
9. Never eat or drink in the laboratory.
10. Keep work areas clean and tidy at all times. Bring only notebooks and lab manuals or written lab procedures to the work area. All other items, such as purses and backpacks, should be left in a designated area.
11. Do not engage in horseplay.

First Aid

12. Always report all accidents or injuries to your teacher, no matter how minor. Notify your teacher immediately about any fires.
13. Learn what to do in case of specific accidents, such as getting acid in your eyes or on your skin. (Rinse acids from your body with lots of water.)
14. Be aware of the location of the first-aid kit, but do not use it unless instructed by your teacher. In case of injury, your teacher should administer first aid. Your teacher may also send you to the school nurse or call a physician.
15. Know the location of emergency equipment, such as the fire extinguisher and fire blanket, and know how to use it.
16. Know the location of the nearest telephone and whom to contact in an emergency.

Heating and Fire Safety

17. Never use a heat source, such as a candle, burner, or hot plate, without wearing safety goggles.
18. Never heat anything unless instructed to do so. A chemical that is harmless when cool may be dangerous when heated.
19. Keep all combustible materials away from flames. Never use a flame or spark near a combustible chemical.
20. Never reach across a flame.
21. Before using a laboratory burner, make sure you know proper procedures for lighting and adjusting the burner, as demonstrated by your teacher. Do not touch the burner. It may be hot. And never leave a lighted burner unattended!
22. Chemicals can splash or boil out of a heated test tube. When heating a substance in a test tube, make sure that the mouth of the tube is not pointed at you or anyone else.
23. Never heat a liquid in a closed container. The expanding gases produced may blow the container apart.
24. Before picking up a container that has been heated, hold the back of your hand near it. If you can feel heat on the back of your hand, the container is too hot to handle. Use an oven mitt to pick up a container that has been heated.

Using Glassware Safely

- Use plastic containers, graduated cylinders, and beakers whenever possible. If using glass, students should wear safety goggles.
- Use only nonmercury thermometers with anti-roll protectors.
- Check all glassware periodically for chips and scratches, which can cause cuts and breakage.

Using Chemicals Safely

25. Never mix chemicals "for the fun of it." You might produce a dangerous, possibly explosive substance.

26. Never put your face near the mouth of a container that holds chemicals. Many chemicals are poisonous. Never touch, taste, or smell a chemical unless you are instructed by your teacher to do so.

27. Use only those chemicals needed in the activity. Read and double-check labels on supply bottles before removing any chemicals. Take only as much as you need. Keep all containers closed when chemicals are not being used.

28. Dispose of all chemicals as instructed by your teacher. To avoid contamination, never return chemicals to their original containers. Never simply pour chemicals or other substances into the sink or trash containers.

29. Be extra careful when working with acids or bases. Pour all chemicals over the sink or a container, not over your work surface.

30. If you are instructed to test for odors, use a wafting motion to direct the odors to your nose. Do not inhale the fumes directly from the container.

31. When mixing an acid and water, always pour the water into the container first and then add the acid to the water. Never pour water into an acid.

32. Take extreme care not to spill any material in the laboratory. Wash chemical spills and splashes immediately with plenty of water. Immediately begin rinsing with water any acids that get on your skin or clothing, and notify your teacher of any acid spill at the same time.

Using Glassware Safely

33. Never force glass tubing or thermometers into a rubber stopper or rubber tubing. Have your teacher insert the glass tubing or thermometer if required for an activity.

34. If you are using a laboratory burner, use a wire screen to protect glassware from any flame. Never heat glassware that is not thoroughly dry on the outside.

35. Keep in mind that hot glassware looks cool. Never pick up glassware without first checking to see if it is hot. Use an oven mitt. See rule 24.

36. Never use broken or chipped glassware. If glassware breaks, notify your teacher and dispose of the glassware in the proper broken-glassware container. Never handle broken glass with your bare hands.

37. Never eat or drink from lab glassware.

38. Thoroughly clean glassware before putting it away.

Using Sharp Instruments

39. Handle scalpels or other sharp instruments with extreme care. Never cut material toward you; cut away from you.

40. Immediately notify your teacher if you cut your skin when working in the laboratory.

Animal and Plant Safety

41. Never perform experiments that cause pain, discomfort, or harm to animals. This rule applies at home as well as in the classroom.

42. Animals should be handled only if absolutely necessary. Your teacher will instruct you as to how to handle each animal species brought into the classroom.

43. If you know that you are allergic to certain plants, molds, or animals, tell your teacher before doing an activity in which these are used.

44. During field work, protect your skin by wearing long pants, long sleeves, socks, and closed shoes. Know how to recognize the poisonous plants and fungi in your area, as well as plants with thorns, and avoid contact with them. Never eat any part of a plant or fungus.

45. Wash your hands thoroughly after handling animals or a cage containing animals. Wash your hands when you are finished with any activity involving animal parts, plants, or soil.

End-of-Experiment Rules

46. After an experiment has been completed, turn off all burners or hot plates. If you used a gas burner, check that the gas-line valve to the burner is off. Unplug hot plates.

47. Turn off and unplug any other electrical equipment that you used.

48. Clean up your work area and return all equipment to its proper place.

49. Dispose of waste materials as instructed by your teacher.

50. Wash your hands after every experiment.

Using Sharp Instruments

◆ Always use blunt-tip safety scissors, except when pointed-tip scissors are required.

Animal and Plant Safety

◆ When working with live animals or plants, check ahead of time for students who may have allergies to the specimens.

◆ When growing bacteria cultures, use only disposable petri dishes. After streaking, the dishes should be sealed and not opened again by students. After the lab, students should return the unopened dishes to you. Students should wash their hands with antibacterial soap.

◆ Two methods are recommended for the safe disposal of bacteria cultures. *First method:* Autoclave the petri dishes and discard without opening. *Second method:* If no autoclave is available, carefully open the dishes (never have a student do this) and pour full-strength bleach into the dishes and let stand for a day. Then pour the bleach from the petri dishes down a drain and flush the drain with lots of water. Tape the petri dishes back together and place in a sealed plastic bag. Wrap the plastic bag with a brown paper bag or newspaper and tape securely. Throw the sealed package in the trash. Thoroughly disinfect the work area with bleach.

◆ To grow mold, use a new, sealable plastic bag that is two to three times larger than the material to be placed inside. Seal the bag and tape it shut. After the bag is sealed, students should not open it. To dispose of the bag and mold culture, make a small cut near an edge of the bag and cook in a microwave oven on high setting for at least 1 minute. Discard the bag according to local ordinance, usually in the trash.

◆ Students should wear disposable nitrile, latex, or food-handling gloves when handling live animals or nonliving specimens.

End-of-Experiment Rules

◆ Always have students use antibacterial soap for washing their hands.

A

acoustics The study of how well sounds can be heard in a particular room or hall. (p. 58)

amplitude modulation Method of transmitting radio signals by changing the amplitude of the waves. (p. 97)

amplitude The maximum distance the particles of a medium move away from their rest positions as a wave passes through the medium. (p. 19)

angle of incidence The angle between an incoming wave and an imaginary line drawn perpendicular to the surface of the barrier or new medium. (p. 24)

angle of reflection The angle between a reflected wave and an imaginary line drawn perpendicular to the surface of the barrier. (p. 24)

antinode A point of maximum amplitude on a standing wave. (p. 28)

B

beats The regular changes in loudness of a sound when two sounds of different frequencies are played together. (p. 59)

bioluminescence Light produced by organisms as a result of a chemical reaction. (p. 93)

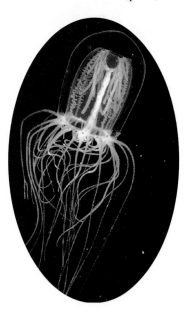

C

camera Optical instrument that uses lenses to focus light and record an image of an object. (p. 135)

cochlea A fluid-filled cavity behind the inner ear. (p. 63)

complementary colors Any two colors that combine to form white light or black pigment. (p. 126)

compression The part of a longitudinal wave where the particles of the medium are close together. (p. 17)

concave lens A lens that is thinner in the center than at the edges. (p. 120)

concave mirror A mirror with a surface that curves inward. (p. 115)

cones Cells on the retina that detect color. (p. 131)

constructive interference The interference that occurs when two waves combine to make a wave with a larger amplitude. (p. 26)

controlled experiment An experiment in which all factors except one are kept constant. (p. 157)

convex lens A lens that is thicker in the center than at the edges. (p. 120)

convex mirror A mirror with a surface that curves outward. (p. 116)

cornea The transparent front surface of the eye. (p. 130)

crest The highest part of a transverse wave. (p. 16)

D

decibel (dB) A unit of measurement of loudness. (p. 47)

density Ratio of the mass of a substance to its volume. (p. 43)

destructive interference The interference that occurs when two waves combine to make a wave with a smaller amplitude. (p. 27)

diffraction The bending of waves around a barrier. (p. 26)

diffuse reflection Reflection that occurs when parallel rays of light hit a rough surface and all reflect at different angles. (p. 113)

dissonance The sound produced when notes that have no musical relationship are played together. (p. 55)

Doppler effect The apparent change in frequency of a sound as the source moves in relation to the listener. (p. 50)

E

ear canal A narrow region leading from the outside of the human ear to the eardrum. (p. 62)

eardrum A small, tightly stretched, drumlike membrane in the ear. (p. 63)

echolocation The use of reflection of sound waves to navigate and to locate prey. (p. 68)

elasticity The ability of a material to bounce back after being disturbed. (p. 43)

electromagnetic radiation The energy transferred by electromagnetic waves. (p. 77)

electromagnetic spectrum The range of electro-magnetic waves placed in a certain order. (p. 81)

electromagnetic waves Transverse waves that transfer electric and magnetic energy. (p. 77)

energy The ability to do work. (p. 14)

eyepiece lens A lens that magnifies the image formed by the objective lens. (p. 134)

farsightedness Condition that causes a person to see nearby objects as blurry. (p. 132)

fluorescent lights Lights that glow when an electric current causes ultraviolet waves to strike a coating inside a tube. (p. 91)

focal point The point at which rays of light meet, or appear to meet, after being reflected (or refracted) by a mirror (or a lens). (p. 115)

frequency modulation Method of transmitting radio signals by changing the frequency of the waves. (p. 98)

frequency The number of complete waves that pass a given point in a certain amount of time. (p. 22)

gamma rays Electromagnetic waves with the shortest wavelengths and highest frequencies. (p. 88)

hertz (Hz) Unit of measurement for frequency. (p. 22)

hologram A three-dimensional photograph formed by the interference between two laser beams. (p. 140)

hypothesis A possible explanation for a set of observations or answer to a scientific question; must be testable. (p. 156)

illuminated Words used to describe an object that can be seen because it reflects light. (p. 90)

image A copy of an object formed by reflected or refracted rays of light. (p. 114)

incandescent lights Lights that glow when something inside them gets hot. (p. 90)

index of refraction The amount a ray of light bends when it passes from one medium to another. (p. 118)

infrared rays Electromagnetic waves with higher frequencies and shorter wavelengths than radio waves. (p. 83)

infrasound Sound waves with frequencies below 20 Hz. (p. 48)

intensity The amount of energy per second carried through a unit area by a wave. (p. 46)

interference The interaction between waves that meet. (p. 26)

iris The ring of colored muscle around the pupil of the eye. (p. 130)

larynx Two folds of tissue that make up the human voice box. (p. 41)

laser A device that produces coherent light. (p. 137)

lens A curved piece of glass or other transparent material that is used to refract light. (p. 120)

longitudinal wave A wave that moves the medium parallel to the direction in which the wave travels. (p. 16)

loudness Perception of the intensity of a sound. (p. 47)

luminous Word used to describe an object that can be seen because it emits light. (p. 90)

magnetic resonance imaging (MRI) A process that uses radio waves to form pictures of the inside of the human body. (p. 83)

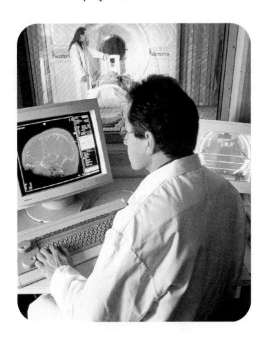

manipulated variable The one factor that a scientist changes during an experiment. (p. 157)

mechanical wave A wave that requires a medium through which to travel. (p. 15)

medium Material through which a wave travels. (p. 15)

microscope Optical instrument that forms enlarged images of tiny objects. (p. 135)

microwaves Radio waves with the shortest wavelengths and the highest frequencies. (p. 81)

middle ear The space behind the eardrum. (p. 63)

mirage An image of a distant object caused by refraction of light as it travels through air of varying temperature. (p. 119)

music A set of tones and overtones combined in ways that are pleasing to the ear. (p. 54)

nearsightedness Condition that causes a person to see distant objects as blurry. (p. 132)

neon lights Glass tubes filled with neon that produce light. (p. 92)

node A point of zero amplitude on a standing wave. (p. 28)

noise A mixture of sound waves with no pleasing timbre and no identifiable pitch. (p. 55)

objective lens Lens that gathers light from an object and forms a real image. (p. 134)

opaque A material that reflects or absorbs all light that strikes it. (p. 112)

operational definition A statement that describes how a particular variable is to be measured or a term is to be defined. (p. 157)

optical fiber Long, thin strand of glass or plastic that can carry light for long distances without allowing the light to fade out. (p. 140)

optic nerve Short, thick nerve that carries signals from the eye to the brain. (p. 131)

photoelectric effect The movement of electrons in a substance when light is shined on it. (p. 79)

photon A tiny particle or packet of light energy. (p. 79)

pigment An opaque substance used to color other materials. (p. 126)

pitch Perception of the frequency of a sound. (p. 48)

plane mirror A flat mirror that produces an upright, virtual image the same size as the object. (p. 114)

polarized light Light that vibrates in only one direction. (p. 78)

primary colors Three colors that can be used to make any other color. (p. 125)

primary wave A longitudinal seismic wave. (p. 33)

pupil The hole through which light enters the eye. (p. 130)

radar A system of detecting reflected radio waves. (p. 82)

radio waves Electromagnetic waves with the longest wavelengths and lowest frequencies. (p. 81)

rarefaction The part of a longitudinal wave where the particles of the medium are far apart. (p. 17)

ray Straight line used to represent a light wave. (p. 113)

real image An inverted image formed where rays of light meet. (p. 115)

reflecting telescope Telescope that uses a concave mirror to gather light from distant objects. (p. 134)

reflection The bouncing back of a wave when it hits a surface through which it cannot pass. (p. 24)

refracting telescope Telescope that uses two convex lenses to form images. (p. 134)

refraction The bending of waves as they enter a different medium. (p. 25)

regular reflection Reflection that occurs when parallel rays of light hit a smooth surface and all reflect at the same angle. (p. 113)

resonance The increase in the amplitude of vibration that occurs when external vibrations match the object's natural frequency. (p. 28)

responding variable The factor that changes as a result of changes to the manipulated variable in an experiment. (p. 157)

retina The layer of cells that lines the inside of the eyeball. (p. 131)

rods Cells on the retina that detect dim light. (p. 131)

secondary color Any color produced by combining equal amounts of any two primary colors. (p. 125)

secondary wave A transverse seismic wave. (p. 33)

seismic wave A wave produced by an earthquake. (p. 33)

seismograph Instrument used to detect and measure earthquakes. (p. 34)

sodium vapor lights Bulbs containing solid sodium plus neon and argon gas that produce light. (p. 92)

sonar A system of detecting reflected sound waves. (p. 67)

sonogram An image formed by an ultrasound machine. (p. 69)

sound A disturbance that travels through a medium as a longitudinal wave. (p. 40)

spectroscope An instrument used to view the different colors of light produced by different sources. (p. 90)

standing wave A wave that appears to stand in one place, even though it is really two waves interfering as they pass through each other. (p. 27)

surface wave A wave that occurs at the surface between two mediums. (p. 17)

telescope Optical instrument that forms enlarged images of distant objects. (p. 134)

thermogram An image that shows regions of different temperatures in different colors. (p. 85)

timbre The overall quality of a sound. (p. 53)

total internal reflection Complete reflection of light by the inside surface of a medium. (p. 142)

translucent A material that scatters light as it passes through. (p. 112)

transparent A material that transmits light. (p. 112)

transverse wave A wave that moves the medium in a direction perpendicular to the direction in which the wave travels. (p. 16)

trough The lowest part of a transverse wave. (p. 16)

tsunami Surface wave on the ocean caused by an underwater earthquake. (p. 33)

tungsten-halogen lights Bulbs containing a tungsten filament and a halogen gas that produce light. (p. 93)

ultrasound Sound waves with frequencies above 20,000 Hz. (p. 48)

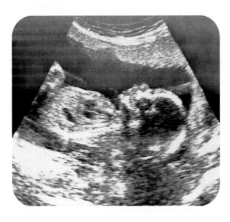

ultraviolet rays Electromagnetic waves with frequencies higher than visible light, but lower than X-rays. (p. 86)

variable Any factor that can change in an experiment. (p. 157)

vibration A repeated back-and-forth or up-and-down motion. (p. 15)

virtual image An upright image formed where rays of light appear to meet or come from. (p. 114)

visible light Electromagnetic waves that are visible to the human eye. (p. 86)

wave A disturbance that transfers energy from place to place. (p. 14)

wavelength The distance between two corresponding parts of a wave. (p. 21)

X-rays Electromagnetic waves with higher frequencies than ultraviolet rays, but shorter than gamma rays. (p. 87)

Acknowledgments

Staff Credits

The people who made up the **Science Explorer** team—representing design services, editorial, editorial services, electronic publishing technology, manufacturing & inventory planning, marketing, marketing services, market research, online services & multimedia development, production services, product planning, project office, and publishing processes—are listed below.

Carolyn Belanger, Barbara A. Bertell, Suzanne Biron, Peggy Bliss, Peter W. Brooks, Christopher R. Brown, Greg Cantone, Jonathan Cheney, Todd Christy, Lisa J. Clark, Patrick Finbarr Connolly, Edward Cordero, Robert Craton, Patricia Cully, Patricia M. Dambry, Kathleen J. Dempsey, Judy Elgin, Gayle Connolly Fedele, Frederick Fellows, Barbara Foster, Paula Foye, Loree Franz, Donald P. Gagnon Jr., Paul J. Gagnon, Joel Gendler, Elizabeth Good, Robert M. Graham, Kerri Hoar, Joanne Hudson, Linda D. Johnson, Anne Jones, Toby Klang, Carolyn Langley, Russ Lappa, Carolyn Lock, Cheryl Mahan, Dotti Marshall, Meredith Mascola, Jeanne Y. Maurand, Karen McHugh, Eve Melnechuk, Natania Mlawer, Paul W. Murphy, Cindy A. Noftle, Julia F. Osborne, Judi Pinkham, Caroline M. Power, Robin L. Santel, Suzanne J. Schineller, Emily Soltanoff, Kira Thaler-Marbit, Mark Tricca, Diane Walsh, Pearl Weinstein, Merce Wilczek, Helen Young.

Illustration

Carmella M. Clifford: 63tl
Kathy Dempsey: 20ctr, 30, 45, 60, 94, 122, 128
John Edwards & Associates: 15, 16, 17, 25, 26, 37, 41t, 50, 51, 104, 105, 106
David Fuller: 100br
Andrea Golden: 148
Jared Lee: 42, 62, 76
Martucci Design: 81, 162, 163, 164
Matt Mayerchak: 35, 71, 107, 160, 161
William McAllister: 96
Fran Milner: 130, 131t, 145
Morgan Cain & Associates: 19, 20, 21, 24, 27, 28b, 33, 41ctr, 47, 48, 53, 59, 67, 84-85, 103, 154, 155
Ortelius Design Inc.: 100tl, bl, 101bl, br, 138, 139
Stephanie Pershing: 37
Matthew Pippin: 10, 28-29
Precision Graphics: 77, 90, 97, 98, 101t, 113, 114, 115, 116, 118, 119, 120, 121, 127, 132, 134, 135, 136, 137, 140, 143
Tim Spransy: 66
Roberta Warshaw: 109
J/B Woolsey Associates: 63tr, 78, 79, 82, 102, 158

Photography

Photo Research: Paula Wehde
Cover Image: horn, John Martucci; background, Alfred Pasieka/Science Photo Library/Photo Researchers

Nature of Science
Page 8t, Rob Trubia/Westlight; **8b,** Courtesy of Christine Darden; **9,** HO/AP/Wide World Photos; **11l,** AP/Wide World Photos; **11r,** Courtesy of Christine Darden.

Chapter 1
Pages 12-13, Jim Pickerell/Folio, Inc.; **14t,** Richard Haynes; **14b,** Rob Gilley/Adventure Photo & Film; **16,** Richard Megna/Fundamental Photographs; **18t,** Richard Haynes; **18b,** Chris Cole/Duomo; **21, 24, 30, 31,** Richard Haynes; **32b,** Lynette Cook/Science Photo Library/Photo Researchers; **34t,** Andrew Ratkino/TSI; **34 inset,** Russell D. Curtis/Photo Researchers.

Chapter 2
Pages 38-39, Bob Kramer /The Picture Cube; **40,** Richard Haynes; **41,** Russell D. Curtis/Photo Researchers; **43,** Russ Lappa; **44t,** The Granger Collection, NY; **44b,** Eric Risberg/AP Wide World Photos; **45, 46,** Richard Haynes; **48,** Matt Bostick; **49t,** Mark C. Burnett/Stock Boston; **49b,** Martin Bough/Fundamental Photographs; **52t,** Richard Haynes; **52b,** Cosmo Condina/TSI; **54,** Michael Newman/PhotoEdit; **55,** Stanley Rowin/The Picture Cube; **56l,** Spencer Grant/The Picture Cube; **56r,** Nancy Brown/The Stock Market; **56-57,** Peter Saloutos/The Stock Market; **56-57t,** Doug Martin/Photo Researchers; **57r,** PhotoDisc Inc.; **57b,** Index Stock; **58,** David Ball/The Stock Market; **59,** Neil Nissing/ FPG International; **60-61, 62,** Richard Haynes; **64,** Stephen Frisch/Stock Boston; **65,** Michael Newman/PhotoEdit; **67,** Corbis; **68t,** Mitch Reardon/Photo Researchers; **68b,** Francois Gohier/Photo Researchers; **69t,** Merlin D. Tuttle, Bat Conservation International/Photo Researchers; **69b,** Charles Gupton/The Stock Market, **69 inset,** Telegraph Color Library/FPG International; **70 all,** Richard Megna/Fundamental Photographs.

Chapter 3
Pages 74-75, Alex Bartel/Science Photo Library/Photo Researchers; **76, 79t,** Richard Haynes; **79b,** Russ Lappa; **80,** Richard Haynes; **82,** Matthew McVay/TSI; **83l,** Jim Roshan; **83r,** Eric Miller/Liaison International; **83b,** Vecto Verso/Leo de Wys, Inc.; **85,** Alfred Pasieka/Science Photo Library/Photo Researchers; **86t,** Fundamental Photographs; **86b,** Ron Sutherland/Science Photo Library/Photo Researchers; **87,** RNHRD NHS Trust/TSI; **88,** Alfred Pasieka/Science Photo Library/Photo Researchers; **89,** Nordion/Visuals Unlimited; **91,** Bill Horsman/Stock Boston; **92t, 98** Kunio Owaki/The Stock Market; **92b,** Phil Degginger; **93t,** Aneal E. Vohra/Unicorn Stock Photos; **93b,** Charles Seaborn/TSI; **95,** Richard Haynes; **97,** Russ Lappa; **99,** Bruce Forster/TSI; **101,** AP/Wide World Photos; **102,** David Ducros/Science Photo Library/Photo Researchers; **106,** Richard Haynes.

Chapter 4
Pages 110-111, Arthur Gurmankin/Mary Morina/Visuals Unlimited; **112t,** Russ Lappa; **112b,** Andy Levin/Photo Researchers; **113l,** Coco McCoy/Rainbow; **113m,** Michael A. Keller Studios LTD./The Stock Market; **113r,** Skip Moody/Rainbow; **114 both,** Corel Corp.; **115, 116,** PhotoDisc Inc.; **117t,** Richard Haynes; **117b,** Russ Lappa; **118,** Peter A. Simon/The Stock Market; **119t,** John Kieffer/Peter Arnold; **119b,** John M. Dunay IV/Fundamental Photographs; **120 both,** David Parker/Photo Researchers; **121,** Richard Megna/Fundamental Photographs; **122,** Russ Lappa; **123t,** Richard Haynes; **123b,** David Young-Wolff/PhotoEdit; **124tl,** Breck P. Kent; **124b,** Grant Heilman Photography; **125 both,** Michael Dalton/Fundamental Photographs; **126l** Ralph C. Eagle/Photo Researchers; **126 inset,** Jerome Wexler/Photo Researchers; **126r, 127 both,** Russ Lappa; **128,** Richard Haynes; **129,** John Coletti/Stock Boston; **130 both,** L.V. Bergman & Associates; **132,** PhotoDisc Inc.; **133t,** Richard Haynes; **133b,** Camerique, Inc./The Picture Cube; **135t,** Richard T. Nowitz/Photo Researchers; **135b,** Jan Hinsch/Science Photo Library/Photo Researchers; **138t,** Corbis; **138b,** Scala/Art Resource, NY; **139t** Grant Heilman Photography; **139m,** Corbis; **140,** Blair Seitz/Photo Researchers; **141tl,** Jon Goell/The Picture Cube; **141tr,** Bob Daemmrich/Stock Boston; **141ml,** E.R. Degginger; **141m,** Grant Heilman Photography; **141mr,** Spencer Grant/Photo Researchers; **141bl,** E.R. Degginger; **141br,** Will & Deni Mcintyre/Photo Researchers.

Interdisciplinary Exploration
Page 146, Everett Collection, Inc.; **147,** Hans W. Silvester/Rapho/Liaison International; **149l,** TITANIC (c) 1997 Twentieth Century Fox Film Corporation and Paramount Pictures Corporation. All rights reserved.; **149r,** Photofest; **150l,** The Kobal Collection; **150r,** Photofest; **150b, 150-151b,** Russ Lappa; **151,** The Kobal Collection.

Skills Handbook
Page 152, Mike Moreland/Photo Network; **153t,** Foodpix; **153m,** Richard Haynes; **153b,** Russ Lappa; **156,** Richard Haynes; **158,** Ron Kimball; **159,** Renee Lynn/Photo Researchers.